KU-516-367

BOGNOR REGIS COLLEGE OF EDUCATION
LIBRARY

AUTHOR (Isr) INTERNAT. SEMINAR on Biomechanics	ACCESSION No 42361
TITLE Biomechanics	CLASS No 612·76

Books are to be returned on or before
the last date below

BOGNOR REGIS COLLEGE OF EDUCATION
LIBRARY

AUTHOR INTERNATIONAL SYMPOSIUM ~~MARTENWALGERNJWBO~~	ACCESSION No 42,361
TITLE BIOMECHANICS	CLASS No 612·76

WS 1001841 7

Biomechanics

Medicine and Sport

Vol. 2

Editor: E. JOKL, Lexington, Ky.

Advisory Board: K. LANGE ANDERSEN, Norway; P. BECKMANN, Germany; H.N. BLEASDALE, England; D. BRUNNER, Israel; A. CARLSTEN, Sweden; G. LA CAVA, Italy; R. DIETRICH, German Democratic Republic; A. DIRIX, Belgium; F.N. DUKES-DOBOS, Switzerland; B. EISEMAN, United States; S. FIRSOV, Soviet Union; A. GALLEGO, Spain; E. GEBHARDT, Germany; L. GEDDA, Italy; A.M. GEISSA, United Arab Republic; L. GUTTMANN, England; M. HALHUBER, Germany; K. HÄNTZSCHEL, German Democratic Republic; E. HAY, Mexico; W. HOLLMANN, Germany; M. IKAI, Japan; S. ISRAEL, German Democratic Republic; F. JANDA, Czechoslovakia; E. JOKL, United States; M. KARVONEN, Finland; E.J. KLAUS, Germany; A.V. KOROBKOV, Soviet Union; J. KRAL, Czechoslovakia; H. KRAUS, United States; F. KREUZER, Holland; S.P. LETUNOV, Soviet Union; R. MARGARIA, Italy; D. MATEEFF, Bulgaria; H. MELLEROWICZ, Germany; N. NEMESSURI, Hungary; J. PARIZKOVA, Czechoslovakia; F. PLAS, France; L. PROKOP, Austria; W. RAAB, United States; H. REINDELL, Germany; H. ROSKAMM, Germany; G. SCHOENHOLZER, Switzerland; E. SIMON, Israel; E. STRAUSZENBERG, German Democratic Republic; K. TITTEL, German Democratic Republic; F. ULMEANO, Rumania; A. VENERANDO, Italy; S. WOLOCZYN, Poland; N.K. ZIMKIN, Soviet Union.

Published for and on behalf of Research Committee
International Council of Sport and Physical Education
UNESCO

19 68

Baltimore, Maryland   University Park Press   Manchester, England

Proceedings of the First International Seminar on Biomechanics,
Zürich, August 21-23, 1967

Biomechanics

Technique of Drawings of Movement and Movement Analysis

Edited by J. WARTENWEILER, Zürich · E. JOKL, Lexington, Ky.
M. HEBBELINCK, Bruxelles

with 215 figures and 17 tables

Baltimore, Maryland   University Park Press   Manchester, England

Originally published by S. Karger AG, Basel, Switzerland
Distributed exclusively in the United States of America and Canada by
University Park Press, Baltimore, Maryland

Library of Congress Catalog Card Number 70–372983
Standard Book Number (SBN) 8391–0026–4

BOGNOR REGIS COLLEGE
OF EDUCATION

Acc. No.	Class
18177	

S. Karger AG, Arnold-Böcklin-Strasse 25, 4000 Basel 11 (Switzerland)

All rights, including that of translation into other languages, reserved.
Photomechanic reproduction (photocopy, microcopy) of this volume or
parts thereof without special permission of the publishers is prohibited.

Copyright 1968 by S. Karger AG, Basel
Printed in Switzerland by Buchdruckerei Kohlhepp AG, Neuallschwil
Clichés: Aberegg-Steiner, Bern

Index

VII. Applied Biomechanics in Work

VIII. Applied Biomechanics in Sports

IX. Clinical Aspects

Introduction

The International Council of Sport and Physical Education of UNESCO aims at the establishment of a broad conceptual basis of the global sports movement which during the past decades has developed almost entirely along empirical lines. Through its Research Committee, the Council has initiated numerous study teams and organized groups of experts from many countries who deal with the three fundamental categories of contemporary culture: 'scientific', 'humanistic', and 'physical', in their relationship to sport and physical education. It is in this context that a comprehensive image of the impact of the global sports movement upon society at the present stage of its development can be envisaged.

'Biomechanics' belongs to the first of the above three sectors. Its study contributes to the identification of 'the theater of the events' —to quote a simile applied by the 16th century French philosopher Jean Fernel—on which 'the event itself' takes place. 'The event itself' is the human performance in its manifold forms.

The International Council of Sport and Physical Education cooperates with S. Karger, Basel, in publishing from time to time representative volumes to detail scope and nature of a number of academic disciplines whose methodology and theoretical prerequisites are applied in an effort to evaluate content and meaning of the phenomena with which the world-wide sports movement confronts us.

Among these disciplines, biomechanics or, as the subject is referred to by many of its American students, kinesiology, occupies an important place. One of the reasons is that communication of meaningful messages from man to man is accomplished through a variety of movements, including of course, speech. SHERRINGTON related to this fact by saying 'the muscle is the cradle of recognizable mind'.

The Council's overall policy is to serve the all-embracing purpose of Unesco whose credo is 'that all conflicts of man originate in the minds of man and that an unceasing appeal must thus be made to the mind of man in an effort to lessen the conflicts of which history tells'. The international sports movement affords a new opportunity to cultivate inter-human relations. The Council's work, therefore, assumes a significance of its own. The special task of the Council's Research Committee is to formulate policy, to detail technical aspects of its work, and to guide administrative action. The Committee is convinced that—to quote Heine—

'the thought precedes the deed so as lightning precedes thunder'.

E. JOKL, Lexington, Ky., USA, President

Research Committee, International Council
of Sport and Physical Education, UNESCO

Editor 'Medicine and Sport'.

Preface

Biomechanics, a New Science

Biomechanics is a new branch of science. It comprehends knowledge of the interplay of mechanical forces underlying all human movements, their autonomic support, neurological initiation, integrated control, perceptual accompaniments, as well as their 'central design'.

Major *fields of research* in biomechanics are:
1. movement patterns in space and time;
2. energy production and activity distribution in the musculature;
3. the 'steering' of movements through the nervous system;
4. psychosomatic phenomena associated with motor acts.

Research methods of biomechanics include cinematography, stroboscopy, light-tracing and electronic recording, recording of angles (goniography), displacement, velocity, acceleration forces as well as electrophysiology, more especially electromyography.

Areas of *application* of biomechanics are:
1. trade, crafts, industry and agriculture;
2. sport and physical education;
3. medical rehabilitation;
4. the creative arts.

Multi-Disciplinary Approach to Research in Biomechanics

Research in Biomechanics involves methods derived from a variety of scientific disciplines, chief among them:

Physics: for assessment of *mechanical, thermic, electrical* and other components of human motor acts.

Anatomy: for analysis of *morphological* prerequisites for movements.

Physiology: for identification of *functional* parameters of relevance for the understanding of motor phenomena.

Psychology: for consideration of the role played by *mental* processes in the design, initiation, control and perceptual representation of movements.

Classification of Motor Manifestation

The conceptual classification of the empirical evidence from which biomechanical research derives reflects the multifaced nature of motor problems in their entirety.

The following classification has been found practical:

1. Content of Motor Acts

a) purposive movements (e.g. hitting a nail into a wall with a hammer);
b) expressive movements (e.g. laughing).

2. Magnitude of Movements

a) mass movements (involving action of major parts of the body);
b) small movements (such as those reflecting skill of movements of hands and fingers).

3. Nature and Degree of Resistance

a) movements against *external resistance* (e.g. in putting the shot);
b) *ballistic movements* (e.g. leg movements in running);
c) movements involving *patterned resistance* of antagonistic muscle forces (e.g. moving from static attitude to arabesque in ballet dancing).

4. Design

a) *elementary movements* (assessment of displacement of single body components) (e.g. arm swinging, with body at rest);
b) *combined movements* (involving displacement of two or more body components in one unity of function):

    – co-movements: (e.g. thrust with lunge in fencing);
    – counter-movements: (e.g. arm swinging while walking);
    – movements involving phasic displacement (e.g. throwing);
c) *joint movements* (involving displacement of two or more body components in separate unities of function) (e.g. arm and leg movements in crawl swimming);
d) *superimposed* ('focal and satellite') *movements:* (e.g. moving arm from left to right with fingers forming symbolic movements, such as in Hindu dancing).

Nature of Task

Two fundamental tasks confront the science of biomechanics namely identification of

1. General Characteristics of Optimal Execution of Movements

Rhythm
Continuity of force development, acceleration and deceleration, approaching repetitive sinus prototype.

Co-ordination
Development of force release, acceleration and deceleration of body segments (transfer of impulse) in keeping with objective of total motor performance.

Relaxed Intervals
Antagonistic muscles acting alternatively, without extended overlap.

Anticipatory Initiation of Motor Act
Movements aiming at maximal performance initiated by counter displacements of body components resulting in:
    – optimal positioning of joints;
    – lengthening of range of effective action;
    – facilitation of force release.

2. Variations

'Motor Personality'
Somatic typology studies of individual human characteristics. Until recently, 'somato-typing' concerned itself almost exclusively with *mor-*

phological research even though other implications of the issue were recognized by Kretschmer, Sheldon, Tanner and Parnell. Nevertheless, the study of a *functional* somatic typology is in its infancy. It is the task of biomechanics to develop it.

Skill

Variations in the execution of movements may reflect lack of skill. Movement tests reveal nature and scope of such variations, as well as the extent to which training may influence them.

Vocational guidance and the sports sciences have elaborated many tests in the section under reference.

Pathological Interference

A special category of deviation from optimal movement patterns may result from disease or injury. The study of such deviations is of major relevance to clinical medicine.

J. WARTENWEILER, President
ICSPE-Working Group on Biomechanics

Address of welcome by the President of the Seminar, Prof. Dr. Jürg Wartenweiler

Ladies and Gentlemen,

I have the honour to welcome you on behalf of the Organizing Committee of the First International Seminar on Biomechanics.

You have come from many countries to hold scientific discussions and to become acquainted with each other. Professor ERNST JOKL, President of the Research Committee of the International Council of Sport and Physical Education, suggested some time ago the inclusion of studies on biomechanics in the program of the International Council. I thank him for the confidence placed in our Swiss research centre to which he entrusted the organization of the Seminar. Also I would like to express my appreciation of the support we have received from Dr. EMANUEL SIMON, vice-president, and Professor MARCEL HEBBELINCK, secretary general, of the Research Committee.

The scientific study of movements dates back over at least 100 years. In 1873, H. VON MAYER, Zürich, the anatomist, well-known through his discovery of the 'spongiosa structure' of osseous tissue, published his magnum opus 'Die Statik und Mechanik des menschlichen Knochengerüstes'. About the same time the French physiologist MAREY undertook his classic studies on walking and running. His co-worker DEMENY elaborated Marey's findings in his book 'Mécanisme et Education des Mouvements'. A few decades later the Zürich physiologist W.R. HESS introduced new experimental techniques designed to throw light upon the central co-ordination of movements and their autonomic accompaniments.

Psychological aspects of the human motor act were given attention 40 years ago by KRÜGER and KLEMM in Leipzig who applied psychometric methods to the study of the issue; by KRETSCHMER in Marburg who correlated morphological, functional and personality features of different somatypes; and by F.J.J. BUYTENDIJK whose monograph 'Allgemeine Theorie der menschlichen Haltung und Bewegung' is now considered a classic.

The trend during the past decades towards industrial rationalization extended not only towards engineering processes but also towards human movements. Attempts to economize the latter were undertaken by many investigators whose efforts resulted in the establishment of a new discipline of research, now called 'human engineering'.

On an increasing scale, research studies of movements in sport and athletics are now yielding information on nature and scope of the human motor system. Next to the arts and crafts, sport is the one sector of movement research in which the greatest variety of performances offer themselves for analysis.

From these remarks you will, I hope, see that biomechanics has grown into a major scientific of its own. By learning to know more about human movements, we are bound to learn more about the nature of man.

Begrüssung durch den Generalsekretär
der Nationalen Schweizerischen UNESCO-Kommission,
Dr. Charles Hummel

Meine sehr verehrten Damen und Herren!

Es ist mir eine große Ehre, Sie nicht nur im Namen der Nationalen Schweizerischen Unesco-Kommission hier willkommen zu heißen, und Ihnen eine ergebnisreiche Tagung zu wünschen, sondern Ihnen auch die Grüsse der schweizerischen Behörden zu überbringen. Diesen Grüßen füge ich den Dank an die Organisatoren bei, welche das 1. Seminar für Biomechanik in die Wege geleitet und offensichtlich so gut vorbereitet haben, daß sich eine über Erwarten große Zahl von Teilnehmern aus nicht weniger als 26 Staaten hier in Zürich eingefunden hat. Ein Fachgespräch über so viele Grenzen hinweg ist an sich schon ein großer Erfolg, wofür man den Initianten dieses Seminars herzlich gratulieren kann.

Wenn man das Programm dieses 1. Seminars für Biomechanik näher anschaut, die eindrucksvolle Liste hochspezialisierter Referate durchgeht, welche in der Mehrzahl sportmedizinischen Themen gewidmet sind, so könnte man sich fragen, was für Beziehungen denn zwischen der Unesco, der Organisation der Vereinten Nationen für Erziehung, Wissenschaft und Kultur, und den hier zur Diskussion gebrachten Problemen bestehen. Mit andern Worten: *Was hat die Unesco mit dem Sport zu tun,* daß sie so eng mit dem Weltrat für Sport und Leibeserziehung zusammenarbeitet?

RENÉ MAHEU, der gegenwärtige Generaldirektor der Unesco, hat diese Frage anläßlich einer Ansprache vor dem Weltrat für Sport und Leibeserziehung sehr prägnant beantwortet: ‚Sport bedeutet *Erziehung,* und zwar Erziehung in ihrer konkretesten und wirklichsten Form: Erziehung des Charakters. Sport bedeutet auch *Wissenschaft,* denn nur durch die geduldige Erkenntnis seines Wesens kann der Sportler seine Leistungen steigern. Sport ist auch *Kultur,* denn mit den vergänglichen Gesten, die er in Zeit und Raum zeichnet – für nichts, für das Vergnügen, wie *Platon* sagt –, läßt er durch ihre dramatische Übersteigerung die ureigensten und damit auch die tiefsten Werte des Volkes, ja der menschlichen Rasse, an die Oberfläche steigen. Sport ist aber auch Kultur, weil er Schönheit schafft.‘

Die Unesco ist sich der erzieherischen Bedeutung des Sportes und seiner wichtigen Rolle in der menschlichen Gesellschaft im Laufe der letzten Jahre in stets wachsendem Maße bewußt geworden, so daß dem Sport heute im Programm der Unesco ein fester Platz zukommt; und ich bin überzeugt, daß in den kommenden Jahren dieser Platz immer bedeutender werden wird.

Von den vielfachen Verknüpfungen der Unesco mit dem Sport seien nur drei hier stichwortartig aufgezeigt.

XVIII

1. Sport und Jugend. Vor genau drei Jahren fand in Grenoble eine außerordentlich wichtige, von der Unesco organisierte Konferenz statt. Sie war dem Problem der Jugend gewidmet. Eingehende Untersuchungen über die heutige Situation der Jugend in aller Welt waren ihr vorausgegangen und die Debatten dieser Konferenz führten zu einer Reihe wichtiger Empfehlungen, welche die Tätigkeit der Unesco im Bereiche der Jugendfragen entscheidend beeinflußt haben. Die Bedeutung des Sportes als wesentliches Element der Ertüchtigung, der Gesundung und der Erziehung der Jugend kam dabei entscheidend zum Ausdruck.

Wenige Wochen nach dieser Konferenz von Grenoble wurde in Tokio das «Manifest über den Sport» proklamiert. Ihm fügte der Generaldirektor der Unesco eine Botschaft bei, worin er einmal mehr die pädagogischen und sozialen Aspekte des Sportes hervorhob.

2. Sport und Kultur. Wesentliches Merkmal unserer Kultur der Gegenwart ist der Gewinn an Freizeit breitester Kreise der Bevölkerung und gleichzeitig die Notwendigkeit einer sinnvollen Gestaltung dieser Freizeit. Sinnvolle Gestaltung der Freizeit heißt aber auch, und vor allem, Vorbereitung auf die gesteigerten Anforderungen der modernen Arbeitsprozesse und des Lebens in der Gegenwart überhaupt. Das ist der Grund, weshalb die Unesco und andere, ähnliche Organisationen dem Thema der Erwachsenenbildung eine so zentrale Bedeutung beimessen. Was aber für die Jugenderziehung gilt, gilt hier ebenfalls: auch hier ist der Sport wichtiges Bildungs- und Erziehungselement. Er wird damit zu einem der Träger unserer modernen Freizeit-Kultur.

3. Sport und internationale Verständigung. Hauptanliegen der Unesco ist das Wirken für Frieden und Völkerverständigung. Auch hier kann der Sport, der über alle Grenzen hinweg Menschen zu gemeinsamem Tun vereint, im Sinne der hohen Ziele der Unesco wirken. Allerdings müssen wir eingestehen, daß der Sport für nationalistische Propaganda mißbraucht werden kann und auch oft mißbraucht wird, aber daneben gibt es in weit größerem Maß die echte Begegnung im Zeichen des Sportes von Menschen verschiedener Kulturkreise. Das Seminar, das Sie hier zusammengeführt hat, ist dafür ein Beispiel.

In allen Gesprächen über die großen Probleme unserer Zeit wird immer wieder sichtbar, daß nur die rein menschlichen, die ethischen Qualitäten uns eine sinnvolle Zukunft garantieren können. Voraussetzung jeder moralischen Haltung ist aber die Selbsterkenntnis. Der Sport führt einerseits zur Lust an der Bewegung und der Beherrschung des eigenen Körpers, anderseits aber auch zur Erfahrung der eigenen Grenzen. Und das ist wohl das entscheidende Moment aller Erziehung.

Allocution de bienvenue du Président de la Société Suisse de Médecine Sportive, le Dr Pierre Krieg

Monsieur le Président, Mesdames et Messieurs,

Le Prof. CHAILLEY-BERT, Président de la Fédération internationale de médecine sportive, actuellement au Japon, m'a prié de vous adresser ses vœux les plus cordiaux pour la réussite de ce premier Séminaire international de biomécanique. La société suisse de médecine sportive que j'ai l'honneur de représenter ici, est heureuse également d'être associée à ce congrès.

Comme l'a relevé votre Président, il peut paraître paradoxal d'étudier de manière toujours plus approfondie le mouvement, alors que se perd progressivement l'habitude de l'effort physique. La machine remplace en effet presque toujours avantageusement le travail musculaire de l'homme, mais ce dernier qui doit essayer de dominer la machine est soumis à des travaux, à des occupations qui exigent une grande concentration et une grande habileté dans ses mouvements. Nous sommes donc soumis de plus en plus à des efforts du système nerveux, efforts encore aggravés par le rythme de vie que nous menons. Et puis nous sommes victimes de notre confort qui nous permet de subsister sans effectuer beaucoup de mouvements.

Les médecins doivent s'intéresser toujours davantage à ce problème car même si en général leur intérêt pour le sport n'est que relatif, ils constatent journellement les méfaits sur l'organisme humain, du manque de mouvement: déformation de la colonne vertébrale chez les adolescents, arthrose vertébrale chez l'adulte trop sédentaire ou soumis aux trépidations de la voiture ou de certaines machines, affections articulaires dégénératives et affections cardio-vasculaires touchant des individus toujours plus jeunes.

Dans la grande majorité de ces affections, le mouvement bien conduit va développer une musculature éfficiente, qui permettra de mieux soutenir le squelette, donnera une plus grande souplesse à l'appareil articulaire et améliorera le système circulatoire en procurant un meilleur tonus au cœur et aux vaisseaux.

Il ne faut pas oublier l'effet extrêmement utile du mouvement sur le système nerveux. Les physiologistes nous montrent en effet que la pratique des sports, en particulier les jeux de balle et de gymnastique, raccourcissent les temps de réaction et augmentent de manière générale les performances des fonctions nerveuses. Ainsi, la pratique des sports augmente la faculté d'intégrer de nouveaux automatismes et facilite l'acquisition de l'habileté. L'exemple de l'école à mi-temps réalisée à Vanves près de Paris est frappant: les enfants que l'on soumet à des mouvements les plus divers et adaptés à leur âge durant chaque après-midi, suivent parfaitement le programme scolaire normal et présentent même moins d'échecs que les autres. Il va sans dire que leur développement physique est bien meilleur.

XX

Il est donc urgent que tous ceux qui s'occupent de près ou de loin de l'éducation au sens le plus large du terme ou de la santé en général, prennent conscience de ces problèmes afin de faciliter aux jeunes générations l'adaptation à la vie moderne.

Le programme de ce séminaire atteste de la diversité de vos études et du grand nombre de chercheurs qui analysent le corps humain en mouvement. En complétant nos connaissances du mouvement par la physiologie, la biochimie et la psychologie, la biomécanique doit nous ouvrir de nouveaux champs d'application dans la pratique des sports, dans l'industrie et dans la rééducation fonctionnelle.

Je souhaite que ce congrès vous apporte beaucoup de satisfaction.

Begrüssung
durch den Regierungspräsidenten des Kantons Zürich, Dr. Walter König

Meine sehr verehrten Damen und Herren!

Es ist mir eine Ehre und ein Vergnügen, Sie im Namen des Regierungsrates des Kantons Zürich zur Eröffnung des I. Internationalen Seminars für Biomechanik in Zürich begrüßen zu dürfen. Sicher wird diese Zusammenkunft von Wissenschaftern aus 26 Ländern der Entwicklung der Biomechanik wesentliche Impulse geben, den persönlichen Kontakt zwischen Ihnen fördern und so auch über das engere Fachgebiet hinaus zum gegenseitigen Verständnis beitragen. Besonders freut es mich, daß Sie Zürich als Ort Ihres ersten Zusammentreffens gewählt haben. Ich hoffe, daß Sie sich in Zürich wohlfühlen und mit angenehmen Erinnerungen an diese Stadt in Ihr Heimatland zurückkehren werden.

In meiner Eigenschaft als Erziehungsdirektor des Kantons Zürich habe ich ein ganz unmittelbares Interesse an Ihrer Tagung. Nicht nur, weil Wissenschaft und Forschung zum Aufgabenkreis meiner Direktion gehören, sondern, und dies vor allem, weil mir die Ertüchtigung der Jugend dringendstes Anliegen ist. Allen Bemühungen in dieser Richtung wäre nicht der gewünschte Erfolg beschieden, wenn sie sich auf den geistigen Bereich beschränken und die Förderung einer gesunden körperlichen Entwicklung vernachlässigen würden. Daß gerade für die Hebung der körperlichen Gesundheit und Leistungsfähigkeit der Jugend unter den heutigen Lebensverhältnissen besondere Anstrengungen nötig sind, brauche ich in Ihrem Kreise nicht näher auszuführen. Ich bin überzeugt davon, daß wir hiebei von der noch jungen Wissenschaft der Biomechanik eine wesentliche Hilfe erwarten dürfen, und wünsche dem I. Internationalen Seminar für Biomechanik in diesem Sinne viel Erfolg.

Worte zur Eröffnung der Buchausstellung
von Prof. Dr. Josef Recla, Graz

Die Biomechanik eröffnet neue Aspekte
der Leibesübungen, bereichert die
wissenschaftliche Theorie und schafft
ungeahnte Möglichkeiten für die Praxis.

Sportdokumentation – eine vordringliche Aufgabe

In den letzten Jahren hat sich unser Wissen verdoppelt, neue Erkenntnisse und Erfahrungen haben das Bestehende erschüttert – ein neues Weltbild ist im Entstehen. Wir sind mitten im Umbruch, im Aufbruch. Das gilt vor allem auch für den Sport. Fakultäten und Akademien für Körperkultur, Institute für Leibeserziehung, Sporthochschulen leisten eine beachtenswerte Arbeit in Lehre und Forschung. Die Sportwissenschaft hat sich als neue, komplexe Wissenschaft entwickelt. Fülle, Reichhaltigkeit und geistiges Niveau haben eine moderne Literaturarbeit – Bibliographie, Dokumentation und Information – notwendig gemacht. Auslese und Interpretation werden vordringlich. Im internationalen Raum haben sich in den letzten Jahren über dreißig Literaturstellen entwickelt. Intensiv wird die Sportliteratur erschlossen, verarbeitet und vermittelt. Das im Jahre 1960 gegründete Internationale Büro für Dokumentation und Information lenkt als international anerkanntes Zentrum die gesamte Sport-Dokumentation und Sport-Information.

Die Literatur über Biomechanik

Auf Wunsch der Initianten des I. Internationalen Seminars für Biomechanik, hat das Institut für Leibeserziehung der Universität Graz eine Literaturstudie über das Fachgebiet der Biomechanik bearbeitet und vorgelegt:
«Die Biomechanik in der Literatur der Gegenwart» von HELGA und OTTO FLEISS, KARL RINGLI und PETER RÜMMELE, herausgegeben von Prof. Dr. JOSEF RECLA, Vervielfältigung, 109 Seiten, Institut für Leibeserziehung der Universtiät Graz, 1967.
Im ersten Teil dieser Literaturarbeit werden die Grundzüge der Biomechanik des Sports dargestellt, die Untersuchungsmethoden der Biomechanik beleuchtet und eine Zusammenfassung der theoretischen Grundlagen versucht. Der zweite Teil bringt die erreichbare Literatur über Biomechanik des Sports mit bibliographischen Angaben. Die Studie erfaßt 518 Werke, Schriften und Beiträge in Fachzeitschriften des internationalen Raums von 430 Verfassern.

Unbekannte, versteckte Literatur über Biomechanik wurde in der Literatur der Mechanik und Physik, der Medizin, vor allem der Sportmedizin, und der Psychologie gefunden.

Die eigentliche Biomechanik des Sports ist erst neueren Datums. Sie hat sich in den letzten Jahren durch intensive Forschungsarbeit rasch zu einem beachtenswerten Fachgebiet entwickelt. Was den geisteswissenschaftlichen Disziplinen noch nicht voll gelungen ist, kann die Biomechanik heute schon belegen, daß nämlich genug Arbeiten für eine selbständige Wissenschaft des Sports vorliegen.

Die Ausstellung «Literatur über Biomechanik»

Der Leiter der Bibliothek der Eidgenössischen Turn- und Sportschule Magglingen/Schweiz, Herr KARL RINGLI, hat mit viel Liebe, Fachkenntnis und Mühe eine gute Auslese der Literatur über Biomechanik des Sports zusammengestellt und in einer geschmackvoll gestalteten Ausstellung den Teilnehmern des Seminars zugänglich gemacht. Neben den Standardwerken, Büchern und Schriften – in verschiedenen Sprachen aus dem internationalen Raum – sind vor allem die Sonderdrucke wertvoll und beachtenswert. Die Literaturschau ist ein Musterstück einer Ausstellung, wie sie auf jeder internationalen Tagung gestaltet werden sollte!

Biomechanics I, 1st Int. Seminar Zurich 1967
pp. 1–22 (Karger, Basel/New York 1968)

University of Kentucky, Lexington

The Acquisition of Skill*

E. JOKL

Man is capable of two kinds of motor acts: of movements whose
patterns form part of the genetically determined building plan of his
central nervous system; and of movements which originate as mentally
conceived objectives which the neuromuscular system transforms into
kinetic events. Standing and walking are representative of the former;
the use of tools, writing, playing musical instruments, or competing in
a 110 meter hurdles race of the latter.

Not only can human beings carry out movements in the image of
their thinking, but they can also improve upon their execution. The
scope of this improvement ranges from a child's drawings to Michel-
angelo's paintings in the Sistine Chapel; from a beginner's renderings
on the piano to a concert presentation by Arthur Rubinstein; from a
school boy's efforts at the carpenter's bench to the building of wooden
churches in Northern Finland; and from a young track and field
contestant's performances to the feats accomplished by Olympic de-
cathlon finalists.

Cognition and Motor Learning

Nature and appearance of a given motor task observed by us in others
are mediated first through our sense organs. It is only secondarily that
we become acquainted with the inherent properties of tools, imple-
ments, and other material elements involved in motor learning: the
buoyancy of the water in which we swim, the expansion of the space
in which we run or jump, the resistance of the snow on which we
move on skis, the elastic properties of the ball which we bounce, or of

* Presidential Address

the wind which swells the sails of our boat. New categories of cognition engender new motor responses in a continuous *Gestaltkreis*.

Watching and thinking do not suffice for the acquisition of skills, for learning how to ride a bicycle, how to handle a galloping horse, how to skate on ice, how to play tennis. It is through sustained practice alone that the required coordinative potentialities are developed and new cognitive qualities conveyed. The individual thereby gains decisive knowledge of 'I can do it thus' of keeping his balance on the bicycle, of remaining in control of the horse, of skating on ice, of swimming through a river. The initial 'gnostic' approach to the acquisition of skill is supplemented by 'pathic' experience. The process thus initiated of 'building up' increasingly more differentiated postural and spatial schemata of the body, at rest and in action, involves correspondingly more differentiated associations with corporeal awareness, imagery, and memory. It also develops three-dimensional and temporal discrimination. Summation of new sense data reaching the central nervous system leads to new perceptive integration and in turn to progressively more effective motor responses. DENNY-BROWN has referred to this adaptive process as 'morphosynthesis'.

The Parietal Lobes

The acquisition of skill is a protracted process. A given individual's motor capacities are not fully recognizable in the untrained state. This fact is of importance in education, in the arts and in athletics, in physiology, psychology, and very much so in neurology and psychiatry. For example, the relevance of the literature concerning the symptomatology of lesions of the parietal lobes, of the aphasias, apraxias, agnosias, alexias, agraphias, acalculias, of tactile and visual dysfunctions, of the Gerstmann syndrome, and of disorders of the body image, is limited by the fact that performance variants have not been systematically investigated in *healthy* subjects. As long as range and quality of skill in normal people are not identified, the elaborately constructed pyramid of clinical theories in the sector under reference rests on insecure foundations.

MACDONALD CRITCHLEY's statement that 'the ordinary routine neurological examination as well as conventional psychological testing fail to do justice to the nature of parietal disorders alludes to this short-coming. To illustrate, clumsy young boys and girls who also do poorly in their arithmetic lessons and who have difficulties in distinguishing right from left are not infrequently 'discovered' by alert physical training instructors who, of course, are unlikely to interpret such observations as indicative of the presence of a 'congenital type of Gerstmann syndrome'—all the more so since the disabilities are apt to disappear after a few months of intensive physical training.

Four Stages of Acquiring Skill

Every voluntary activity productive of patterned work can be analyzed in four stages. First, in respect of the *idea of the work* to be performed. Second, with a view to the *design of the work* as imagined at the moment when the activity begins. Third, in terms of the fact that a *constructive plan* must encompass the partial activities leading in appropriate sequence to the completion of the task. Fourth, with regard to the motor *technique* employed for the attainment of the objective.

All four components are involved in the acquisition of skill even though there is ordinarily no awareness of such design. However, the validity of the concept can be demonstrated along two lines: by a study of patients with lesions of the parietal lobes who present a syndrome called 'constructional apraxia', and by observations of extraordinarily able and determined individuals who acquire *exceptional skills* irrespective of the fact that they are afflicted with major bodily handicaps. Such a division is in accordance with the distinction made by HUGHLINGS JACKSON between clinical manifestations of 'destroying' and 'discharging' cerebral disorders[1]. I consider it appropriate to extend JACKSON's pathophysiological concept to the interpretation of neuro-

[1] The following quotations are from JACKSON's 'Selected Writings' (2 Volumes, Basic Books, New York 1958):

'Cases of paralysis and convulsions may be looked upon as the results of experiments made by disease on particular parts of the nervous system of man. The study of palsies and convulsions from this point of view is the study of the effects of 'destroying lesions' and of the effects of 'discharging lesions'. (Localisation of movements, Vol. 1, p. 63)... 'Abnormalities of function are of two kinds, minus and plus. In cases of hemiplegia from breaking-up of the internal capsule by clot or softening, there is destruction of fibers and also, of course, loss of function...; while a 'discharging lesion' is a hyperphysiological condition.' ('Hypertonicity in Paralysis', Vol. II, p. 472–3).

'The discharging lesion' is an hyper-physiological 'condition'... and a fit of epilepsy an excessive caricature of the normal physiological process during what is called a voluntary action.' ('Some Implications of Dissolution of the Nervous System', Vol. II, pp. 39 and 43).

motor performances in their entirety, including their vast range of effectiveness and differentiation in *normal* subjects. In studying acquired skills, we thus place in juxtaposition analyses of *performance defects* encountered in patients with destructive cerebral lesions, and evaluations of *exceptional performance achievements* by subjects who are afflicted with anomalies of their *bodily* machinery of execution. If we look upon the functional *sequelae of destructive cerebral lesions* as revealing facets on the 'anti-eidos' of the norm, the case histories of *'handicapped' champion athletes* serve to delineate the outermost boundaries of the field of operation of the human organism's capacity to transform ideomotor concepts into action. The field within these boundaries encompasses the scope of the acquisition of skill.

Constructional Apraxia

Constructional apraxia occurs commonly in parietal disease. It rarely prompts the patient to make specific complaints of its existence. KLEIST defined the condition as a disturbance of the ability to carry out tasks demanding spatial arrangements. Essentially, it is an executive defect within the visuospatial domain—it can be demonstrated by tests in which the patient is asked to copy designs made by the examiner. Figures 1 and 2 document faulty test responses by two patients afflicted with a left frontoparietal and a right temporoparietal tumor, respectively. Most patients who perform inadequately in these tests show little dissatisfaction with their efforts. They are 'not or not fully' aware of having failed, e.g. a housewife who can no longer lay a table for a meal, an experienced dressmaker who begins to have trouble in cutting

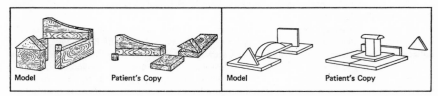

| Model | Patient's Copy | Model | Patient's Copy |

Fig. 1. Three-dimensional constructional tasks. (The patient was given the appropriate bricks, but he helped himself to two others as well.) Right temporoparietal glioblastoma. *Fig. 2.* 'Model' and 'Patient's Copy' by subject afflicted with constructional apraxia due to lesions of parietal lobes. Patient was unable to duplicate the pattern placed before him (after Macdonald Critchley).

out material from a pattern, a previously competent typist who lately encountered difficulties in writing, omitted letters and words, spelled incorrectly and used faulty grammar. MAYER-GROSS believed that constructional apraxia is an expression of 'space-impairment', and that the disturbance under reference includes features of a perceptive as well as of an executive character. It is a sort of visual agnosopraxia, a deficiency not only of cognition but also of action. The condition is related to a syndrome described by GERSTMANN in 1924, viz. of the inability of patients afflicted with parietal lobe lesions to recognize their own fingers, to name them, and to point out individual digits when so directed. MACDONALD CRITCHLEY has reported the case of a woman with a biparietal lesion who had for years worked as a fish-filleter. With the development of her symptoms, she began to experience difficulty in carrying on with her job. She did not seem to know what to do with her knife, would stick the point in the head of a fish, start the first stroke, and then come to a stop. In her own mind, she knew how to fillet fish, but yet she could not execute the maneuver. The foreman accused her of being drunk and sent her home for mutilating fish.

JOHANNES LANGE pointed out that the hand plays the part of a tool which connects our 'personal space' with the 'space around us.' The same statement can, of course, be made in respect of the sensory, proprioceptive, and motor potentialities of the human body as a whole; however, it applies most demonstrably to the hands. The acquisition of skill implies the establishment of new levels of relations between personal and extra-personal space, an accomplishment whose effectiveness presupposes functional integrity of the cerebral cortex, more especially of the parietal lobes.

HUGHLINGS JACKSON's concepts of *discharging* lesions were derived from observations of patients with epileptic seizures. However, the problem also relates to the initiation of *normal* movements. Its study belongs to neurophysiology as a whole and not exclusively to neuropathology. It involves the broad problem of the transformation of ideomotor patterns into skilled movements. The fact that many *handicapped individuals,* because they were unable to adopt the customary techniques of execution of *standardized athletic tasks,* attain extraordinary performances through *unusual coordinative approaches,* throws new light upon the theory of the acquisition of skill.

Harold Connolly, one of the greatest hammer throwers of all time and winner of the Olympic gold medal in 1956, has a severely crippled left arm caused by a combined injury of both upper and lower brachial plexuses due to a birth trauma. The condition led to a marked growth defect as well as generalized pareses and paralyses of the muscles of the affected arm.

Karoly Takacs of Hungary ranks as one of the best marksmen (pistol shooting) in the world. When, as a young student, he participated in the Olympic Games in 1936, he was already known as an outstanding performer. In 1938, he was involved in an accident which necessitated amputation of the right arm midway between elbow and wrist; he subsequently competed, holding his pistol in the left hand. In 1939, he won a world championship. At the Olympic Games in London in 1948 and in Helsinki in 1952, he was awarded gold medals. The 1956 Games in Australia were his fourth Olympic competition.

Lis Hartel of Denmark was declared the world's leading equestrienne at the dressage competitions of the Olympic Games in Helsinki in 1952, and Stockholm in 1956. Since her school days, Mrs. Hartel had been a good rider. At the age of 23, seven years before her first Olympic contest, she suffered an attack of poliomyelitis which caused major irremediable paralyses of all four extremities whose mobility and strength were reduced by more than 50 per cent. At Helsinki she still had to use leg braces and crutches for standing and walking.

Because of the irremediable nature of their handicaps, the three athletes seemed to belong to the category of 'the lame and the halt' of whom the Bible speaks with compassion; to a class of human beings who throughout history have been looked upon as 'les misérables', to whom no alternative was left but to accept their destiny with resignation. The significance of the above mentioned case histories lies in the fact that they demonstrate the fallacy of such an attitude. Confronted with physical defects of considerable magnitude, the three champions changed their destiny by making defiant as well as heroic decisions of their own. Prometheus-like, they challenged fate itself. The athletic techniques which they learned to master did not rest upon reflex-controlled inborn patterns of execution like those of standing, walking, and running. Rather, they had to be synthesized from 'new' and 'original' mental images whose realization required powerful motivation and sustained perseverance. For their execution original techniques had to be developed.

As regards the *idea of the work to be performed,* the 15th century French physiologist Jean Fernel wrote, 'What geography is to history, such is anatomy to medicine. Both represent theaters of events.' Likewise, the acquisition of skill is a prerequisite for the execution of a large variety of purposive tasks; with them of what SHERRINGTON has called the 'communication of mind', and the creation of esthetic values.

The evolution of objectives necessarily precedes the synthesis of motor patterns to materialize them. Invariably exceptionally gifted individuals act as pathfinders. This statement applies to the crafts, to technology, to the arts, as well as to sport. This is shown by the existence in every sphere of human interest of 'schools' whose didactic techniques aim at the cultivation of specific skills.

Selected references to the history of sport and physical training will illustrate. Prior to the second half of the 18th century the attainment of maximal physical performances was a matter of little concern. The summits of the Swiss Alps did not challenge the inhabitants of the valleys to climb them. However, when in 1787 Saussure conquered Mont Blanc, his achievement motivated many people to acquaint themselves with the techniques of mountaineering. At the same time, the desire to explore plains and rivers and forests everywhere in the world received a powerful stimulus. Such skills as were needed for the implementation of these desires were perfected. Around the end of the 18th century, the German naturalist, Alexander von Humboldt, undertook expeditions to the Northern and Southern hemisphere of the American continent and he described in detail what he had seen. Among those who were enthused by his writings was Charles Darwin.

At all times *new physical skills* were used in the pursuit of new human adventures following in the wake of *new scientific discoveries*. Balloon ascents staged in France during the second half of the 19th century marked the beginnings of the conquest of space. The flight in 1875 by Tissandier, Croce-Spinelli and Sivel of the 'Zenith', fired the imagination of the people of Europe in a manner comparable to the excitement caused by the orbiting of the Russian 'Sputnik' in 1956. During the same period, competitive athletics and swimming became popular. Performances in running, jumping, throwing, etc. were measured, recorded, and compared. A new view of the scope and nature of human powers was engendered. In 1872, Captain Webb swam the British Channel from Dover to Calais in twenty-one hours. Evidently the scope of man's motor aptitude, strength, and endurance was wider than had so far been assumed. Modern science further aided the effectiveness of human skill. The growth of agricultural chemistry led to

major improvements in food production. The infectious diseases were
brought under control. People became bigger and stronger and matured
earlier. The length of life increased. All these achievements were at-
tended by the evolution of new skills. Methods of physical training
were evaluated in research laboratories, first in Germany, France,
England and Italy, and later in other countries. Orthopedic surgeons
and cardiologists became interested in the application of exercise therapy in the management of a variety of diseases. The idea of reha-
bilitating chronically disabled individuals was born.

Standards of human performances in sports and athletics increased
incessantly (Fig. 3). The traditional assumption of a categorical in-
feriority of women had to be revised: many girl swimmers now return
better times than did the world's best male performers but a few
decades ago. Young boys and girls today successfully aspire at performance goals almost beyond imagination only 50 years ago. Evi-

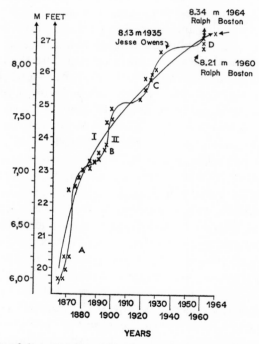

Fig. 3. Development of the world record in the long jump during the past 100 years. (II,
curve showing periodic fluctuations of growth: I, smoothed curve following identifiable
parabolic trend.)

dently, the acquisition of human skill presupposes not only physical powers but also the realization of distinct aims and objectives. The latter in turn are conceived in the image of historical, social, cultural, and scientific precedents.

The problem of *design of a skilled movement* cannot be divorced from that of its notation and of the methods employed to transform the mental image thus engendered into corresponding executive motor acts, a process of which ADRIAN has said that 'the nervous system reacts to relations between stimuli and performs the appropriate task with any part of the motor system that is available. We cannot represent it as a series of machines for operating on the mape of events unless we add a number of devices to make good this fundamental difference. On the sensory side there must be something to abstract the significant elements of a pattern; on the motor side something to do just the reverse, to convert the abstraction into a concrete movement'. In other words, the central nervous system of man 'decodes' efferent and 'codes' afferent streams of impulses of the kind involved in the initiation and control of motor acts.

An area in which didactic techniques designed to establish skill in execution are very far advanced is *keyboard music*. As an example, I refer to the role of the 'study' or of the 'étude', defined in Grove's *Dictionary of Music and Musicians* as 'a class of musical composition of extremely varied scope and design, whose chief object is the cultivation of the powers of execution'.

Facility to play on the keyboard is achieved by practicing technical exercises, such as scales and arpeggios, by each hand separately, consequently by both hands in unison. Up to the middle of the eighteenth century such technical exercises were taught in a dry and unattractive form. In Voltaire's *Candide,* published in 1759, the 'Illustrissimo Lord Prococurante' complained that 'music nowadays is merely the art of executing difficulties and in the end that which is only difficult ceases to please'. Decisive attempts to improve this kind of short-coming were made by Domenico Scarlatti and by Johann Sebastian Bach whose *Notenbüchlein* for his wife Maria Magdalena and his son Friedemann have ever since been used by music teachers. Moreover, Bach, in seeking to establish the perfect relationship of the tempered scales, produced forty-eight preludes and fugues that, besides being inherently beautiful, have remained the classical touchstone of piano pedagogy. More than a century later Chopin who always limbered up for his own concerts by playing from Bach's 'Well-Tempered Clavichord', presented in his twenty-four études a series of 'field of the territory he felt had to be explored in order to enlarge the range of piano technique' (W. BROCKWAY and H. WEINSTOCK, *Men of Music,* New York, 1937). In almost every one of them he dealt with technical problems involved in the new kind of music he was composing. Each étude was designed as an exercise to overcome specific difficulties of execution. The study in thirds (Opus 25, No. 6) and the tremendous one in octaves (Opus 25, No. 10) reveal their teaching purposes at a glance. Even such a passionate outburst as the 'revolutionary' étude (Opus 10, No. 12) is essentially a technical study of the very highest order for the left hand.

These études initiated a world-wide advancement of piano technique just as 150 years before Chopin, Bach had caused an advancement of musical technique in its entirety. The cellist Pablo Casals said that he plays Bach 'as pianists play Chopin'. In setting forth technical problems, both Bach and Chopin created music of great esthetic value, thus providing the motivation without which nobody can be induced to spend the necessary time practising. The best of Chopin's études are among the finest compositions for the piano. It has been truly said that he who can play Chopin's études can play anything in modern piano literature.

The history of the musical study represents a model of methodology for the teaching of advanced skills of all kinds. The time will come when it will serve as a didactic guide for the development of gymnastics and physical training.

Construction plans for all human pursuits which aspire to the attainment of excellence of motor performance demand that the pupil spends a great *amount of time* practising. Track champions devote four to five hours per day to their training. In a comprehensive study of a selected group of Sweden's best girl swimmers, ASTRAND *et al.* found that performances differed in accordance with the volume of training: those girls who swam 60,000 meters per week achieved significantly better results than others who swam 10,000 meters. The former also developed a more pronounced adaptive enlargement of their hearts and a greater capacity to absorb oxygen.

Eighty years ago John Ruskin, the British art critic, made a statement whose validity extends beyond the field to which it was meant to apply:

'If we were to be asked abruptly, and required to answer briefly, what qualities chiefly distinguished great artists from feeble artists, we should answer, I suppose, first, their sensibility and tenderness; secondly, their imagination; and thirdly, their industry. Some of us might, perhaps, doubt the justice of attaching so much importance to this last character, because we have all known clever men who were indolent, and dull men who were industrious. But though you may have known clever men who were indolent, you never knew a 'great' man who was so; and, during such investigation as I have been able to give to the lives of the artists whose works are in all points noblest, no fact ever looms so large upon me—no law remains so steadfast in the universality of its application—as the fact and law that they are all great workers. Nothing concerning all great workers is a matter of more astonishment than the quantity they have accomplished in the given length of their life; and when I hear a young man spoken of, as giving promise of high genius, the first question I ask about him is always— Does he work?'

Ruskin's law is equally valid in respect of the acquisition of skill. Its significance is greater than that of any other determinant of performance. In statistical parlance one would say that sustained practice is a determinant of the first order whose effectiveness is aided by a variety of determinants of second, third, etc. order, each of them related to the objective under reference. For example, TANNER has identified a number of *anthropometric* characteristics of successful participants in a variety of athletic contests; REINDELL of Freiburg, Germany, has described profound discongruities of patterns of *cardiovascular adaptation* between Olympic long distance cyclists and weight lifters; in my own laboratory, *diverse personality features* were found to distinguish successful basketball players from outstanding swimmers. There is overwhelming evidence showing that each kind of athletic performance depends upon the specific morphology of functional or psychological states. At the same time, the personal history of every champion athlete reveals the determining role played in his career by intensive, sustained training. Intensive, sustained training is an indispensable prerequisite for athletic as well as artistic success. Without it the full potentialities of neuromotor skill cannot unfold themselves.

I like to quote from an account given by Eva Bosakova, the Czechoslovakian gymnastic champion, of the years of preparation which preceded her Olympic victories in the contest on the balancing beam in 1956 and 1960. When Miss Bosakova was 15 years old her father, himself an outstanding gymnast, began to supervise her training:

'He prescribed daily thirty minute periods of work on the beam during which it was necessary to remain on the apparatus constantly in action, walking, hopping, turning, and again walking without rest. I spent hundreds of hours and uncounted kilometers walking and running on the beam'.

After some time the beam became her favorite gymnastic event. 'I constantly searched for new methods of training, elements, and arrangements for my exercises. In the process I gained complete confidence, accustomed myself to unfamiliar situations, and lost all fear of falling. Each exercise period lasted more than one hour. During this time, I went through my whole routine five to seven times. Afterwards, I worked on individual phases of the exercises and their connections, selected passages and their combinations. At the height of my career, it took me from about six to eight months to acquire mastery of a new exercise such as those prescribed for the Olympic Games.'

It is thus that skill is acquired. Sustained practice of concisely designed sequences of movements establishes advanced levels of control of differentiation, and of precision of motor acts such as are beyond the integrative control of the untrained.

The *constructive plan* for the execution of a skilled movement also presupposes *memory* for its structure as well as for the components from which it is synthesized.

STRAUS has shown that memory is selective. Of our daily actions we generally do not retain details but remember only 'the whole' and 'the remarkable'. To register, STRAUS says, means to disengage and to arrest the fleeting from the continuum of confrontations with the world. If an event is to be remembered, it must be different and separable from other things. It has to have 'marks of distinction', marks which the observer can identify. Yet, not each and every difference makes an event remarkable. There must be a significant change in the flow of events. STRAUS' thesis is that only the new, or the *Novum,* can be disengaged, arrested, registered, and recalled. This statement applies to ideas, concepts, emotional experiences, as well as to motor performances. The capacity to disengage components of the motor act involved in the training of performances demanding skill presupposes *intelligence;* to identify them as *'Nova'* didactic competence.

The *Novum* cannot be measured. It represents a specifically human happening of 'historical dimensions'. As to the memorability of *motor* events, only *'focal acts'* can thus be 'disengaged'. The term 'focal act' was coined by SHERRINGTON who distinguished between 'grades of acts'. We think, he wrote, of ourselves as engaged from moment to moment in doing this or that. This is a convenience of speech. At any given time, there is but one 'focal doing' which presents the keypiece of the performance to which all other motor events are subordinate. The crack pistol shot can hit his target whether he stands, sits, or lies. Postures and movements that are but contributory to the focal act are called 'satellite movements'. Satellite movements fit into the total pattern of the act—but they do not enter the field of awareness. Only to the 'focal act' can awareness be attached and if so to but one act at a time. No individual is ever the seat of two focal acts at once, nor can two events be simultaneously recorded as memory traces. Both the main act of the moment and the memory trace thus enjoy a special position.

'The main act', SHERRINGTON says, 'seems to each of us, amid a natural world we do not control, a happening which we do control. It seems to me I do it not at the dictation of the inevitable. In turning to it I do not seem to myself to be merely carrying out something already completely fixed for me by the past. I am restricted to one such act at a time for it is always an act which demands my fully integrated self. I cannot, therefore, break away from a deterministic world in several directions at once. As to the one main act which I am allowed, it seems to me I have freedom of choice'.

Terms like 'the main act' or 'freedom of choice' have different connotations in different stages of the process of acquisition of skill. Even though the objectives of all differentiated motor performances are specific, their execution cannot be so in the beginning. For instance, in sport as well as in the arts a long period of general physical conditioning and practice of component parts of the complex performance precedes the attainment of mastery of the task in its final form. Success or failure are eventually assessed in accordance with *technical,* as well as *interpretive* criteria. The development of music into a cultural pursuit of the highest order is largely due to the fact that its content has been rendered identifiable through the elaboration of *staff notation.* An artist's ability to perform a particular composition from staff notation is a hallmark of his competency, even though it is true that there are also other critical aspects of his performance. At the height of their concert careers some of the greatest pianists of this century, among them Busoni and Gieseking, could memorize a composition simply by looking at the score sheet and thereupon play it without further practice. In 1961, Oxford University Press published a textbook by the viola virtuoso William Primrose under the meaningful title *'Technique is Memory.'* It deals with 'the relationship between memory, concentration, and accuracy, and the topography of the fingerboard'.

As a result of the perfection of staff notation, the student of music today has access to the collective technical and esthetic experiences of the past. He can acquaint himself with and memorize them. The athlete cannot to the same extent benefit from the skill and knowledge gained by others. However, the progressive improvement during the past decades of all performances in sport is in part due to the advancement of techniques of what Medawar calls 'extrasomatic hereditary communication', through techniques which conceptualize and record acquired information and render it accessible to every beginner. Attempts to elaborate a system of staff notation of movements in physical education, sport and athletics are currently beginning to yield results which are comparable to those which in the past two and a half centuries have facilitated developments in the communication of music. Promising efforts in the graphic representation of motor performances have recently been made in choreography, as well as in the transcription of the modern dance, of gymnastics and of calisthenics. Universally recognizable memory traces are made available, to serve every athlete as guides during his training.

Didactic Procedures

Most didactic procedures which are applied in athletic training today were identified first from observations of successful performers. The situation is the same as that in music which is taught on the basis of what Bach and Haydn and Mozart and Mendelssohn and Brahms have written, even though analytical studies undertaken *post festum* have contributed to their understanding and enjoyment as well as to the acquisition of such skills as are necessary for the performance of the compositions under reference. The following is a summary of an interview with the Princeton University basketball player Bill Bradley[2]:

[2] JOHN MCPHEE, in 'The New Yorker', January 23, 1965.

Bradley's hook shot consists of the high-lifted knee of the Los Angeles Lakers' Darrell Imhoff, the arms of Bill Russell of the Boston Celtics, who extends his idle hand far under his shooting arm and thus stabilizes the shot, and the general approach of Kentucky's Cotton Nash. Bradley carries his analyses of shots further than merely identifying them with pieces of these players. 'There are five parts to the hook shot', Bradley explains. As he continues, he picks up a ball and stands about eighteen feet from a basket. 'Crouch', he says, whereupon he crouches and demonstrates the other moves. 'Turn your head to look for the basket, step, kick, and follow through with your arms.' Once, as he was explaining this to me, the ball curled around the rim and failed to go in.

'What happened?' I asked him.

'I didn't kick high enough', he said.

'Do you always know exactly why you've missed a shot?'

'Yes', he said, missing another one.

'What happened that time?'

'I was talking to you. I didn't concentrate. One of the secrets of shooting is concentration'.

Accompaniment of Mind

In the initial stages of practising a new task, all acquired skills are characterized 'by accompaniment of mind'. At first, awareness is concentrated on *mechanical* aspects of the act. With increasing skill however, the motor event becomes progessively more automatic and the mind now concerns itself with its *aims*. On the highest levels of technical perfection performance and performer seem to merge in the attainment of the objective, and with it of experiences mediated by its realization. Man's capacity for transforming the former into the latter represents the physiological basis of all motor pursuits in which *technical* mastery is the prerequisite for the creation of *esthetic* and *emotional* values. In *Johann Sebastian Bach's b-minor mass,* ritual, text and music combine to convey the idea of the transubstantiation of the bread and of the wine. The *Greek drama* demonstrates the transforming power of 'catharsis', of the reverberation in the mind of the onlooker of the happenings on the stage. In lyrical poetry, literary allegory causes reality to undergo a magic change: in *Heinrich Heine's Dichterliebe* tears turn into flowers and sighs into a chorus of nightingales. Corresponding categories of transformation are accompaniments of the acquisition of all skills of a high order of differentiation. The significance of the superb feats of the three handicapped champions to whom reference was made earlier cannot be fathomed in their entirety in terms of the athletic success attained by them; their triumph actually altered their entire lives.

During the Victorian age, 'ladies' were not expected to indulge in sport. The saying 'a horse sweats, a man perspires, but a lady only glows' reflects the restrictive views held at the time. Since then, social attitudes have undergone a profound change, with the result that millions of girls have indulged in sports, gymnastics and games; competed in swimming, on track and field, and on horseback; have climbed mountains and swam through a thousand rivers and lakes. They have derived therefrom some of the most valuable experiences of their lives.

SHERRINGTON has emphasized that our bodies are the one part of nature of which we have 'direct' knowledge. One may well add that there are grades of such direct knowledge, and that the differentiation of skill which comes with sustained practice facilitates its expansion. The average city dweller can no longer acquire such knowledge. SUSAN LANGER has pointed out that town people today know nothing of the earth's productivity; that they do not know the sunrise and rarely notice when the sun sets. Ask them what phase the moon is in or when the tide in the harbor is high, and likely as not they cannot answer. Seed time and harvest are nothing to them. The power of nature is not felt by them as a reality. Realities are to them the motors that run elevators or electricity over the wires; or the crates of foodstuffs that arrive by night; or the concrete and brick, bright steel and dingy woodwork that take the place of earth and waterside and sheltering roof for them. Nature, as man has always known it, he knows no more.

However, man's capacity to acquire skill continues to place into his hands a key which opens doors to a world of values inside himself by acquainting him with potentialities which are inherent in the world around all of us. The skilled motor act, SHERRINGTON wrote, 'seems to clinch the distinction between self and not-self'. The doer's doings affirm the self.

The problem of 'the distinction of the self and not-self', as SHERRINGTON saw it, represents one of the key issues of the border-territory between neurophysiology and philosophy. Its exploration has been furthered by contemporary exponents of phenomenology, chief among them ERWIN STRAUS to whose writings I have refered, and JURG ZUTT.

The Inner Attitude

In a paper entitled 'Die innere Haltung' ZUTT has analyzed the problem, starting out from the following question: 'What do I mean when I speak of a person assuming an attitude, e.g., a friendly, soldierlike, philosophical, or negative attitude?' What happens if I represent something which I am not; if a child pretends to be an adult, a horse, or a railway engine; or if a grown-up imitates another person with a view to ridiculing him; or if an actor gives 'his version' of a literary figure on the stage?

In such situations, ZUTT says, something is set in motion in us, an attitude is 'adopted' which corresponds with the idea of the person or subject before our mind. Something is constituted in us which attains a measure of independence *vis-à-vis* the 'I', something from which details of our subsequent behavior derive, as it were, automatically. If I wish to play the part of a conceited person, I do not decide, step by step, to raise my eyebrows, to lower my eyelids, to lift my chin, to drop the corners of my mouth, to cross my arms, to hold my fingers rigidly extended, etc. All my postures and movements are engendered by a single act of adoption of an inner attitude.

If I do so with a view to playing the part of a given character or person, e.g. on the stage, I establish in myself a state from which my subsequent actions flow with an evident degree of independence; at the same time the 'I' is capable of observing the situation as if from outside. One could also say that by assuming an inner attitude, a person introduces into himself features of another person while his observant 'I' retains its relationship with the outside world and with it an awareness of the arbitrariness of the situation.

Attitude, Posture and Movement

A close relationship exists between a person's inner attitude and his *posture* and *movements*. That from a given inner attitude *motor acts* derive spontaneously has already been mentioned. *Vice versa,* postures and movements may elicit corresponding mental experiences. It is virtually impossible for me to assume the attitude of a conceited man unless I carry out the movements which in my view characterize his behavior. Of course, I can *imagine* his as well as other attitudes. But the *experienced* situation engendered by the commensurate *motor acts* is different from that brought about by *mere imagination*.

The conclusion seems to be warranted that specific nuances of awareness which accompany a given inner attitude depend upon the motor acts which express it. To a degree, motor acts are prerequisites of experienced attitudes. Motor acts may actually establish commensurate attitudes: a devout Catholic will find it impossible to go through the ritual motions of the Holy Mass without engendering in his mind a state akin to that which attendance at Mass itself evokes. Evidently, motions are directly represented in our awareness.

Expressive movements and their corresponding experiences are two facets of the same phenomenon. The German word 'Haltung'—in combination with the adjectives 'äussere' and 'innere'—relates to both. The English language requires for the semantic identification of the same phenomenon two different substantives, namely, 'posture' and 'attitude'. But the fact remains that to every purposive movement are attached specific expressive connotations. The latter attain their meaning only in relation to the body in its entirety: it is not the same if I raise my eyebrows and wrinkle my forehead; or if I do likewise and at the same time look searchingly around the room; or place a cupped hand behind one ear.

Experience and Expression

What about the *original* doer, the person who experiences in *reality* situations of the kind whose *playful* representation we have considered? Does he not also assume an inner attitude? Do not details of his actions also derive automatically from his inner attitude? If so, what is the difference? The difference lies in the position of the 'I'. The original doer's inner attitude is *not* that of a *quasi* foreign person; it is his own. His 'I' identifies itself with his inner attitude of the moment. Contrariwise, the 'I' of the individual who acts or poses or pretends does not establish such identification. *Identification with one's inner attitude, as compared with observation of one's inner attitude by the 'I', are mutually exclusive states.* The former presupposes *subjective* participation; while the latter involves confrontation and *objectivation.* In contrast to the original doer, the 'actor' always maintains a distance between the 'I' and the event.

Since inner attitudes determine all voluntary actions, every voluntary motor performance possesses expressive characteristics. A task as simple as taking a book from the table can be executed in a shy, hasty, impatient, or disinterested manner.

Expression and Experience

In speaking of *voluntary* motor acts we do not include bodily events which are controlled by the *autonomic* system even though the latter is invariably mobilized during deliberate movements. Insofar as willed acts involve participation of the *vegetative* realm, they are not reflected in our awareness with that quality of experience which attaches to the *motor* performance *sensu strictiori.* The difference between the two qualities need not be consciously appreciated. However, the fact remains that the two mental states are not synonymous even though they influence each other.

The scope and nature of expression of which different parts of the body are capable vary. The *legs* cannot to the same extent convey expressive detail as can the *hands;* while the muscles of the *face* are more communicative than those of the hands. The highest degree of expressive differentiation attaches to the movements of *speech.* In any given situation the 'meaning' of voluntary movements corresponds with the individual's inner attitude: as the actor plays his self-chosen role on the stage, his manner of speech is in agreement with his pantomime, his postures, and his movements. If a child converses over the telephone with his teacher, he is likely to assume a respectful attitude even though he knows that the teacher can not see him. *Bodily movements and speech form a communicative entity.* This is so because at any one time a person can assume but *one* inner attitude. To reiterate SHERRINGTON: 'Mind can never be attached to more than one purpose'.

Thought, Language and Motor Behavior

We are, of course, able to think without expressing our thoughts in language. However, whenever we do express our thoughts in language, we commit our entire voluntary musculature to a unified style of expression. True, the degree of recognizability of this relationship differs from situation to situation. But the mutual dependence between thinking and speaking and posture and movements is clearly demonstrable. If a visitor interrupts me while I work in my laboratory, I may react thus: 'I cannot allow anybody to disturb me now'; but I may respond differently, e.g. so: 'My visitor is, I know, a reasonable person; he will understand if I say that I prefer him to call tomorrow'. My gestures accompanying these two different responses will differ accordingly, and their respective verbal expression will establish different inner attitudes which in turn are to determine my motor behavior.

Though inner attitudes change frequently, certain fundamental trends remain constant over long periods. This is the reason why it is possible to speak of a person as sincere, or honest, or proud, or courteous. Such assessments are derived from our knowledge of his movements, gestures, and words—to reiterate, there are no other means of communication between people. Each individual's personality is characterized by an element of constancy which pervades his inner attitudes and thus also his motor behavior.

Affects

Our awareness and with it our attitudes are influenced by *affects*. If a person is sad, he usually assumes an attitude of sadness. Everybody will then recognize him as being sad. But he may hide his sadness, even pretend to be gay. It is impossible to say that his gaiety is a mere bodily facade and that his sadness remains totally unchanged behind the mask. We have already mentioned that all expressive movements are represented in our awareness and that gestures, movements, and language are accompanied by corresponding states of awareness. Evidently, sad and gay affects can exist side by side, even though the sad person who pretends to be gay does not experience his gaiety in the same manner in which a truly gay person does. Thus, there is a difference between the state of awareness of a person whose attitudes and affects correspond, and that of one in whom no such correspondence prevails. The perceptive outside observer recognizes the difference.

The essential distinction between *affects* and *inner attitudes* is that I am capable of adopting inner attitudes in accordance with my wishes;

but that I am unable to do so in respect of my affects. I cannot make up my mind to be happily excited or to be sad, but I can make up my mind to play the role of a conceited man. The distinction between inner attitude and the affects is also reflected in the close relationship between inner attitude and voluntary movement. This relationship has no parallel in respect of the affects. We speak of *'being affected'*, but of *'assuming an attitude'*. The passive form in the first, and the active in the second indicate the categorical discongruity of the two states.

Autonomic Accompaniments

The affects exert an influence upon the *autonomic* system, e.g. upon our heart beat or the blood flow through our skin—we may become 'pale with fright', or 'flushed with excitement'. Affects also may modify perspiration, digestive functions, etc. In contrast to the inner attitude, the affects and thus their autonomic manifestations are independent of our will. Just as we cannot directly modify the influence of an affect upon the function of our heart or stomach, it is impossible for us to escape the *mental* impact of an affect.

We can—within limits—hide an affect 'before the world'. But we cannot hide it before ourselves. We can also reinforce an affect by assuming a commensurate inner attitude, e.g. that which an athlete assumes when he participates in a competition. In this instance the affect tends to engender a corresponding inner attitude. This is an example of a categorical interrelation. We speak of persons being 'crushed by despair' or 'elevated by joy'. In fact, a distinct mental effort is needed to assume an inner attitude that is *not* in agreement with an affect. An affect may be so overwhelming that it is impossible to hide it. In such a situation we say that the 'affected' person is 'unable to control himself'. An affect cannot be extinguished through deliberate assumption of an antagonistic inner attitude.

On Being Civilized

Since the neuro-muscular system of man is his sole medium of interpersonal communication, its differentiation through training represents a major determinant of the individual's capacity to act and to react.

The acquisition of skill thus attains a significance of its own. It enlarges his scope of action, the range of his experience and thus of his freedom. The enjoyment which comes from competing in a tennis match is inaccessible to those who are not acquainted with the skills of the game; the keyboard of the piano means nothing to those who are not familiar with the technique of playing on it. If I have failed to acquire skills, I am restricted in respect of taking action upon my environment. My experiences will thereupon be confined to a correspondingly narrowed field. *Vice versa,* if I am conversant with a multiplicity of skills; if I can perform in the worlds of sports and arts and crafts and languages, I have access to a richer and more diversified life. Kant wrote 200 years ago that the more civilized a person is, the better can he meet the demands with which life in its present form confronts him. The ability to do so, Kant held, is one of the hallmarks of being civilized.

References

ADRIAN, E.D.: Physical Background of Perception (Oxford/London 1947).
ASTRAND, P.-O.; ENGSTRÖM, L.; ERIKSSON, B.O.; KARLBERG, P.; NYLANDER, I.; SALTIN, B. and THOREN, C.: Girl swimmers, Acta paediat. Suppl. *147,* (1963).
CRITCHLEY, MACDONALD: The Parietal Lobes (Arnold, London 1953).
DENNY-BROWN: cit. by CRITCHLEY.
FRUCHT, A.H.: Die Grenzen der menschlichen Leistungsfähigkeit im Sport (Akademie Verlag, Berlin 1960).
GEBSATTEL, V.E. v.: Prolegomena einer medizinischen Anthropologie (Springer, Berlin 1954).
GERSTMANN, J.: Fingeragnosie: Eine umschriebene Störung der Orientierung am eigenen Körper. Wien. klin. Wschr. *37:* 1010–1012 (1924).
JACKSON, HUGHLINGS: Selected Writings, Vols. 1 and 2 (Basic Books, New York 1958).
JOKL, ERNST: The Scope of Exercise in Rehabilitation (Thomas, Springfield 1964).
KLEIST, K.: Über Apraxie. Mschr. Psychiat. Neurol. *19:* 269–290 (1906).
LANGE, J.: Agnosien und Apraxien; BUMKE, O. and FOERSTER, O.: Hb. d. Neurol. *6:* 807–960 (Springer, Berlin 1936).
LANGER, SUSAN: Reflections on Art (Oxford/New York 1961).
MAYER-GROSS, W.: Some Observations on Aproaxia. Proc. Roy. Soc. Med. *28:* 1203–1212 (1935).
REINDELL, H. *et al.:* Herz-Kreislauf-Krankheiten und Sport (Barth, München 1960).
SHERRINGTON, CHARLES: Man on his Nature (Cambridge/London 1940).
STRAUS, E.: Phenomenology of Remembering. Acta psychother. *8:* 334–351 (1960).
STRAUS, E.: Psychologie der menschlichen Welt (Springer, Berlin 1960).
TANNER, J.M.: The Physique of the Olympic Athlete (Allen and Unwin, London 1964).
ZUTT, J.: Die innere Haltung. Mschr. Psychiat. Neurol. *73:* 52 (1929).

Author's address: Professor E. JOKL, University of Kentucky, *Lexington,* Kentucky (U.S.A.).

I. Technique of Motion Studies:
Cinematographic and Photographic Methods

Biomechanics I, 1st Int. Seminar Zurich 1967
pp. 23-32 (Karger, Basel/New York 1968)

Bürgerhospital Saarbrücken – Orthopädische Abteilung (Prof. Groh) und Institut für angewandte Physik und Elektrotechnik (Prof. Eckart) Universität des Saarlandes, Saarbrücken

Kinematische Bewegungsanalyse

H. Groh und W. Baumann

1. Kinematische Bewegungsanlayse

Die historische Entwicklung der Untersuchung menschlicher Körperbewegung, die 1679 mit dem Italiener Borelli beginnt und bis 1895
zu dem Deutschen Otto Fischer reicht, kann in diesem Rahmen, so
reizvoll sie an sich ist, nicht dargestellt werden. Wenn ich heute versuche, einige Fragen der *kinematischen Bewegungsanalyse* Ihnen darzustellen, so möchte ich drei Dinge zeigen:

1. Verschiedene Methoden der Darstellung und Veranschaulichung
von Bewegungsabläufen durch Fotobild und Filmbild.

2. Einige Ergebnisse der quantitativen physikalischen Analyse von
Filmbildern.

3. Die zukünftige Entwicklung neuer analytischer Methoden durch
neue Meßgeräte.

Wir unterscheiden zwischen der anschaulichen Darstellung von Bewegungsabläufen und der physikalischen Analyse von Bewegungsabläufen. Veranschaulichung von Bewegungsabläufen ist möglich durch
fotografisches Einzelbild – Stroboskop- oder Reihenbild – Trommelkamerabild – filmähnliches Reihenbild – Lichtspurbild – Filmbildserie –
Ringfilm – Ringtrickfilm.

Bei der physikalischen Analyse von Bewegungsabläufen stehen uns
zur Verfügung:

1. Die Filmbildanalyse mit der Möglichkeit der Bestimmung von
Weg, Geschwindigkeit, Beschleunigung und Kräften.

2. Die Kombination von Lichtpunktfilm und direkter Beschleunigungsmessung an den Gliedachsen.

3. Die automatische elektronische Analyse durch eine Auswertanlage.

2. Methoden zur Darstellung von Bewegungsabläufen

Das *Stroboskopbild* zeigt verschiedene Phasen einer Bewegung auf einer Platte. Es eignet sich vorwiegend zur Veranschaulichung eines Bewegungsablaufes, vor allem als Farbbild. Es kommt zur Überdeckung der Glieder, wenn der Körper im Raum nicht fortbewegt wird. Bei einem Start z.B. findet eine zu geringe Fortbewegung im Raum statt (Abb. 1).

Die *Trommelkamera* aber erlaubt die zeitliche Auflösung, auch wenn keine Fortbewegung im Raume stattfindet. Wegen der hohen zeitlichen Auflösung können auch extrem schnelle Vorgänge dargestellt werden, z.B. wie eine Pistolenkugel eine Glaswand durchschlägt. Das ist

Abb. 1. Stroboskopbild eines Startes – Überdeckung der Glieder wegen zu geringer Fortbewegung im Raum.

Abb. 2. Trommelkamerabild eines Startes – Das Maximum liegt bei 50 m/sec Filmgeschwindigkeit.

in der Biomechanik kein Vorteil, weil die hohe Frequenz bei der relativ langsamen menschlichen Körperbewegung nicht nötig ist (Abb. 2).

Beim *Lichtspurbild* wird die Fotoplatte im Dunkeln bei offenem Verschluß durch das Dauerlicht von Glühlämpchen, die am Körper angebracht sind, belichtet. Abbildung 3 zeigt das Lichtspurbild eines Startes. Abgebildet sind: Fußgelenk, Kniegelenk, Hüftgelenk, Handgelenk, Ellenbogengelenk, Schultergelenk, Kopf. Bei Anbringung eines räumlichen Maßstabes und intermittierenden Lichtquellen wäre eine räumliche und zeitliche Auswertung der Lichtspurbilder möglich. Das Verfahren bietet keinen Vorteil gegenüber der Kinematographie. Es ermöglicht allerdings eine anschauliche und ästhetische Betrachtung menschlicher Körperbewegung.

Abb. 3. Beim Lichtspurbild wird der Bewegungsablauf der Gliederachsen kontinuierlich aufgezeichnet.

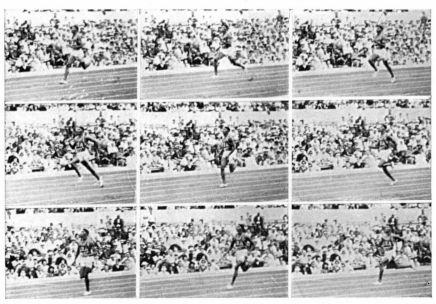

Abb. 4. Bildserie des 400 m-Laufes von Otis DAVIS auf der Olympiade in Rom 1960 (Nett).

Bildserien von Filmen lassen ein anschauliches Erleben und Studieren von Bewegungsabläufen zu (Abb. 4).

Alle diese Methoden sind ausschließlich geeignet zur anschaulichen Darstellung von Bewegungsabläufen. Sie werden daher in reichem Maße und mit Erfolg im Unterricht und zu Lehrzwecken angewandt.

3. Zur quantitativen Analyse von Bewegungsabläufen durch die Kinematographie

Aus Filmbildern läßt sich eine Analyse der Kinematik der Bewegung durchführen, wenn ein räumlicher und zeitlicher Maßstab vorhanden ist, wenn also der Abbildungsmaßstab und die Bildfolgefrequenz bekannt sind. Es wurden zu diesem Zweck Meßstäbe im Objektraum angebracht. Als zeitlicher Maßstab wurde die Bildfolgefrequenz der Kamera auf einem Oscillographen registriert. Die Gelenkachsen der Versuchsperson wurden markiert. Zur Auswertung wird auf dem Projektionsbild entweder die Lage dieser Gelenkpunkte ausgemessen oder es werden die von den Gliederachsen miteinander gebildeten Winkel ausgemessen.

Wir haben die Winkelmessung vorgezogen, da sich die Fehler bei der Abstandmessung der Gelenkachsen als zu groß erwiesen haben.

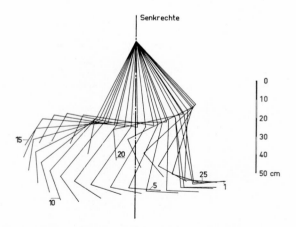

Abb. 5. Beinbewegung beim 100 m-Lauf – Reduktion der Beinbewegung auf eine Rotation um die feststehende Hüftgelenkachse.

Der Meßfehler bei der Winkelmessung beträgt ± 0,5°. Die entsprechenden Gliederlängen werden unmittelbar an der Versuchsperson
durch Meßband bzw. Röntgenbild bestimmt.

Für die Beinbewegung beim 100 m-Lauf ergibt sich Abbildung 5.
Es ist die Fortbewegung im Raum auf eine Rotation der Glieder des
Beines um die als feststehend gedachte Hüftgelenkachse reduziert. So
ergibt sich die reine Gliederbewegung des Beines beim 100 m-Lauf.

Trägt man den Winkel der Gliedmaßen in ein Koordinaten-System
ein und verbindet die Meßpunkte der Einzelbilder durch eine glatte
Kurve, dann erhält man die Wegkurve des Fußballens. Die Zeitdauer der
Abstoßphase des Fußes ist mit 50 ms außerordentlich kurz. Die Differentiation dieser Wegkurve führt zur Geschwindigkeitskurve. Die Maximal-
geschwindigkeit des Fußballens errechnet sich dabei mit 12 m/sec =
43 km/h. Nochmalige Differentiation führt zur Beschleunigungskurve.
Die maximale Beschleunigung des Fußballens wurde mit 42 g errechnet.

Errechnet man aus den Filmbildern die Bewegung des Beinschwerpunktes um die Hüftgelenkachse (Abb. 6), so erhält die Beschleunigungskurve ein ausgeprägtes Maximum am Ende der Abstoßphase
des Fußes am Boden. In der kurzen Abstoßzeit des Fußballens von
50 m/sec (10-14). erhält der Beinschwerpunkt eine Beschleunigung von
max. 22 g. Die Kraft, mit der der Beinschwerpunkt dabei bewegt
wird, errechnet sich mit rund 300 kp.

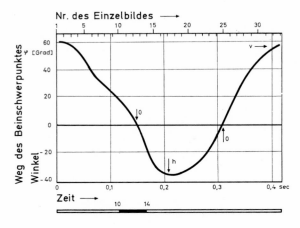

6a

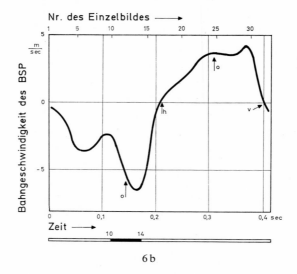

6 b

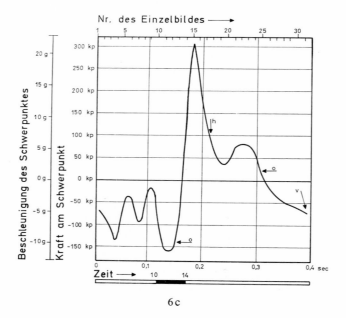

6 c

Abb. 6. Wegkurve – Geschwindigkeitskurve – Beschleunigungskurve des Beinschwerpunktes beim 100 m-Lauf. Dauer der Abstoßphase 50 ms – Maximalbeschleunigung 22 g – die bewegende Kraft liegt bei 300 kp.

o = O-Durchgang, h = hintere Umkehr, v = vordere Umkehr.

Eine exakte Fehlerrechnung der rein formal durch Differenzieren gewonnenen Geschwindigkeits- und Beschleunigungskurven ergibt folgendes (Abb. 7). Der von uns bei der Winkelmessung begangene Fehler vergrößert sich zwangsläufig als Gauss'sche Fehlerfortpflanzung bei der Geschwindigkeitskurve und noch mehr bei der Beschleunigungskurve. Die Breite der aufgezeichneten Wegkurve bedeutet einen Meßfehler von ± 0,5°. Dieser Meßfehler vergrößert sich bei Ableitung der Geschwindigkeit deutlich, aber nicht wesentlich (Abb. 7b). Bei der Beschleunigungskurve (Abb. 7c) wird der Fehler so groß wie die Beschleunigungswerte selbst. Die gestrichelte Kurve ist der errechnete Wert der Beschleunigung. Die durchgezogenen 2 Kurven bezeichnen die Fehlergrenzen. Jede innerhalb dieser einhüllenden Kurven eingezeichnete glatte Beschleunigungskurve hat den gleichen Anspruch auf Richtigkeit, wie die von uns errechnete. Aus diesem Grunde ist die kinematographische Methode zwar geeignet zur Berechnung von Weg und Geschwindigkeit, nicht aber zur Ermittlung der Beschleunigung.

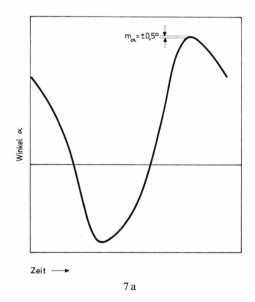

7 a

Abb. 7. Fehlerrechnung: 7a Wegkurve – *7b* Geschwindigkeitskurve – *7c Beschleunigungskurve.* Der Fehler erreicht die Größenordnung der Beschleunigungswerte selbst.

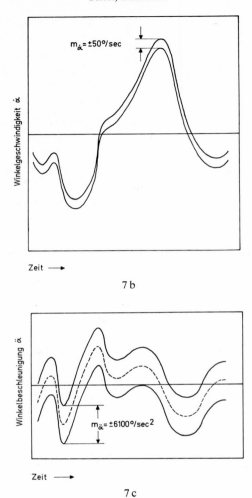

7 b

7 c

4. *Bewegungsanalyse aus Lichtpunktfilm und direkter Beschleunigungsmessung*

Gerade die Beschleunigung und die mit ihr verbundene Kraft sind aber die wesentlichen physikalischen Kenngrößen einer Bewegung. Um sie zu ermitteln, haben wir einen neuen Weg eingeschlagen. Wir messen die Beschleunigung unmittelbar durch Beschleunigungsmesser. Diese werden in Höhe der Gelenkachsen an den Gliedern fixiert. Die

Übertragung der Meßwerte zum Registriergerät erfolgt drahtlos mit einem mehrkanaligen UKW-Sender.

Um die Richtung der einzelnen ständig bewegten Beschleunigungsmesser zu erfassen, werden sie mit kleinen Lichtquellen versehen. Der gleichzeitig mit der Beschleunigungsmessung aufgenommene Lichtpunktfilm gibt den Ort und die Bewegungsrichtung der einzelnen Beschleunigungsmesser an. Damit kann ihre Zuordnung zum Koordinatensystem des Raumes berechnet werden.

Dieses Verfahren kombiniert das hohe örtliche Auflösungsvermögen des Films mit der ausgezeichneten zeitlichen Auflösung der Beschleunigungsmesser. Damit ist eine Analyse der Kinematik und der menschlichen Körperbewegung mit genügender Genauigkeit möglich.

5. Automatische elektronische Auswertanlage

Die außerordentliche Vielzahl von Einzelinformationen und Rechenoperationen macht es bereits bei wenigen Bewegungsphasen zu einem unmöglichen Unterfangen von Hand auszuwerten. Wir werden deshalb unsere Meßkurven und Filmbilder mit einer elektronischen Anlage automatisch auswerten (Abb. 8). Das Prinzip der automatischen Auswertanlage ist folgendes: Der Filmstreifen, der die Lichtpunkte oder die Beschleunigungskurven als Information trägt, wird von dem Elek-

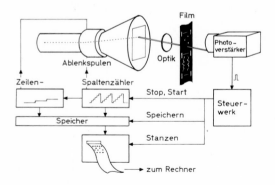

Abb. 8. Schaltbild einer automatischen Auswertanlage: Braun'sche Röhre – Filmstreifen – Fotoverstärker – Steuerwerk – Speicher – Lochstreifen. Die Koordinatenwerte der Kurvenpunkte werden in Lochstreifen gestanzt und mittels Programm durch einen Elektronenrechner ausgewertet.

tronenstrahl eines BRAUN'schen Rohres – links oben – abgetastet. Der
Punkt durchläuft ähnlich wie beim Fernsehbild die ganze Bildebene
zeilenweise. Trifft er eine Information, d.h. eine Hellstelle auf dem
Film – oben Mitte – dann wird der Strahl über Fotoverstärker und
Steuerwerk (rechts) gestoppt. Der Koordinatenwert des Meßpunktes
wird als Nummer der Zeile und als Nummer der Spalte – links un-
ten – festgestellt, einem Speicher – links unten – übergeben und in
Lochstreifen – ganz unten – gestanzt. Auf diese Weise wird Bild für
Bild abgetastet und sämtliche Koordinatenwerte der Lichtpunkte und
Beschleunigungskurven in Lochstreifen gestanzt.

Mit Hilfe eines speziellen Programmes werden durch einen Elektronenrechner Filmbilder und Beschleunigungskurven einander zuge-
ordnet. Der Rechner liefert in kurzer Zeit alle Informationen zur Bewegungsanalyse, die man aus Lichtpunktfilm und Beschleunigungskurven gewinnen kann.

Diese Anlage bietet vielfältige Möglichkeiten für Serienuntersu-
chungen, auch der menschlichen Körperbewegung.

Adresse des Autors: Prof. Dr. H. GROH, Rastbachweg 2, D-66 *Saarbrücken* (Deutschland)

Biomechanics I, 1st Int. Seminar Zurich 1967
pp. 33–36 (Karger, Basel/New York 1968)

Fakultät für Körperkultur und Sport, Abteilung Biomechanik, Karls-Universität, Prag

Verarbeitung von biomechanischen Informationen durch die Detektionsphotomethode

A. Nováк

Einleitung

Bewegungsanalysen mittels Film sind heute weit verbreitet. Die Methode gibt direkte Informationen über den Bewegungsablauf in Raum und Zeit. Die weiteren Charakteristiken der Kinematik, Geschwindigkeit und Beschleunigung, lassen sich graphisch oder rechnerisch ableiten und führen zur Dynamik über.

Analyse des Kugelstoßens mit Film und Koordinatenwand

Beim Kugelstoßen darf die Bahn der Kugel als in einer Ebene liegend betrachtet werden. Fertigt man Filme für Bewegungsstudien des Kugelstoßens an, kann man sich die Arbeit wesentlich vereinfachen, wenn hinter dem Stößer ein zur Wurfebene paralleles Koordinatennetz mitgefilmt wird. Bei Bedarf könnte diese Technik auch bei schwenkbarer Kamera Anwendung finden, sofern nur die gefilmten Bewegungen genügend genau parallel zum Koordinatennetz bleiben und die Meßpunkte am Körper sorgfältig eruiert werden (z.B. Umrisse genügen dafür nicht mehr!).

Für die Auswertung kann das Bewegungsbild durch zentrale Projektion in die Koordinatenebene oder noch besser, das Koordinatennetz in die Stoßebene übertragen werden.

Als bekannte Größe (siehe Abb. 2) treten auf:

m Distanz Kamera–Bewegungsebene (ist ständig zu beobachten)
n Distanz Kamera–Netzebene

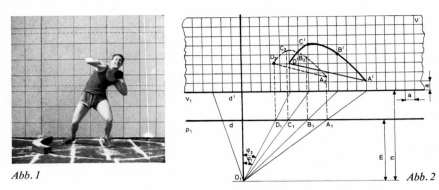

Abb. 1   *Abb. 2*

Abb. 1. Die Aufnahme des Kugelstößers mit der Koordinatenwand.
Abb. 2. Das Schema der Überführung zentraler Projektion (volle Linie) auf die senkrechte Projektion (gestrichelte Linie).

a Seite des Quadrats am Koordinatennetz.

Es gilt: $d : d' = m : n = k$.

Dazu kommt noch die Verkleinerung der Aufnahme oder Auswertung $1 : x$. Die Seite des Quadrats für das Auswertungsnetz ist dann $a_x = a \cdot k \cdot \frac{1}{x}$.

Damit lassen sich Winkel direkt und Längen maßstäblich ausmessen. z.B.

Für die Gesamtverkleinerung $1:17$ zeichnen wir ein Auswertungsnetz mit Quadraten mit Seiten $a_x = 30 \cdot \frac{7,50}{8,75} \cdot \frac{1}{17} = 1,51$ cm. In dieses Netz tragen wir nach den Filmaufnahmen die einzelnen Positionen ein und erhalten die Bahn der Kugel (Abb. 3).

In der Abstoßphase geht die Bahn der Kugel durch die Positionen 0–5. Aus der Aufzeichnung messen wir (oder errechnen aus den Koordinaten) die Länge der einzelnen Bahnabschnitte Δs_i für i = 1–5 von Position 0 ausgehend und transferieren sie auf die wirkliche Größe (Maßstab der graphischen Darstellung ist $1:17$, den abgemessenen Wert multiplizieren wir also mit 17).

Die Bildfrequenz der Kamera war $f = 21$ Bildwechsel/s. Das Zeitintervall zwischen zwei Nachbarpositionen ist also $\Delta t = \frac{1}{21}$ s.

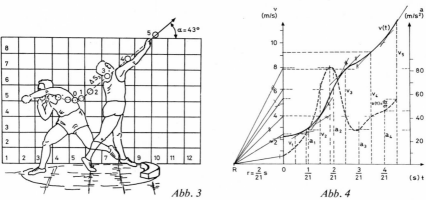

Abb. 3   *Abb. 4*

Abb. 3. Graphische Verarbeitung der Filmaufnahme. Die Kugelbahn erscheint in dem
Quadratnetz so, als ob die Koordinatenwand in der Bewegungsebene wäre.
Abb. 4. Graphische Darstellung des Verlaufes der Geschwindigkeit und Beschleunigung
der Kugel in der Abstoßphase.

Zur Berechnung der Durchschnittswerte der Geschwindigkeit und
der Beschleunigung benützen wir die bekannten Formeln $v_i = \dfrac{\Delta s_i}{\Delta t}$
und $a_i = \dfrac{\Delta v_i}{\Delta t}$. Die Resultate können wir in Tafeln eintragen, über-
sichtlicher zeigt jedoch die graphische Darstellung den Verlauf dieser
Werte in Abhängigkeit von der Zeit (Abb. 4). Die Beschleunigung
wurde hier auch durch graphische Derivation abgeleitet.

Auf Grund der bekannten Beschleunigung können wir auch die
Kraft, die auf die Kugel einwirkt, ermitteln. Diese Kraft ist das Produkt
der Kugelmasse und der Muskelbeschleunigung. Die Resultate, die wir
erhalten, sind allerdings nur aproximativ.

Der Abstoßwinkel aus der graphischen Darstellung der Bahn gemessen, ist $\alpha = 43°$ (Abb. 3). Für diesen Winkel und die errechnete
Abstoßgeschwindigkeit $v = 11,4$ m/s erhalten wir theoretisch durch
Einsatz in die Formel für die Wurflänge eine Leistung $d = 13,14$ m.
Die wirkliche gemessene Leistung betrug 13,25 m. Die Werte stimmen
fast überein, bei der Berechnung wurden nicht alle Umstände in Erwä-
gung gezogen (z.B. die Höhe des Loslassens der Kugel).

Kurze Schlußfolgerungen

Aus dem Verlauf der Geschwindigkeit und der Beschleunigung, aus
der Form der Bahn und der Richtung der Bewegung kann man

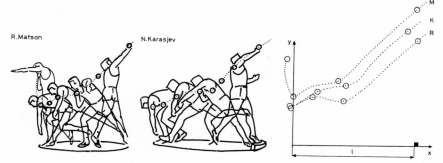

Abb. 5. Der Kugelstoß des MATSON und KARASJEV (nach KUTJEV).
Abb. 6. Der Vergleich der Kugelbahnen bei MATSON (M), KARASJEV (K) und bei unserem Kugelstößer (R).

Schlüsse, die den Grad der Technik sowie die Funktion des Organismus angehen, machen.

Der Kugelstößer (ein Hochschüler), dessen Stoß untersucht wurde, hatte noch so manche Mängel. Die Bahn der Kugel sank ihm nach dem Hupfschritt unter die waagrechte Ebene, wogegen bei prominenten Kugelstößern, welche wir auf der Abbildung 5 sehen, MATSON und KARASJEV, dieser Mangel nicht vorkommt. (Die Abbildungen wurden aus der Zeitschrift LEGKAJA ATLETIKA entnommen). Ersichtlich ist dies besonders bei gemeinsam schematisch eingezeichneten Bahnen auf Abbildung 6. Der Verlauf der Kugelbahn des KARASJEV ist aber nicht so ökonomisch wie bei MATSON.

Ein größerer Abstoßwinkel (α auf Abb. 3) beeinflußt die Abstoßgeschwindigkeit ungünstig. Die Schnelligkeit in der Abstoßphase steigt nicht zügig, die Beschleunigung schwankt (Abb. 4) was auf eine falsche Einschaltung der Kraft und die Notwendigkeit der Anstrengungserhöhung hinweist.

Die konkreten Erkenntnisse, die wir auf Grund der objektiven Informationen erhalten haben, sind von überzeugendem Wert. Solche Erkenntnisse verbessern dann die Trainingsarbeit im Sport.

Literatur

HOCHMUTH, G.: Biomechanik (DHfK, Leipzig 1962).
KUTJEV, N.: Jadro tolkajut mastera. Legkaja atletika *12:* 8–9 (1966).
NOVÁK, A.: Biomechanika telesnych cvičení (SPN, Praha 1965).

Author's address: A. NOVÁK, M.D., Ujezd 450, *Praha 1* (CSSR).

Biomechanics I, 1st Int. Seminar Zurich 1967
pp. 37–41 (Karger, Basel/New York 1968)

Yugoslav Institute for Physical Culture, Belgrade

Analysis of Movement by Film

R. Gombac

Filming

Technique is usually analysed on the basis of the visible form of movement and on the basis of mechanical elements which are obtained from the film. In order to obtain all data needed from the film, it is necessary to film the movement under specific predetermined conditions. In this respect, from our experience, the following points should be mentioned:

1. Filming should be done with a fixed camera in order to permit computing of the distance element of movement.

2. Before filming the action, distance marks placed in the line of movement should be photographed by the camera.

3. The field of vision should include two to three static objects or points (pole, part of a building, or the like). These will serve as points of orientation when data are taken from the screen.

4. Time elements are also essential for computations. It is necessary to establish the time lapse between two frames, or the operating speed of the camera.

5. The operating speed at which the camera should be set depends on the speed of the movement to be photographed, the number of 'movement segments' needed for proper analysis, and the type of camera.

Description of Method

The simplest form of graphic presentation of movement based on film is the contourogram. It is obtained by transposing one, two or more contours of the athlete observed.

Before developing the contourogram it is necessary to determine the characteristic positions of the technique being analysed. These positions are transposed from the film on to paper.

Based on the contourogram, certain definite conclusions on the athlete's technique may be reached. In each movement there are established regularities. Sometimes it is sufficient to examine a specific position or positions only in order to be able to determine whether the preceding technique was correct or not, or whether from such a position further movement may be carried out properly.

The second form of this method is the cyclogram, which is obtained by transposing specific points from the film onto paper (such as, centers of joints, parts of the object, etc.). By tying up the points the trajectory is obtained.

The analysis of the trajectory of specific points offers considerable information about the technique. If, at the same time, the speed of the point's movement, acceleration and acting forces are determined, there are sufficient elements for a detailed analysis.

For detailed analysis the two forms, contourogram and cyclogram, are usually combined. Contours are tied to the trajectory of certain points, for which space and time elements of movement are determined (Fig. 1).

Fig. 1

Technique of Work

The first step is to accurately determine the speed of the camera. This is done by viewing that part of the film on which the stop watch is recorded. The number of frames per second and, subsequently, the *unit of time* are thus determined.

The next step is determinig the *multiplier*. This is the number by which each distance between points should be multiplied in order to determine the actual distance of their.movement in space. This factor is computed on the basis of the photographed distance marks.

The graphic presentation of the movement is the following step. It consists in taking down the contours and points under observation. Which frames will be used in the process depends on the speed of the camera, velocity of movement, type of movement and other factors.

When all necessary data have been transposed from the film, computation may begin. This whole procedure is presented in the following example:

Table of Mechanical Values

Shot putting

No. of frames	'd' (mm)	'D' (m)	'V' (m/sec)	'a' (m/sec²)	'P' (kg)
146	5,1	0,054	3,51	29,25	21,00
147	6,5	0,068	4,42	59,15	42,00
148	8,0	0,084	5,46	67,60	49,00
149	9,8	0,103	6,69	79,95	58,00
150	10,0	0,108	7,02	21,45	15,50
151	10,7	0,113	7,34	20,80	15,00
152	11,5	0,121	7,86	33,80	24,50

Legend:
d = distance between points observed
D = distance covered in unit of time
V = speed of shot
a = acceleration
P = strength

Speed of camera = 65 f/s; Unit of time = $t = \dfrac{1}{65}$ sec

Multiplier – M = 10,53

Example for calculating the stated values for frame No. 149.

Distance: $D = d \times M = 0{,}098 \times 10{,}53 = 0{,}103$ m

Speed: $V = \dfrac{D}{t} = \dfrac{0{,}103}{\dfrac{1}{65}} = 0{,}103 \times 65 = 6{,}69$ m/sec

Acceleration: $a = \dfrac{V_2 - V_1}{t_2 - t_1} = \dfrac{\dfrac{6,69 - 5,46}{1}}{65} = 1,23 \times 65 = 79,95 \ \text{m/sec}^2$

$$\boxed{-\ t_2\ -\ t_1\ =\ t}$$

Strength: $P = m \times a = 0,725 \times 79,95 = 58,00 \ \text{kg};$ $\boxed{m = \dfrac{G}{g}}$

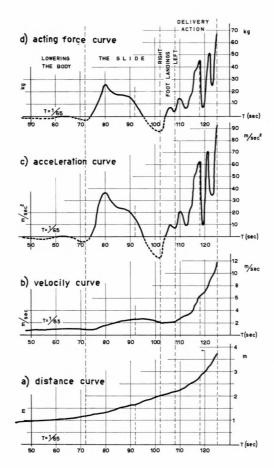

Fig. 2

In this manner, all values may be computed for each unit of time. The values of the vertical and horizontal movement may be separately computed, if desired.

The obtained values are more easily analyzed when presented in the form of a diagram (Fig. 2). The horizontal axis is the time axis, and it remains unchanged for each diagram. The vertical axis represents the computed values. In this way, all values can easily be read for each moment of analyzed action.

This method may be applied for registering all movements performed in a plane, or which are closely related to movements in the plane. However, it is not suitable for analyzing movements in which the third dimension has a significant role.

Author's address: R. GOMBAC, M.S., Yugoslav Institute for Physical Culture, Kneza Viseslava 42, *Belgrade-8* (Yugoslavia).

Biomechanics I, 1st Int. Seminar Zurich 1967
pp. 42–44 (Karger, Basel/New York 1968)

St. Mary's College, Twickenham

Analysis of Film – The Segmentation Method

B.J. Hopper and J.E. Kane

For many years the slow-motion film has been used by students of physical movement to observe and correct defects in technique and to suggest lines along which improvement might be made.

However, it is possible to extend the use of such films to study the development of the force-pattern involved in the action and to see to what extent it corresponds to the optimum one suggested by mechanical considerations; and this can be done because the specific movement given to the body of an athlete, gymnast, or other performer, and recorded on film, is completely determined by the forces brought into play at the different stages of the action.

Although it is obvious that the results obtained by the use of dynamometers, force-platforms, etc. carry potentially greater weight than the indirect estimation of forces from the movements revealed on film; yet this equipment may not always be readily available, and, furthermore, requires the presence of the performer. The segmentation method is one way of attempting to obtain the same information more simply.

Many athletic and gymnastic activities involve a straight run-up to the point where the main effort is made, so that a suitably-placed camera can get a record of this effort as the performer crosses the field of view. If the action has been filmed against accurately-positioned background-markers, the motion at right-angles to the camera-shot can be measured on a known scale: particularly the motion of each chosen part, or "segment" of the body (upperarm etc.), from one frame of the film to subsequent ones. Given the frame-rate, and assumimg the relative masses of the segments to be known with reasonable precision, the path of the center of gravity of the body in this particular plane can be worked out; or, more usually, the variation of its horizontal and vertical position with time can be plotted. Measurements from this latter graph give horizontal and vertical components of force at every stage.

Technique of the Method

One of the frames to be studied is projected on squared paper pinned to a fixed board mounted at right-angles to the optical axis of the projector. The projection-distance is adjusted to give a suitable scaling-down of the picture; say 1/12. This is obtained from the position of the background markers. If a commercial film is being used, with no such markers, a reasonable estimate of distance can be made from other things such as the known height of the performer, or that of standard pieces of apparatus used by him.

Such other marks as are likely to prove useful are drawn in on the squared paper, and a run-through of the film is then carried out to see if others, not in view on the first frame, appear on others subsequently examined. A check is also made to see if the projected pictures show the chosen marks in exactly the same relative positions. If, through panning or otherwise there are discrepancies, it may be desirable to make corrections to co-ordinates plotted from the squared paper.

The next step is to pin a set of sheets of translucent typing copy-paper, or similar material, over the squared master-sheet and to project the first frame on to it: pencilling in the fixed marks, as before, on the top sheet. The outline of the body of the performer, or the estimated positions of the centers of gravity of each of his segments is now drawn on the top sheet, which is numbered and torn off. The same procedure is adopted with the next frame on the new sheet, and with all the others required for the analysis.

The relative masses of specific components of the average male or female may be obtained from medical and other sources, and it has to be assumed that the subject being studied conforms closely with the figures used. It is for this reason that attempts to achieve greater ac-curacy by increased precision of measurement have limited value, parti-cularly when only a fair estimate of the position of a hidden compo-nent can be made. It is convenient to number the individual positions of the centers of gravity of the segments, the somewhat doubtful posi-tions of the hidden ones being indicated as having reduced reliability.

It is now necessary to place these numbered and marked sheets in turn over the master-sheet; to bring the background markings on them into co-incidence, and to read off the co-ordinates of each segment-position from the horizontal and vertical axes shown on the squared paper. This is sometimes done on top of a sheet of glass illuminated from underneath, but this is by no means necessary. The co-ordinates for each segment are entered in columns on prepared tabular sheets, the arrangement making it easy for subsequent calculation. This in-volves the multiplication of each co-ordinate by the percentage of body-mass of the segment to which it refers; the addition of such products; and their final division by 100. From this information the position of G for the whole body is found for every frame: a position which can then be marked-in by making use of the master sheet, its axes and background marks.

Difficulties, Limitations, etc.

1. Non-standard Mass Distribution

This has been mentioned already. Deviations from the standard mass distribution seldom make a difference to the plotted points which is as great as the random error introduced by the estimation of segmental center of gravity positions. The existence of a deviation of this type will be apparent if the measured vertical acceleration of the performer in an airborne action is not that of a freely-falling body. If the subject is available he could be made to perform a somersault over a trampoline in order to confirm his suitability for analysis by this method. If analysis of rotary motion is being undertaken, his angular momentum about the relevant axis through his center of gravity should be found to be constant in such an airborne phase.

2. Covering of one Part of the Body by Another

This is usually most serious in the case of the remote arm, which at some stage will be hidden by the trunk. Fortunately, the number of frames for which its position cannot be viewed are few, and the unknown co-ordinates of this component have to be found by interpolating between earlier and later ones which are in view. It often happens that the disappearance occurs during an airborne phase; e.g. in the hurdling stride, for which the path of the center of gravity can be determined without using information from all frames of the film.

3. Errors of Obliquity

There is only one point at which the camera-shot is at right-angles to the action being studied, and although all measurements are made with respect to the accurately-spaced distance-markers covering all parts of the field of view, such markers will not appear in their correct relative positions unless the pictures are projected with apparatus having the same optical characteristics as the camera. The need for making corrections for the distortion introduced is something that may arise, particularly if the camera has had to be panned in order to take in a wide field of view.

It must be appreciated that segmentation only gives a simple method of obtaining a more precise estimate of the position of the center of gravity than a single visual estimate will give. Its accuracy, and therefore its use for this type of detailed analysis, has to be assessed for each film studied. It is a method in which, given a suitable film, precision depends on how much time and care is taken in using it. If a quick, preliminary survey shows that a film is capable of giving more detailed information, then not only can the horizontal and vertical components of the acceleration of the center of gravity be calculated from the distance-time graph, but the angular movement of each segment around it can be measured in order to find what changes in angular momentum take place during the action. These can then be related to the turning-moment of the force acting on the performer as the movement proceeds.

Author's address: B.J. HOPPER and J.E. KANE, St. Mary's College, Strawberry Hill, *Twickenham* (England).

Biomechanics I, 1st Int. Seminar Zurich 1967
pp. 45–52 (Karger, Basel/New York 1968)

Institut für Leibesübungen der Universität Frankfurt

Lichtspuraufnahmen – Technik und Möglichkeiten

F. Fetz

I. Einführung

Im Bestreben, Bewegungsabläufe exakt zu beschreiben, zu analysieren und ihre wichtigsten Eigenschaften in objektiven Kennlinien darzustellen, wurden viele Untersuchungsmethoden entwickelt. Eine davon ist die Lichtspurmethode. Sie dient dazu, Ortsveränderungen ausgewählter, mit Lichtquellen markierter Punkte zu verfolgen. Bei dauergeöffnetem Verschluß werden die Lichtspuren von einem geeignet aufgestellten Photoapparat auf einer Platte festgehalten. Der Schwerpunkt der folgenden Betrachtungen liegt im Gebiet der Biomechanik der Leibesübungen.

Soweit die Technik der Lichtspuraufnahmen anwendbar ist und die erreichbare Genauigkeit den Versuchsanforderungen entspricht, wird die Methode infolge ihrer Einfachheit und Billigkeit anderen kinematographischen Methoden, Chronophotographie und Zeitlupenfilme, vorzuziehen sein.

Vor allem französische Gelehrte (MAREY, DEMENY u.a.) trugen in den letzten Jahrzenten des 19. Jahrhunderts zur Vervollkommnung der Chronophotographie bei. Die von MAREY vorgenommene Abstraktion der Chronophotographie auf am Körper angebrachte Streifen mußte in ihrer Weiterentwicklung notwendig zur Lichtspuraufnahme (Zyklographie) führen. FISCHER und BRAUNE verwenden (1895) anstelle der weißen Streifen bereits GEISSLERsche Röhren und bedienen sich damit der eigentlichen Lichtspuraufnahmen [9, S. 15]. Die Lichtspuraufnahme ist als eine Sonderform der Chronophotographie zu betrachten, bei der man sich auf Markierung besonders interessanter Punkte beschränkt und diese zu direkten oder indirekten Lichtquellen macht.

II. Technik der Lichtspuraufnahmen

Die Technik der Lichtspuraufnahmen wird jeweils von der Aufgabenstellung diktiert. Sind nur räumliche Formen gefragt, so genügen häufig einfache Taschenlampen als Lichtquellen. Will man aber Geschwindigkeiten und Beschleunigungen berücksichtigen, dann sind periodisch unterbrochene Lichtspuren erforderlich. Bei großen Beschleunigungen (Verzögerungen) müssen erschütterungsunempfindliche Geräte eingesetzt werden.

Aufgabenstellungen und zugehörige Techniken

1. Bestimmung räumlicher Bahnen ausgewählter bewegter Punkte bei einfachen motorischen Abläufen.

Zugehörige Techniken der Lichtspuraufnahme: Einfache an Körper oder Gerät befestigte Lichtquellen und gewöhnliche Photoapparate, evtl. Wahl besonderer Wellenlängen des Lichtes (bei Ausführung in Helligkeit); Glühbirne oder kleine Spiegel zur Lichtreflexion.

Einige Beispiele mögen Einblick in die Vielfalt der Anwendungsmöglichkeiten dieser Methode geben.

a) Formanalysen zur Bestimmung des *Übungseffektes* oder des Fertigkeitsniveaus. Abbildung 1 zeigt die Lichtspuren von Beinkreisen, die eine Vp. zu Beginn und am Ende einer etwa sechswöchigen Übungszeit ausgeführt hat (ERDMANN). Mit Hilfe der Streuung der Lichtspuren auf konjugierten Durchmessern kann man den Übungseffekt berechnen.

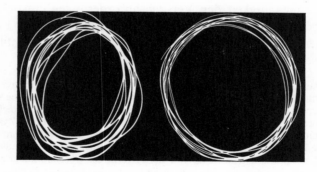

Abb. 1. Beinkreise zu Beginn und am Ende einer etwa sechswöchigen Übungszeit.

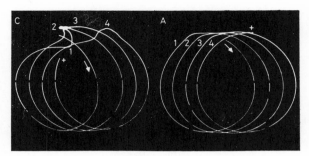

Abb. 2. Fersenpunktkurven von je 4 Rollen rückwärts am Barren von Vp. verschiedener Leistungsklassen.

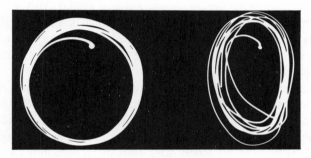

Abb. 3. Armkreise ohne und mit Belastung des Unterarms.

Abbildung 2 gibt Lichtspuren des Fersenpunktes bei Rollen rückwärts am Barren wieder (O. HANEBUTH, [7] S. 45). Die Lichtspuren zeigen deutliche Unterschiede im motorischen Fertigkeitsniveau.

b) Untersuchung des *Belastungseinflusses* auf den räumlichen Bewegungsablauf. In Abbildung 3 werden Lichtspuren von je 10 Armkreisen ohne und mit Belastung des Unterarms festgehalten (FETZ [4] S. 94). Durch derartige Untersuchungen kann man beispielsweise zu optimalgewichtigen Sportgeräten für die verschiedenen Altersstufen kommen.

c) *Technik- und Stiluntersuchungen.* Durch Formanalysen können Eigenheiten der jeweiligen Techniken und des Stils untersucht werden. Dieser Sektor gehört zu den wichtigsten Anwendungsbereichen der Lichtspurmethode. Aus solchen Analysen können wichtige Korrekturen für das praktische Training hervorgehen. Eigenarten der Technik und der persönlichen Prägung zeigen die Lichtspuren beim Gewichtheben (Abbildung 4, D.D. DONSKOI [2] S. 164).

115 kg   135 kg

Abb. 4. Lichtspuren beim Gewichtheben.

d) *Gestaltcharakter der Motorik.* Zu den ersten Anwendungen der Lichtspurmethode im Bereich der Sportmotorik gehören die Untersuchungen MÖCKELMANNS zum «Gestaltcharakter der Motorik» [14].

e) Untersuchung intraindividueller *Formkonstanz (Präzision)* bei Bewegungsabläufen (Abb. 1).

f) Untersuchungen der Raumgestaltung in Kunstturnen oder Gymnastik. Die Raumgestaltung ist ein qualitätsbestimmender Faktor bei der Beurteilung von Kürübungen. In vielen Fällen ist es möglich, mit Hilfe von Lichtspuraufnahmen ein gutes Bild der Raumgestaltung, z.B. bei Kürübungen an Reck oder Barren zu erhalten (Abbildung 5 zeigt Lichtspuren des Fußpunktes bei einer einfachen Übungsverbindung am Reck (O. HANEBUTH [7] S. 47).

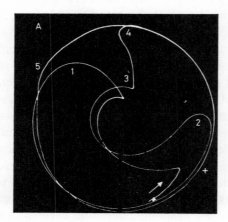

Abb. 5. Fußpunktkurve einer Übungsverbindung am Reck.

2. Bestimmung räumlich-zeitlicher Faktoren oder Merkmale ausgewählter bewegter Punkte bei motorischen Abläufen.

Zugehörige Techniken: Intermittierendes Licht (Glimmlampen
ohne Nachleuchten bzw. Glühbirnen, Abbildungen 6 und 7, von be-
kannter Frequenz oder Sektorenblende zur Unterbrechung des Licht-
weges vor dem Objektiv) und Photoapparat bzw. Spiegelung intermittierenden Lichts an ausgewählten Punkten und Photoapparat (oder
Filmkamera).

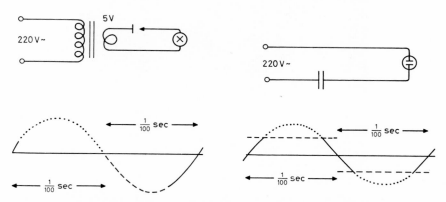

Abb. 6. Schaltung und Leuchtschema der Glühbirne (aus Fetz, F. [4] S. 175).
Abb. 7. Schaltung und Leuchtschema der Glimmlampe (aus Fetz, F. [4] S. 175).

Mit intermittierendem Licht können alle Formanalysen hinsichtlich
Technik, Stil usw. durch Einbeziehung zeitlicher Faktoren verbessert
werden.

Entsprechende Studien eignen sich zur biomechanischen Grund-
lagenforschung:

a) Untersuchungen zum Prinzip der konstanten Figurzeit. Auf
Abbildung 8 sind Lichtspuren einfacher Schreibbewegungen festgehal-
ten. Sie sind geeignet, die konstante Figurzeit derartiger motorischer
Produktionen zu belegen (Fetz [4] S. 169).

b) Zusammenhang von Krümmung und Bewegungsgeschwindig-
keit. Auf Abbildung 9 sind die Lichtspuren wiedergegeben, die eine
Vp. auf den Auftrag hin, einen Kreis mit Beschleunigungen und
Verzögerungen zu zeichnen, gestaltet hat.

Abbildung 10 verdeutlicht den Zusammenhang, den Krümmung
und Bewegungsgeschwindigkeit beim obigen Versuch eingehen.

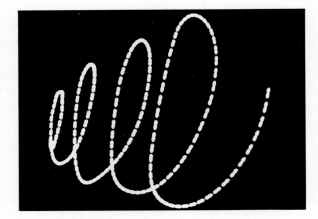

Abb. 8. Lichtspur einfacher Schreibbewegungen (aus FETZ, F. [4] S. 169).

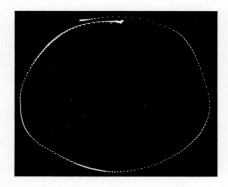

Abb. 9. Kreis mit Beschleunigungen (aus FETZ, F. [4] S. 179).

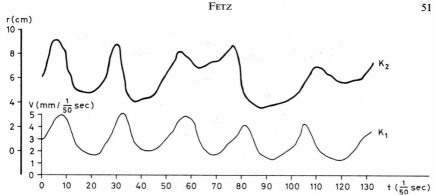

Abb. 10. Krümmungs- und Geschwindigkeitsdiagramm bei obiger Kreisgestaltung (aus FETZ, F. [4] S. 180).

III. Schwierigkeiten und Grenzen der Lichtspurmethode

Bewegungen müssen mehr oder weniger in einer Ebene (evtl. mehrere Kameras) ablaufen.

Verzerrungen bei großräumigen Bewegungen bzw. bei großem Bildwinkel. Gegenmittel: Teleoptik oder Verzerrungskorrektur. Auswertungsgenauigkeit ist auch durch Bildformat, Bildschärfe und Korngröße beschränkt.

Absolute Weg-, Geschwindigkeits- und Beschleunigungsuntersuchungen verlangen Vergleichsmaßstab (Eichung der Lichtspurstriche).

Aufnahmen bei Tageslicht erfordern Anwendung besonderer Wellenlängen (UV) und entsprechenden Filmmaterials. Geschwindigkeit oder Beschleunigung des KSP bzw. entsprechender biomechanischer Punkte können mit Lichtspuraufnahmen nicht genau ermittelt werden.

Literatur

1. DERWORT, A.: Untersuchungen über den Zeitablauf figurierter Bewegungen beim Menschen, Pflügers Arch. ges. Physiol. 661–675, *240:* (1938).
2. DONSKOI, D.D.: Biomechanik der Körperübungen: 163–165 (Sportverl., Berlin 1960).
3. ERDMANN, F.: Präzisionsleistungen menschlicher Motorik (Untersuchung der räumlichen Zielgenauigkeit an Hand- und Fußkreisen). Unveröffentl. Vorprüfungsarbeit, Institut für Leibesübungen (Frankfurt a.M. 1966).

4. FETZ, F.: Beiträge zu einer Bewegungslehre der Leibesübungen (Österr. Bundesverlag, Wien 1964).

5. HANEBUTH, O.: Gymnastik mit oder ohne Handgerät?, in: Die Leibeserziehung, 2, 2–7 (1953).

6. HANEBUTH, O.: Der Rhythmus in der Lehre und Gestaltung des Kunstturnens, in: Leibesübungen 12; 3–12 (1961).

7. HANEBUTH, O.: Rhythmisches Turnen – eine sportliche Kunst (Limpert, Frankfurt a.M. 1964).

8. HOCHMUTH, G.: Biomechanik. Lehrbrief. (Leipzig 1962).

9. KIETZ, G.: Gang und Seele. (Barth, München 1966).

10. KLEITER, K.: Zum Problem der konstanten Figurzeit. Unveröffentl. Vorprüfungs-arbeit, Institut für Leibesübungen (Frankfurt a.M. 1965).

11. MECKL, B.: Die Oberarmkippe am Barren, in: Praxis der Leibesübungen 12, 183 (1961).

12. MECKL, B.: Die Kippe vorlings am Reck, in: Praxis der Leibesübungen 1, 7 (1963)

13. MENZEL, G.: Stiluntersuchungen beim Lauf mit Hilfe von Lichtspurmethode und Reihenbild. Unveröffentl. Arbeit (Marburg 1955).

14. MÖCKELMANN, H.: Der Gestaltcharakter der Motorik und seine Bedeutung für die körperliche Erziehung. Habil. (Gießen 1933).

15. SONNTAG, R.: Das Bodenturnen unter dem Aspekt der Raumaufteilung, in: Theorie und Praxis der Körperkultur 15: 11, 984–989 (1966).

Adresse des Autors: Prof. Dr. F. FETZ, Institut für Leibesübungen der Universität Frankfurt, Frauenlobstraße 5, D-6 Frankfurt a.M. (Deutschland).

Biomechanics I, 1st Int. Seminar Zurich 1967
pp. 53–60 (Karger, Basel/New York 1968)

Abteilung Biomechanik-Motorik der Sektion Sportwissenschaft
(Direktor: Prof. Dr. habil. W. SCHRÖDER) der Friedrich-Schiller-Universität, Jena

Die digitale Erfassung kinematischer Parameter
der menschlichen Bewegung

W. GUTEWORT

Einführung

Die industriell angebotenen Möglichkeiten einer vollautomatischen Registrierung numerisch erfaßter Meßergebnisse durch Digital-recorder, der sehr geringe Zeitaufwand bei der Aufbereitung und Auswertung des Zahlenmaterials durch die Möglichkeit der programmierten elektronischen Datenverarbeitung und die damit verbundene Wirtschaftlichkeit solcher Methoden legt auch für die Bewegungsanalyse die Entwicklung digitaler Verfahren nahe. Der Aufbau einer *Kinemetrie* zur Gewinnung primärer Meßdaten und die direkte, rechnerische Ableitung von Kennziffern der menschlichen Bewegung sind eine gegenwärtig vorrangige Aufgabe[1].

1. Batteriegespeister Impulsgenerator zur Steuerung von Stroboskopglimmlampen

Zur Herstellung von Meßbildern mit zeitlich exakt definierten Lichtspuren entwickelten wir in Zusammenarbeit mit Mitarbeitern des VEB Carl Zeiss Jena einen tragbaren, batteriegespeisten Impulsgenerator als Meßsignalgeber.

Der Rechteckwellengenerator mußte klein, leicht, stoßfest, betriebs- und unfallsicher sein, da er an einer geeigneten Stelle des Körpers der Versuchsperson angebracht wird. Er steuert kleine Glimmlampen, die mittels Lochgummistreifen an den interessierenden Körperpunkten befestigt werden. Die Transformation von exakten Rechteckimpulsen im NF-Bereich ist unter den gegebenen Bedingungen nicht ratsam. Es wurde der Weg gewählt, die Hochspannung für die Glimmlampen mit

---

[1] Vgl. GUTEWORT, W. und PÖHLMANN, R.: Biomechanik – Motorik. Theor. u. Pr. d. Körperkultur. *15:* 595–604 (1966) und BALLREICH, R.: Entwicklungstendenzen in der Bewegungslehre der Leibesübungen. Leibeserziehung *15:* 424–428 (1966).

einem HF-Transverter zu erzeugen und die Glimmlampen mit HF zu speisen. Hierdurch ließen sich im Verein mit einer geeigneten Wahl der Gasfüllung der Glimmlampen photoaktive und der Sensibilisierung des verwendeten Filmmaterials (NP 27 von ORWO WOLFEN) entsprechende spektrale Abstrahlungscharakteristiken erzielen.

Der HF-Generator wird elektronisch mit einer stufenweise wählbaren Frequenz getastet. Die Tastimpulse werden mit einem astabilen symmetrischen Multivibrator erzeugt. Der Generator wurde mit einem Zählfrequenzmesser mit digitaler 7-Ziffern-Anzeige und einem Zählbetragdrucker mit einer Quarzfrequenz von 1 MHz geeicht, so daß der absolute Fehler der Meßanordnung $\pm$ 1 μs betrug.

2. Aufnahmebedingungen und Versuchsdurchführung

Für die Erfassung der Bewegung in 2 Koordinaten wurde eine Praktisix IIa mit Biometar 2,8/50 verwendet. Räumliche Bewegungen wurden mit neuentwickelten terrestrischen Stereomeßkammern des VEB Carl Zeiss Jena aufgenommen. Das Objektiv blieb während des gesam-

Abb. 1. Terrestrische Stereomeßkammer SMK 5,5/0808 des VEB Carl Zeiss Jena, 1200 mm Basis.

ten Bewegungsablaufes geöffnet. Um eine kontrastreiche, gut auswert-
bare Lichtspur zu erhalten, sind ein dunkler Hintergrund und eine
dunkle Kleidung der Versuchsperson sinnvoll. Lichtwerte von 4 bis 6
sollten nicht überschritten werden.

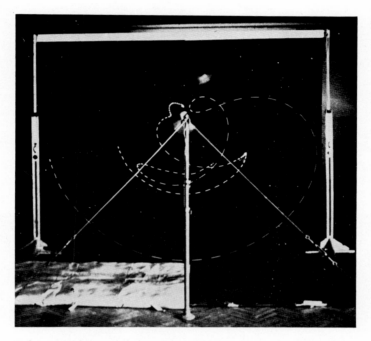

Abb. 2. Fuß- und Hüftkurve bei einer Schwungkippe am Reck (Gesamtaufbau).

Die Abbildungen 3 und 4 zeigen im Vergleich sehr deutlich die
wesentlich kleineren Meßschritte und die präzisere Meßpunktmar-
kierung bei der Impulslichtphotographie.

Da der Innenwiderstand des HF-Generators hoch ist und mit einer
zur Nervenreizung unwirksamen Hochfrequenz gearbeitet wird, werden die Vpn. auch bei Beschädigung der Apparatur nicht belästigt.
Der Maßstab wird durch die Aufnahme einer Nivellierlatte in der
Bewegungsebene erfaßt.

Nachteile der Methode bleiben die beschränkte Umfeldhelligkeit
und das Mitführen der Apparatur.

Abb. 3. Zyklo-Chrono-Photographie eines gymnastischen Schrittsprungs (4 Bilder/sec; für Meßzwecke ungeeignet).

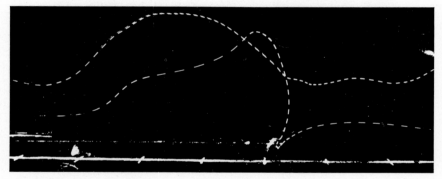

Abb. 4. Der gleiche Schrittsprung der künstlerischen Gymnastik wie Abbildung 3. Die Lichtspuren zeigen den Weg der Hüfte und des Fußgelenks vom Schwungbein.

Die digitale Auswertung der Meßphotos

1. Einbildvermessung mittels Meßmikroskop oder Profilprojektor

Für die Auswertung der Abbildungen von Bewegungsbahnen, die annähernd in einer Bewegungsebene ablaufen, d.h. wo die Zentralprojektion in eine Ebene ohne wesentliche Meßfehler möglich ist, benutzten wir Meßmikroskope bzw. Profilprojektoren. Unsere Erfahrungen haben gezeigt, daß diese Methode bei einer Genauigkeitsanforderung von etwa $\frac{1}{100}$ mm sehr gut zur raschen und wirtschaftlichen Bildvermessung eingesetzt werden können. Das Meßphoto befindet sich auf einem Koordinatenmeßtisch,

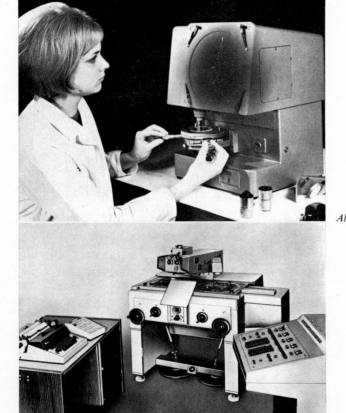

Abb. 5

Abb. 6

Abb. 5. Profilprojektor 200 des VEB Carl Zeiss Jena. Auf der kreisrunden Mattscheibe ist das vergrößerte Projektionsbild der Lichtspur zu sehen. Links unten befindet sich der Koordinatenmeßtisch mit der Halterung für die Meßphotos und den beiden Mikrometerschrauben.

Abb. 6. Gesamtansicht des *Stecometer* mit automatischer Registriereinrichtung. In der Bildmitte das Meßgerät, rechts das Steuerpult und links der Schreibautomat mit Streifenlocher und Lochstreifenleser.

der durch Mikrometerschrauben in x- und y-Richtung verschiebbar ist. Die Skalenwerte auf den Meßtrommeln betragen 0,01 mm.

Der entsprechend dem gewählten Objektiv 10-, 20- oder 50fach vergrößerte Bildausschnitt erscheint als Projektion auf einer Glasmattscheibe, wo das Projektionsbild auch direkt mit einem Glasmaßstab vermessen werden kann. Der hierbei auftretende Fehler beträgt $\pm (1 + \frac{150}{V} + \frac{L}{2}) \mu$m. (V = Vergrößerung; L = Meßlänge in mm).

2. Anwendung der analytischen Photogrammetrie

Eine weit höhere Meßgenauigkeit bei gleichzeitiger Verringerung des Arbeitszeitaufwandes, vor allem aber die Möglichkeit der räumlichen Erfassung bietet der Präzisionsstereokomparator *'Stecometer'* des VEB Carl Zeiss Jena.

Mit dem *Stecometer* können alle Meßbilder auf Glas oder Film bis zu einem Bildformat von 24×24 cm sowohl als Einbildvermessung in zwei Bildkoordinaten x' und y" als auch mittels Zweibildvermessung

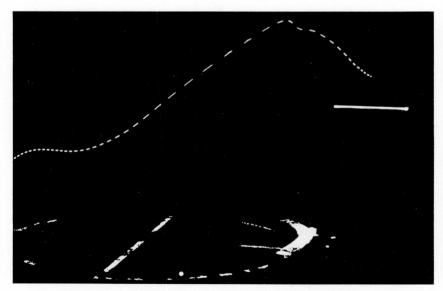

Abb. 7. Weg der Stoßhand beim Kugelstoß. (Verbunden mit der elektronischen Berechnung des optimalen Stoßwinkels in Abhängigkeit von der Abfluggeschwindigkeit und der Abstoßhöhe).

in drei Koordinaten durch zusätzliche Messung der Koordinatenparal-
laxen Px und Py punktweise analytisch ausgewertet werden. Die auf den
Bildträgern befestigten Meßbilder können über ein feststehendes Dop-
pelmikroskop mit einem Auflösungsvermögen von maximal 90 Linien/
mm betrachtet werden.

Die Einstellung in x'- und y''-Richtung erfolgt an Handrädern mittels einer eingespiegelten Leuchtmeßmarke, während die Parallaxen-
messung mit Fußscheiben vorgenommen wird. Der mittlere Koordina-
tenfehler beträgt ± 0,002 mm.

3. Automatische Meßwertregistrierung und elektronische Datenverarbeitung

Die Registrierung der Meßwerte erfolgt im *Stecometer* vollautomatisch
durch die Betätigung eines Fußpedals. Die analogen Informationen
werden über Drehmelder digital umgesetzt und entweder auf einen
Schreibautomaten als Koordinatenpunkttabelle in μm in Klartext aus-
gedruckt oder auf einen Streifenlocher als externen Speicher gegeben.
Von hier aus kann die Weiterverarbeitung sowohl im on-line als auch
im off-line-Verfahren über einen Lochstreifenleser in einem Computer
erfolgen. Aus wirtschaftlichen Gründen benutzten wir einen programm-
gesteuerten Kleinrechenautomaten *Cellatron 2c*. Die Programmierung
war so vorgenommen, daß der angeschlossene Schreibautomat Soem-
tron 527 in Tabellenform für jedes Intervall zwischen zwei Meßpunk-
ten folgende Werte ausdruckte:

1	2	3
Nummer des Meßbildes	laufende Punktnummer	zurückgelegter Weg s
4	5	6
Geschwindigkeit v	Beschleunigung b	Änderung der 3 Richtungscosinusse

Die vollständige Messung und Berechnung aller kinematischen
Größen eines Kugelweges beim Kugelstoß in ca. 70 Meßschritten
nahm etwa 40 Minuten in Anspruch.
Die enorme Verkürzung des Zeitaufwandes für die Meßwertermitt-
lung bei gleichzeitiger Verkleinerung der Meßzeitintervalle und Erhöhung der Meßgenauigkeit und die dadurch ermöglichte maschinelle
und elektronische Aufbereitung des Meßmaterials verbunden mit den

vielfältigen positiven Erfahrungen bei der Anwendung dieses Verfahrens auf die unterschiedlichsten biomechanischen und motorischen Fragestellungen legen die Vermutung nahe, daß diese Methode der Bewegungsobjektivierung und -analyse auf digitaler Basis sich künftig zu einer wertvollen Bereicherung der Möglichkeiten der Bewegungsaufzeichnung entwickeln wird.

Literatur

1. EDEN, J.A.: Measuring Instruments for the Analytical Photogrammetry. Conference of Commonwealth Survey Officers (1963) Paper No. 39.
2. HALLERT, B.: Test Measurements in Comparators and Tolerances for Such Instruments. Photogrammetric Engineering. 301–314 (1963).
3. HALLERT, B.: Bestimmung der Präzision und Genauigkeit eines Stereokomparators. Schweiz. Z., Vermess., Kulturtechn. Photogramm. 271–280 (1963).
4. HARLEY, I.A.: Some Notes on Stereocomparators. The Photogrammetric Record. 194–209 (1963).
5. HOTHMER, J.: Instrumentelle und methodische Fragen der analytischen Photogram metrie. Z. Vermesswesen. 233–245 (1962).
6. KERN, H.-G.: Ergebnisse von Testmessungen am Präzisionsstereokomparator Stecometer des VEB Carl Zeiß Jena. Vermessungstechnik *14:* 21–26 (1966).
7. MARK, R.-P.: Die Leistungsfähigkeit des Stecometer mit automatischer Registriervorrichtung. Vermessungstechnik *13:* 214–218 (1965).
8. PETROV, V.A.: Metody issledovanija i biomechaniceskij analis v sportivnoj technike. (Forschungsmethoden und biomechanische Analyse in der Sporttechnik). Teorija i praktika fiziceskoj kultury *30:* 8–11, H. 5 (1967).
9. SZANGOLIES, K.: Allgemeine Betrachtungen über die analytische Photogrammetrie. in VEB Carl Zeiß Jena Nachrichten, Kompendium 'Photogrammetrie', Sonderband IV. (Fischer Jena 1963).
10. SZANGOLIES, K.: Die Verwendung von Rechenautomaten für die photogrammetrische Auswertung. in VEB Carl Zeiß Jena Nachrichten, Kompendium 'Photogrammetrie', Sonderband IV (Fischer Jena 1963).

Die Abbildungen 1 und 6 sind Werkphotos des VEB Carl Zeiss Jena. Alle übrigen Aufnahmen entstanden in Zusammenarbeit studentischer Forschungszirkel des Instituts für Körpererziehung und der Hochschulfilm- und Bildstelle der Friedrich-Schiller-Universität Jena.

II. Technique of Motion Studies:
Mechanical and Electronical Measurements

Biomechanics I, 1st Int. Seminar Zurich 1967
pp. 61–66 (Karger, Basel/New York 1968)

Faculty of Physical Education and Sport Bratislava

The Electrogoniographic Method and its Position in the Methodology of Biomechanical Research on Human Motion

M. Koniar

A successful development of physical education and sport is impossible nowadays without a good theoretical foundation. This foundation is importantly enriched by the results of scientific research work, particularly in the field of theory, methods, and sporting technique. Scientific research work in physical education is, however, to a considerable degree, dependent on the stage of development of the technical sciences, especially on that of electrical engineering. The recording techniques make possible the study of the quantitative and qualitative sides of various phenomena. The higher the degree of measuring technique development, the deeper is it possible to delve into the bases of the studied phenomena of the laws of movement. This is also the case in the biomechanical study of sporting technique, i.e. studying the physical conditions of human motion in sport.

In the biomechanical study of human motion we use at the present time modern, progressive methods of investigation such as cinematography, stroboscopy, dynamography, electromyography, etc. But even with the exellent qualities of these methods we meet with various difficulties. Thus, for example, the question of the relative position of individual parts of a sportsman's body in various phases of movement gives, when studied by cinematography or stroboscopy, only a partial answer, as the three-dimensional movement cannot be precisely reproduced in a two-dimensional photographic picture or film recording. A similar situation will arise in the dynamic investigation of the movement where we are still not able to ascertain with sufficient preciseness the scope and course of the strength of the functional muscle groups in the course of a sportsman's movement. Therefore, scientific preciseness compels researchers to improve on the methods used up to now and find further progressive methods of movement study.

In recent times attention has been turned to the new method of studying a sportsman's movement, to the so-called *electrogoniographic method* (EGG). The quantities measured by the electrogoniographic method are angle changes in joints, occurring in the course of a sportsman's movements. As the structure of the sportsman's movement and therefore also his sporting technique is evaluated on the bases of continual kinematic and dynamic changes of the individual elements of the body, the angle changes in the joints thus become important indicators of its evaluation. On the basis of the goniographic studies of Karpovich and Gollnick [1] and others we have come to the conclusion that the electrogoniographic method can be used for study not only of angular changes of movements but also of other kinematic phenomena, because the angular changes of movements, recorded by the goniograph, appear here as a function of time. Therefore, we have subjected this method to an analysis, made some experimental research and extended the method of evaluation by further study of the kinematic and dynamic phenomena of movement, which became important indicators for evaluating the sporting technique.

We have been working with this method for 4 years and during these years we have made many experimental studies of the structure of the sportsman's movements in various branches of sport. As the studies require precise measuring of angular data in the joints, we have paid much attention not only to the method of measurement, but also to the instrumental equipment. Therefore, our Faculty of Physical Education and Sport in Bratislava has co-operated with the research institute of the Slovak Academy of Sciences, which supplied the equipment for the electrogoniographic evaluation of the movements.

As scanning equipment resistance, capacitance and inductive transducers were used. The transducers were placed (for swimmers) in a waterproof covering and they were adjusted to the shape of the joint and to the character of the movement. The output signal leaving the

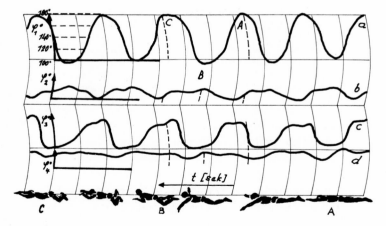

Fig. 1. The synchronized electrogoniographic and cinematographic record of the angular changes of movements in the joints of a swimmer (a – elbow joint, b – wrist joint, c – knee joint, d – ankle joint).

transducer was processed in a measuring and evaluating device, from which it was fed to recording equipment.

When measuring the angular changes of movement in the joints we have observed the standard procedure when measuring the physical variables by transdusers.

The results of measurement were evaluated on the basis of synchronized electrogoniographic and cinematographic recordings. The evaluation was realized in such a way that in the respective time intervals and corresponding positions of the sportsman in the film record we have indicated the magnitude of the angular changes of movement in the joints recorded on an electrogoniogram (Fig. 1). From these angular changes of movement given as a function of time there were derived further kinematic changes of movement representing the movement structure of the sportsman in its kinematic form [2, 3], such as: the angular speeds and accelerations of movements of individual parts of the sportsman's body, the magnitude of the trajectory of movements, the rhythm of movement, the coordination of movements, etc.

As a result of the electrogoniographic analysis of the angular changes of movements in joints as a function of time we have arrived at the following conclusions:

angular changes of movement in the joints recorded on electrogoniograms become very important indicators for the evaluation of a sporting technique as they represent the structure of the movement of a sportsman in its kinematic and dynamic form;

these angle changes of the movements in the joints recorded on the electrogoniogram can be read with an accuracy of $\pm 1°$ in all phases of the sportsman's movement;

the recorded angular changes of movement in the joints representing the structure of the movement of the sportsman in its kinematic form, can be differentiated in the case of the same sportsman in a framework of individual cycles of movement or training seasons, or we can compare them with the angular changes of another, more advanced sportsman;

from the angular changes of movement as a function of time we can derive via mathematical operations some further kinematic phenomena such as: the circular and angular speeds and accelerations of movements, the magnitude of the trajectory of movements, etc. The course of these kinematic changes of movements will be obtained by the graphical derivation of angular changes as functions of time (Fig. 2).

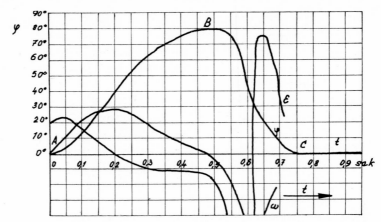

Fig. 2. The course of angular velocity and acceleration of movement in the elbow joint in the individual phases of a swimmer's movement (obtained by graphic derivation of angular changes as a function of time) (ω = angular velocity, ε = angular acceleration, φ = angular changes in the joint).

These curves of velocity and acceleration of movements of individual parts of the sportsman's body make possible the search for relationships between the resulting movement of the sportsman and the movements of individual parts of his body;

electrogoniograms representing time changes of the central angles in the joints become also indicators of changes in the rhythm of movement of the investigated parts of the sportsman's body (Fig. 3). From these electrogoniographic recordings we can ascertain which element of movement is the cause of the eventual change in the resulting rhythm of the sportsman;

the electrogoniograms where the time sequence of angular changes of movements in the joints is recorded on the common time basis also permit investigation of the coordination of movements. The coordination of movements, as the space-time changes of movements of the investigated parts of the sportsman's body, is expressed both by smoothness of the electrogoniographic curves and by the correct time sequence of carrying out the individual movements (Fig. 4). When studying the coordination of movements we must 'therefore start' from the continuity of the curves and from the time sequence of execution of the movements of individual parts of the sportsman's body.

In this way, using the electrogoniographic method, we can evaluate various phenomena of movement of the sportsman. These pheno-

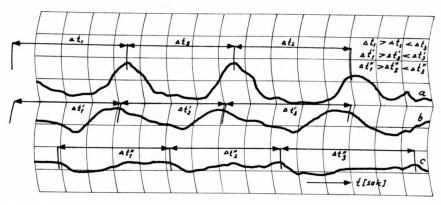

Fig. 3. The rhythm of movement of the individual parts of the sportsman's body in running (a – hip joint, b – knee joint, c – ankle joint).

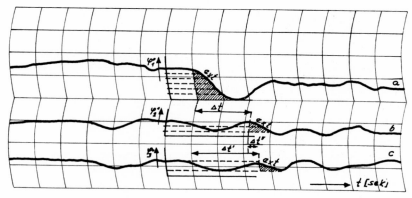

Fig. 4. The coordination of movements in shot-putting (a – hip joint, b – knee joint, c – ankle joint).

mena can be studied not only in isolation but also in their mutual connections and dependencies. This permits us to evaluate the structure of the sportsman's movement in its kinematic expression and to differentiate it from a structure which represents an effective sporting technique.

The studies of kinematic changes in the structure of sport movement, which were processed at our Faculty, are the results of the experimental research on sporting techniques using the electrogoniographic method. From the theoretical analysis and from the experimental research it follows that, for the evaluation of sporting technique, it is necessary to use methods which will describe the structure of the sportsman's movement in its kinematic form in the best and most precise way. From the electrogoniographic studies it appears that the electrogoniographic method fulfills this condition, that is, it makes possible the study of the structure of movement by the sportsman in considerable complexity and it permits the evaluation and the following of changes in the process of acquiring and further improving the effective technique of sporting disciplines, and because of that it can be considered as one of the foremost methods in the biomechanical study of movement.

References

1. GOLLNICK, P.D. and KARPOVICH, P.V.: Electrogoniometric study of locomotion and of some athletic movements. Res. Quart. 35: 357–69 (1964).
2. KONIAR, M. and VIKTORÍN, K.: Skúmanie techniky športovych disciplín elektrogoniografickou metódou. (Fakultná práca FTVŠ, Bratislava 1966).
3. KONIAR, M.: Elektrogoniografické štúdie o kinematickych zmenách štruktúry pohybu plavcov pri osvojovaní a zdokonalovaní techniky plaveckych disciplín. (Dizertačná práca FTVŠ UK, Bratislava 1966).

Author's address: Dr. M. KONIAR, Faculty of Physical Education and Sport, *Bratislava* (CSSR).

Biomechanics I, 1st Int. Seminar Zurich 1967
pp. 67–71 (Karger, Basel/New York 1968)

Service d'Explorations Fonctionnelles Biométriques et Biomécaniques du Centre
Hospitalier de Montpellier

Static and Dynamic Electropodography

P. RABISCHONG

The object of Electropodography is to study the statics and dynamics of plantar pressures in upright walking as well as in standing (one foot or bipodal position).

As technical progress made its way, many authors applied themselves to study the biomechanics of the foot in the attempt of testing plantar pressures. To this day, they mostly have two ways of recording their findings: they either use dynamometrical platforms, equiped with transducers upon with the foot can be tested, or they fit transducers directly under the foot. We believe this latter method gives more information than the former one. At the present time, it allows recordings of localized pressures while preserving the morphology of the electrical complexes.

Method

The electropodographical exploration can be made from two stand points:

In statics, the subject is asked to stand on a hard platform, laying on gauged transducers placed under the main pressure points of the foot sole. This method offers the advantage of testing the distribution of strains under the foot in a bipedal standing position as well as balance reactions in a one foot standing position.

In dynamics, four transducers are fitted into soles adapted to the patient's foot. We use a travelling band in order to be able to make recordings during a longer period of time and under diversified conditions.

Equipment

The Transducers

They are made of gauged strain bridges, mounted on the sides of a block of Araldite. Two kinds of strain bridges are being used.

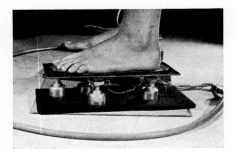

Fig. 1. Static Electropodography—Feet are resting on a platform with four pressure transducers.

– strain bridges gauges at right angle to measure vertical stress by compression.
– strain bridges with 45° gauges to explore shear stress made out of forces parallel to the ground which are the tangential components.

The association of the two kinds of strain bridges in one transducer enables the simultaneous study and dynamic EPG for the recording of compression stress as well as of shear stress. It has been arranged that the compressive forces are indicated by a positive signal while shear stress is considered as *positive* when the friction is forward-backward and *negative* when the friction is backward-forward. In a dynamic electropodography the transducers are gauged with care and placed under four set points on the foot sole: one on the big toe, one on the medial external and internal surface of the foot sole (metatarso phalangeal joints) and one under the heel. In order to allow a precise fitting, the soles are built with velcro braces which prevent any slipping while walking. With the same purpose in mind we have provided for a set of different sizes soles.

The Travelling Band

The use of a travelling band may first appear to be in opposition to normal physiological conditions and one might object that the artificial motion of the floor considerably alters the way the foot pushes against it. Actually, as SCHWARTZ has already proved it, after a period of adaptation which varies according to the person, walking on a travelling band is absolutely comparable with walking on the ground. We have proved of this fact through various experimental tests.

Fig. 2. Dynamic Electropodography—general view of the equipment: travelling band registering device and soles equiped with transducers.
Fig. 3. Soles—One can see 4 transducers under the big toe, metatarsophalangea joints, and the heel.

For a better appraisal of propulsion forces the walking surface is hard and not soft. It is made of metallic slats, 20 cm wide, sliding over a triple rolling system hydraulically powered. This system enables us to use speed variations form 0 to 15 km/h. It can be put into gear and started by the patient himself in the test called 'self-propulsion'. Every 20 cm a magnetic control sends a top into the recording system. One can therefore make a fast estimate of speed and thus obtain the absolutely necessary space component. Hand bars built on each side give a psychological comfort to the patient. It is furthermore possible to set the travelling band into a slanting position in order to study stresses while walking upon a slanted floor.

Recording System

Each transducer sends 2 signals making a total of 16 signals to be simultaneously picked up. In fact, 8 informations can only be fed into the recording system. An EEG pilot has consequently been added to it in order to cope with this drawback. This pilot can select all the different phases of walking, out of 8 different settings. The first one records the top which, as previously pointed out, is an essential space factor and also gives the measurement in cms per step. A dynamometrical walking stick also equiped with a transducer can be used whenever needed by a patient. One can then estimate its function and the adjustment of stress it involves. The other settings are to study the variations of shear stress or of compression stress (as shown in V and VI) on both feet, or on each foot separately (as shown in VII and VIII). The 8 settings used in the dynamic electropodography are set with a short time constant so that the recording is not modified when rapid motions are involved. Four of these settings can be commuted into one continuous chain to allow the recording of pressures in static electropodography. The four remaining settings being used for an electromyographical study with wires.

The Electropodogram

a) In statics the unfolding speed of the paper is 5 mm/s. The purpose of the examination is to study the distribution of strains while standing either on two feet or on one foot. In this latter position the reactions to maintain balance are also recorded: forward or backward as well as lateral oscillations. The range of balance reactions and the distribution of strains can instantly be found out thanks to a gauging system of 1 mm/2 kgs.

b) The dynamic electropodogram is realized by an unfolding paper speed of 25 mm/s. This is a time information in addition to the space information which helps to measure a certain number of parameters. We have classified them into:

1. *Spacial parameters:* measuring the length of a step, measuring the length of a halfstep (from heel strike to the mid-stance phase).

2. *Time parameters:* measuring the time period necessary for a simple stand, then for a double stand, study of the various moments in one step (interval between the time the heel hits the ground and the time the forefoot hits it), measuring the time elapsed during the right to left foot passage and vice-versa, setting forth a possible dodge for support measuring on each transducer the time the foot stays in contact with the floor: heel, medial internal and external sole, big toe.

3. *Time and space parameters:* pace: number of steps per minute; walking speed (band speed in cm/s.).

4. *Pressure parameters* are of a special interest. The findings are quantitative on one hand, measure of the pressures at the four chosen points, on the other hand, qualitative when studying morphology complexes under the different adjustment of strains.

The two main morphological complexes are found at the level of the heel and of the fore-foot:

The heel complex: under pressure it is formed by a steep ascending curve followed by a dome, then a progressive regression of strain synchronized with the contact of the forefoot with the ground. The concomitant study of parallel forces gives a more complete understanding. The double stand is represented by a positive spike, sign of a forward-backward friction representing the gripping of the ground by the extensors at the heel. It is followed by a negative down curve called for by the landing of the foot at the end of the stance phase. It ends by a progressive return to the basic line when the heel looses its contact with the ground. It is impossible to relate with details all the pathological variations of this curve. They are basically of two types and show either a dodge by reduction of strains (the time of contact with the ground is then longer, the curve is flat and spread out) or a reduction of the time of contact only, the maximal strain remaining unchanged.

The forefoot complex: the curve starts 8 to 12/100 sec after the heel strike. It is made of what we have called the 'complex contact-propulsion'. The first of the curve of contact shows a progressive strain synchronized with the release of strain at the heel. It is followed by a curve of propulsion superior to the first one during which the heel has lost all contact with the ground, while at the same time the big toe is pressing on to the ground. The reducing of strain is progressive and usually starts by the outer side of the foot. During a normal walk one notices a more important pressure on the inner side of the foot. This distribution of strains on the forefoot is usually found in average subjects with a physiological toe out of 15°. Any variation of this angulation bears with it an excess of strain on the inner side of the foot with external rotation and excess of strain on the outer side with internal rotation.

A more complete study of parallel forces gives a better understanding of friction factors during the propulsive phase.

In conclusion, we believe this method will bring precise and coded information upon the various normal and pathological gaits.

(The bibliography relative to this paper can be found in the article: "l'Electropodographie, son intérêt en orthopédie, Montpellier-Chirurgical, Tome XIII, No 3, 1967").

Author's address: P. Rabischong, M.D., Chairman of Anatomy, Service d'Explorations Fonctionnelles Biométriques et Biomécaniques du Centre Hospitalier Universitaire, Boulevard Henri IV, *Montpellier* (France).

Biomechanics I, 1st Int. Seminar Zurich 1967
pp. 72–77 (Karger, Basel/New York 1968)

University of Leuven, Institute of Physical Education
(Dir. Prof. Dr. P.P. De Nayer).

Apparatus for Determining the Center of Gravity of the Human Body

E. Willems and P. Swalus

Locating the center of gravity or determining its trajectory during a certain phase of a movement is an important objective of research in human motion analysis.

Therefore, it is not surprising to learn that a method for determining the center of gravity was already described by Borelli in 1679.

Since then several methods have been proposed; the principle of the method described here was adopted by Basler in 1928 and also described by Donskoi in 1961.

The new element in our technique consists in the possibility of measuring the vertical projection of the center of gravity in one plane by only one measurement.

Furthermore, once the calibration is established, it is possible to read immediately, without calculation, the position of the center of gravity in different attitudes.

Principle of the Method

if L = distance between the two supporting points A and B

p = weight of the platform

l = distance between the supporting point A and the center of gravity of the platform

P = weight of the subject

Y = load on the supporting point B

x = distance to be determined between the supporting point A and the center of gravity of the subject.

We can state:

$$L\,Y = l\,p + x\,P$$

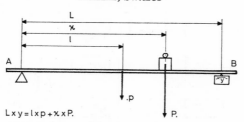

$$L \times y = l \times p + x \times P.$$

Fig. 1. Mechanical principle of the apparatus.

Hence:

$$x = \frac{LY - lp}{P}$$

if the apparatus is calibrated so that
    1 p (i.e. load of the platform without subject)
is not registered, we can state:

$$x = Y \frac{L}{P}$$

L is a constant element by construction.
The only variable to be taken into consideration is the weight of the subject: this is done electronically.

Description of the apparatus

The platform is an aluminium table measuring 1 m by 1 m, reinforced by a system of cables and turnbuckles and hung up on two measuring instruments and one toggle-joint. These three points form a system of perpendicular coordinates the origin of which is the toggle-joint.

The measuring instruments are two load cells, with a power oscillator unit, a carrier amplifier and measuring bridges: all instruments being commercially available and supplied by Vibrometer A.G., Fribourg.

The electronic part is completed by two parallel systems of precision resistances in order to cope with the differences in body weight of the subjects and by two vacuum tube voltmeters calibrated in centimeters in order to enable precise reading[1].

Both outputs can also be connected to an x-y oscilloscope (Fig. 2).

The above mentioned 'division' part works in steps of 100 grams in the range 40–100 kilogram; this represents a maximum error of 1.5 mm in the middle of the platform.

[1]The platform was constructed by the University Technical Experimental Center, Dir. Ir. DE DOBBELEER.

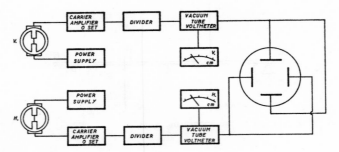

Fig. 2. Block diagram.

Performance Characteristics

The accuracy of the whole system has been tested by means of a calibrating weight of approximately 60 kgs. The results are shown in Figure 3: it is seen that measurements are very precise in the triangle formed by the toggle-joint and the two load cells.

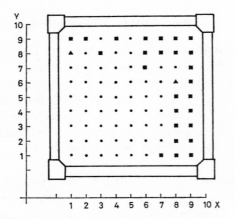

Fig. 3. Errors occurring when calibrating the apparatus.
● error < 2.5 mm. ▲ error 2.5–3.5 mm. ■ error > 3.5 mm.

Evaluation of the Measurements

It is obvious that precise determinations of the center of gravity can be obtained only if these determinations are made simultaneously with

those of the attitude of the subject: the latter can be easily done photo-
graphically at the moment of checking the center of gravity.

When the center of gravity is to be determined in various attitudes,
for instance taken during a certain movement, we can proceed to a
reconstruction of these attitudes based on filmed sequences of the
movements.

In this case the precision of our measurements will greatly depend
on how exactly the subjects have been placed on the platform in the
required attitude.

In order to evaluate this method we proceeded as follows: 9 subjects were put on the platform in a standardised position: lying down
on their sides.

The subjects were chosen from different somatotypes: 3 nor-
motypes, 3 brachytypes, and 3 longitypes, according to Viola-Barbara.

The center of gravity was checked and a photograph was taken;
on this photograph we reproduced precisely the location of the center
of gravity.

Hereafter, each subject was placed on the platform 30 times as
exactly as possible in the same position as the given standard-attitude.

Each time the center of gravity was checked and deviations (distance
and direction) were noticed. We compared our results with those given
by the graphical method described by BRAUNE and FISCHER and according to the indications given by DONSKOI.

Therefore, we calculated the center of gravity 30 times for each
subject on 30 reproductions of the photograph taken of the standard
attitude.

The arithmetic means of the errors of the two methods are represented in Table I.

It appeared that the errors of the graphic method are much greater;
moreover, these deviations originate more from a systematic error than
the ones due to the placement of the subject on the platform.

This was confirmed when examining the distribution of the centers
of gravity checked with regard to the real center of gravity.

If for each subject and for the two methods an angle is traced
having the real center of gravity as the apex, and including the 30 centers of gravity obtained, one notices that for the graphic method these
angles are very acute (5° to 13°), whereas they are much wider for the
apparatus (31° to 155°), one subject even representing a circular repartition (Fig. 4).

Table 1. Arithmetic means and standard errors of the deviations from the real center of gravity (in cm) obtained by the graphic method and our apparatus.

	Graphic Method		Apparatus	
	X̄	SD	X̄	SD
Normotype	8.6	0.27	2.2	0.71
Small normotype	8.1	0.29	1	0.53
Large normotype	7.7	0.40	2.2	0.63
Brachytype	6	0.39	1.7	0.66
Small brachytype	6.5	0.28	3.3	0.92
Large brachytype	6.6	0.50	1.9	0.94
Longitype	5.5	0.46	3.3	0.94
Small longitype	5.1	0.41	2.9	0.86
Large longitype	6.5	0.27	5.1	0.93
Mean	6.7		2.6	

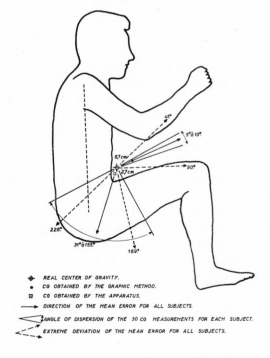

Fig. 4. Location of the real center of gravity, direction of the mean error and dispersion of the 30 C.G. measurements by the two methods.

On the other hand, with the graphic method, the mean tendency of the center of gravity obtained in each of the 9 subjects is situated in very similar directions with regard to the real center of gravity: these directions form angles varying from 41° to 90° with the axis of the trunk of the subject (median 65.5°), whereas with the apparatus these angles vary from 169° to 226°, having a median of 197.5° (for one single subject there was a deviation from this direction at an angle of 354°).

Finally, we can conclude that:

1. The construction of an apparatus for direct determination of the center of gravity by means of a set of electronic weighings and corrections proved to be very satisfactory and practical.

2. If one wants to check the center of gravity based on a photographed position, one notices that:

a) The center of gravity checked by the graphic method does not correspond accurately to the center of gravity of the position photographed. Whatever the somatotype of the subject may be, the center of gravity obtained deviates in the same direction;

b) The apparatus for determining the center of gravity by direct reading gives a more exact localization. Nevertheless, one has to cope with real difficulties when trying to attain a well determined position on the platform. In our experiment there is still a systematic error, which we are trying to eliminate by adapting the technique.

Authors' address: P. SWALUS, University of Leuven, Institute of Physical Education, *Leuven* (Belgium).

Biomechanics I, 1st Int. Seminar Zurich 1967
pp. 78–82 (Karger, Basel/New York 1968)

Orthopädische Abteilung (Vorstand: Prof. GROH) des Bürgerhospitals Saarbrücken und
dem Institut für angewandte Physik und Elektrotechnik (Dir. Prof. ECKART) der Universität
des Saarlandes, Saarbrücken

Über ortsfeste und telemetrische Verfahren zur Messung der Abstoßkraft des Fußes

W. BAUMANN

Eine bei der Fortbewegung des Menschen interessierende physikalische Größe ist die während der Stützphase vom Fuß auf den Boden ausgeübte Kraft. Sie ist in der Orthopädie zur vergleichenden Betrachtung normaler und gestörter Gangbilder ebenso bedeutsam wie im Sport zur quantitativen Untersuchung des Abstoßvorganges als eines leistungsbestimmenden Faktors in den Lauf- und Sprungsdisziplinen.

Dazu muß der Vektor der Kraft als Funktion der Zeit bestimmt werden. Das geschieht am einfachsten und am genauesten mit Hilfe stationärer Kraftmeßplatten (platform). Wir haben 2 solcher Meßplatten gebaut, um die aufeinanderfolgenden Stützphasen von rechtem und linkem Bein zu untersuchen (Abb. 1). Jede Platte ist mit 4 präzise gearbeiteten Aluminium-Trägerröhren fest verbunden. Auf den Trägern sind Halbleiter-Dehnungsmeßstreifen angebracht, die jede Krafteinwirkung auf die Platte in proportionale elektrische Größen, also Widerstands- bzw. Spannungsänderungen umwandeln. Die einzelnen Komponenten der Kraft – in X-, Y- und Z-Richtung – werden gleichzeitig, aber unabhängig voneinander registriert. Die Kraftanzeige ist unabhängig von der jeweiligen Einwirkungsstelle der Kraft auf der Trittfläche. Die Versuchsperson muß also nicht mit dem Fuß auf eine bestimmte Stelle der Platte zielen, sondern nur die Platte überhaupt treffen. Um den Einfluß der Eigenfrequenz des Meßsystems auf das Meßergebnis gering zu halten, haben wir uns auf Plattengrößen von 40×50 cm beschränkt. Der Meßfehler bleibt, bei allen 3 Kraftkomponenten, unter 2%.

Für die fortlaufende Registrierung beliebig vieler aufeinanderfolgender Schritte ist eine solche Anlage naturgemäß nicht geeignet. Die ideale Lösung wäre eine ortsunabhängige Meßeinrichtung, die von der

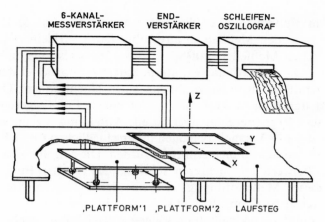

Abb. 1. Schema der ortsfesten Kraftmessung und -registrierung.

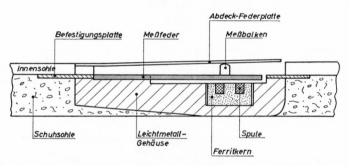

Abb. 2. Schnittbild einer in den Schuh eingebauten Meßkapsel. Maximale Länge ca. 80 mm.

Versuchsperson ohne Behinderung ständig mitgeführt wird und alle gewünschten Meßdaten drahtlos einem Registriergerät übermittelt. Die dabei insbesondere von sportlicher Seite gestellte Forderung nach minimalem Volumen und Gewicht der Meß- und Übertragungseinrichtung hat im allgemeinen einen geringeren Umfang an Information zur Folge, als er mit einer ortsfesten Anlage zu erreichen ist. Das kann einmal betreffen die Genauigkeit der Meßwerte und zum anderen die Anzahl der voneinander unabhängigen Meßgrößen.

Unsere bisherigen telemetrischen Untersuchungen bezogen sich vornehmlich auf die am Fußballen auftretende Abstoßkraft beim sportlichen Lauf und Sprung. Abbildung 2 zeigt das Schnittbild des in den Laufschuh eingebauten Meßwertwandlers: der Meßbalken befindet sich

unter dem Fußballen über die ganze Breite des Fußes. Eine vom
Fußballen auf den Meßbalken ausgeübte Kraft verkleinert den Luft-
spalt zwischen Meßfeder und Spule, vergrößert also die Induktivität
der Spule. Die Induktivitätsvariation ändert proportional der einwir-
kenden Kraft die Resonanzfrequenz eines Hochfrequenz-Oszillators
und wird durch einen Transistorsender einem Empfänger mit ange-
schlossenem Registriergerät übermittelt. Abbildung 3 zeigt einige Ergebnisse, die an 8 Versuchspersonen unterschiedlichen Gewichts in verschiedenen Laufdisziplinen ermittelt wurden. Die einzelnen Meßpunkte
stellen Mittelwerte aus mehreren Schritten des gleichen Fußes dar.

Mit dieser Meßanordnung wird nur der Betrag, nicht die Richtung der Kraft bestimmt. Es läßt sich also ohne zusätzliche Hilfsmittel,
etwa der simultanen kinematografischen Aufzeichnung, nicht zwischen
normalem und tangentialem Anteil der Kraft unterscheiden. Dies
scheint uns kein Mangel der speziellen Anordnung zu sein, vielmehr

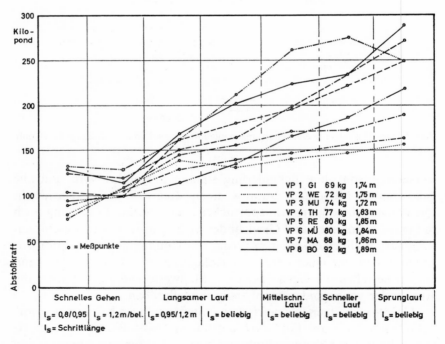

Abb. 3. Abstoßkraft des Fußes von 8 verschiedenen Versuchspersonen in Abhängigkeit
von der Laufgeschwindigkeit.

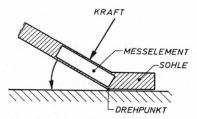

Abb. 4. Meßfehlerquelle: Die vom Fußballen auf das Meßelement ausgeübte Kraft dreht das Meßelement um den Drehpunkt nach unten; die Kraft wird zu klein gemessen.

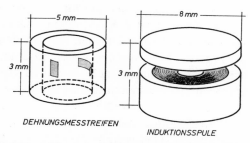

Abb. 5. Meßknöpfe kleiner Dimension. Beide Elemente werden jeweils in Araldit eingegossen.

eine grundsätzliche Eigenschaft aller ortsunabhängigen Methoden zur Messung der Abstoßkraft. Im Gegensatz zur ortsfesten Plattform, deren Koordinatensystem zu jedem Zeitpunkt der Messung mit dem des Raumes übereinstimmt, wird das Koordinatensystem der im Schuh eingebauten Meßdose mit der Bewegung des Beines und den veränderlichen Krümmungen der Schuhsohle ständig gedreht und hat keine feste Beziehung zu den Raumkoordinaten. Hinzu kommt ein mit der Dimension des Meßelements wachsender Meßfehler, da ein Teil der vom Fußballen auf das Meßelement ausgeübten Kraft ein Drehmoment bewirkt und bei der Messung keinen Beitrag liefert (Abb. 4).

Um diesen Mängeln zu begegnen, haben wir kleine Meßelemente entwickelt, wie sie in Abbildung 5 dargestellt sind. Rechts: das von der ursprünglichen Anordnung übernommene Prinzip der variablen Induktivität, links: eine starke Miniaturisierung unserer ortsfesten Kraftaufnehmer mit Dehnungsmeßstreifen. Die fertigen in Kunststoff eingegossenen Meßknöpfe haben ein Gewicht von weniger als 1 Gramm. Es werden Halbleiter-Dehnungsmeßstreifen mit einer aktiven Meßlänge von 1 mm verwendet. Sie gestatten die durch Druckkraft hervorgerufenen Längenänderungen des kleinen Meßröhrchens bis auf 10^{-6} mm genau zu bestimmen.

Diese nur auf Druck in axialer Richtung reagierenden Meßknöpfe werden an entsprechenden Stellen in den Laufschuh eingegossen. Die Anbringung wird an den zu untersuchenden Vorgang angepaßt und erfolgt an den Hauptbelastungspunkten des Fußes, beispielsweise beim Sprint unter den Mittelfußköpfchen. Mit den so präparierten Meßschuhen läßt man die Versuchsperson über die ortsfesten Kraftmeßplatten laufen und mißt dabei einunddenselben Kraftverlauf auf zweierlei Weise: ortsunabhängig als Betrag und ortsfest in den 3 Raumkoordinaten als X-, Y- und Z-Komponente. Damit ist für jeden Zeitpunkt der Stützphase bekannt, wie sich der mit den Meßknöpfen ermittelte Kraftbetrag aus den 3 Komponenten zusammensetzt.

Wir versuchen durch genügend zahlreiche Vergleichsmessungen einen reproduzierbaren Zusammenhang zwischen den beiden Meßergebnissen zu finden, um uns dann von der ortsgebundenen Methode zu lösen und den Kraftvektor beliebig vieler aufeinanderfolgender Stützphasen zu bestimmen. Das geringe Gewicht der Meßknöpfe erlaubt insbesondere behinderungsfreie Untersuchungen an Leistungssportlern in allen Laufdisziplinen.

Adresse des Autors: Dipl.-Phys. WOLFGANG BAUMANN, Institut für angewandte Physik und Elektrotechnik, Universität des Saarlandes, D-66 *Saarbrücken 15* (B.R. Deutschland).

Biomechanics I, 1st Int. Seminar Zurich 1967
pp. 83–86 (Karger, Basel/New York 1968)

University of Birmingham, England

The Use of Force Platforms for the Study of Physical Activity

A.H. Payne

Introduction

In physical activity the human body exerts force against its environment. Study of the magnitude and direction of the force and of the way in which the force changes gives valuable information about the performance which may lead to more efficient and therefore more effective methods of performance. Frequently the force is exerted against the ground through the feet, and in recent years force platforms have been constructed which have permitted the direct measurement of force. A force platform is a plane surface whose displacement due to a force can be measured so as to give information about that force. The ideal platform should be rigid, light and very stiff, so that its displacement is imperceptible to the person performing an activity on it. To measure the very small displacements one has to use sensing devices such as variable transformers, strain gauges and piezo electric crystals in association with electronic equipment for amplification and recording. For complete information of a physical activity the performance on the platform is usually filmed and the use of a continuous motion clock, positioned in the camera field and wired to give pulses on the force records, makes it possible subsequently to relate body movements as shown on the film to changes in the thrust at the feet.

There appear to have been three main lines of force platform evolution after the purely mechanical devices of AMAR [1] and HENRY [6]. The earliest was the triangular, later becoming hexagonal shaped platform using piezo-electric crystals or linear variable differential transformers culminating in the sophisticated apparatus at Kansas State University [5]. A few platforms of WHITNEY's design [9] have been built. They are suspended by cables from strain-gauged cantilevers, and usually require special damping devices.

A third line of development by CUNNINGHAM and BROWN [3] is the simplest in conception but is still in need of improvement. This type is rectangular and is supported by strain-gauged cylindrical posts.

Uses

The force platform has been used with varying amounts of success in fields as diverse, for example, as sprint running and prosthetics design. Most athletics coaches prescribe block spacings for sprinters on the basis of results obtained with a simple apparatus [6]. Recommendations have been made on the height of work stations in industry after experiments with operators performing tasks while standing or seated on force platforms [2, 7]. Prosthetic devices of the lower limb have been improved as the result of comparisons of the forces evoked during normal walking and forces evoked by the amputee fitted with a prosthesis [3]. Research into the durability of floor coverings has also been aided by the use of force platforms [4]. In the purely academic study of biomechanics the force platform is a useful tool and it is in this sphere that much work remains to be done.

The author [8] has used a one metre square platform (aluminium honeycomb suspended by cables to strain gauged cantilevers) to investigate sprinting, shot putting, jumping and weight lifting. A low natural frequency prevented accurate quantitative analysis, but valuable qualitative information was obtained. A higher frequency brass column supported platform of similar size is at present being constructed. Instrumental starting blocks—in effect two small force plates—have been used to investigate the sprint starting action.

Design and Method

One of the major problems involved in the construction of a force platform is concerned with the natural frequency of the apparatus. The forces to be measured must not excite the natural frequency of the platform, for the resulting resonance will make interpretation of the records difficult, if not impossible. The rate of change of force in many normal human movements corresponds to approximately 20 cycles per second, though in some sporting activities this may be considerably higher. For reliable results, therefore, the natural frequency of a force platform should be in excess of 200 cycles per second. This condition is relatively easily obtained with small platforms (usually termed force plates), but from about ¼ square metre upwards difficulties are encountered. Incidentally the human body on the platform does not alter the natural frequency in proportion to the body mass because the human body is not a rigid mass fixed to the platform.

The high inertia of mechanical recording pens makes the use of these instruments undesirable in the force platform apparatus, for a rapid response of the electrical amplifiers and recorder is essential. An ultraviolet recorder with low inertia galvanometers and flat frequency response enables much more faithful recording of the movements of the platform to be made.

A force along one of the measuring axes should not produce an appreciable reading along the other axes, though the amount of this 'cross talk' which is permissible will depend upon the requirements of the experiment. Indeed, the nature of the experiment determines the type and sensitivity of platform required. The characteristics of a platform for measuring the movements of a seated operator in industry may be very different to the characteristics of a platform used for the study of high jumping, and what be necessary in one will be undesirable in the other.

One important requirement in most force platforms is that the recording should be linear over the range of forces to be measured, otherwise interpretation of results becomes difficult. Experiments should be carried out under as near natural conditions as possible—for instance measurement of athletic activities in small rooms usually leads to suspect results. Wherever possible the platform's surface should be level with the surrounding floor or ground and care should be taken that subjects walking or running onto the platform do not adjust their stride in order to land on it correctly.

Results

Interpretation of results should always be carried out with care, for sometimes the force evoked at the feet in an activity may be only very indirectly connected with the desired effect—for example in shot putting and in golf the forces on the external object are not apparent in the force trace obtained from the apparatus, and careful comparison with the filmed record is necessary. Data processing of force traces can be tedious unless some means is available to digitalise the results for processing by digital computer. Relatively cheap electronic analogue computers can be used directly for measuring the integral of the force/time record, which particularly in repetitive industrial movements is of considerable interest to the researcher.

References

1. AMAR, J.: The Human Motor (Dutton, New York 1920).
2. BROUHA, L. and SMITH, P.E., Jr.: Energy expenditure of motions Fed. Proc. *17:* 20 (1958).
3. CUNNINGHAM, D.M. and BROWN, G.W.: Two devices for measuring the forces acting on the human body during walking. Proc. Soc. exp. Stress Analysis. *9:* 75–90 (1952).
4. HARPER, F.C.; WARLOW, W.J. and CLARKE, B.L.: The forces applied to the floor by the foot in walking. National Building Studies Research Paper 32. H.M. Stationery Office, London (1961).
5. HEARN, N.K.N.: Design and construction of a force platform with torque measurement capability: Masters thesis, Kansas State University (1966).
6. HENRY, F.M.: Force-time characteristics of the sprint start. Research Quarterly. amer. Ass. Hlth. phys. Educ. *23:* 301 (1952).
7. KONZ, S.A. and DAY, R.A.: Design of controls using force as a criterion. Human Fact. *8:* 121–127 (1966).
8. PAYNE, A.H.; SLATER, W.J. and TELFORD, T.: The use of a force platform in the study of athletic activities. A preliminary investigation. Ergonomics *11:* 123–143 (1968).
9. WHITNEY, R.J.: The strength of the lifting action in man. Ergonomics *1:* 101–128 (1958).

Author's address: A.H. PAYNE, M. Sc., Lecturer in Physical Education, University of Birmingham, *Birmingham 15* (England).

Biomechanics I, 1st Int. Seminar Zurich 1967
pp. 87–89 (Karger, Basel/New York 1968)

Laboratory of Theory of Gymnastics, University of Copenhagen, Copenhagen

Registration of the Pressure Power (the Force) of the Body on the Floor During Movements, Especially Vertical Jumps

F. Andersen

The force on the floor caused by a man making different movements can be registrated as a function of time by means of a strain-gauge arrangement. We have a platform (Fig. 1) made by plastic fibers, length 1.50 m.

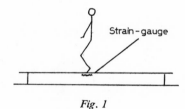

Fig. 1

A man moves from a standing position to a position with bent knees (Fig. 2). The force-time curve will be as shown. By rising again you get the last part of the curve.

If, from a horizontal arm position, you move the arms downwards as quickly as possible and immediately stop them again you will get a curve as shown in Figure 3. You will use the adductors in the shoulder joints in a positive way (concentric) and the abductors in a negative way (eccentric). It is possible to stop the movement more rapidly than you can start it. On the curve it can be seen where the change of force on the floor is greater by stopping than by starting. The opposite movement shows the same thing, and it is possible to compare the force of abductors or adductors by concentric and eccentric work.

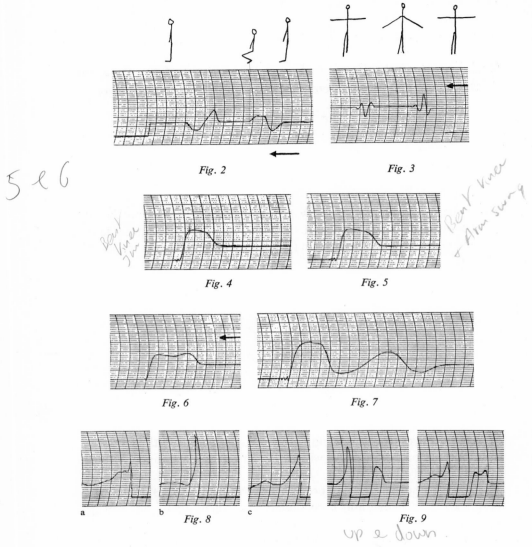

5 e 6

Fig. 2   Fig. 3

Bent knee jum

Bent knee + Arm swing

Fig. 4   Fig. 5

Fig. 6   Fig. 7

a   b   c

Fig. 8   Fig. 9

up e down

If you jump upwards from a position with half bent knee joints you will get the curve shown in Figure 4. It is seen that the force on the floor is about twice the person's weight. If you are using the arms during the jump you will notice that the force will increase as a result of a slower movement of the spring muscles on account of the arm-swing acting as a heavy mass (Figure 5).

From a position with the knees deeply bent you will register the curve of Figure 6 by jumping. And by general high jumping from a standing position the curve will be as in Figure 7.

A downward jump to the floor usually registers as in Figure 8a or in a hard way (Fig. 8b). It is seen that the force on the floor is about 5 times the body weight when you jump in a hard way with only a little knee bending. Also here we see that the negative work of the muscles in the knee joints gives rise to a much bigger force than the positive work.

The last curve (Fig. 9) shows the jump up and down.

Authors' address: Dr. FRODE ANDERSEN, University of Copenhagen, Laboratory of Theory of Gymnastics, *Copenhagen* (Denmark).

Biomechanics I, 1st Int. Seminar Zurich 1967
pp. 90–95 (Karger, Basel/New York 1968)

Purdue University, Lafayette, Ind.

Analysis of Normal Gaits Utilizing a Special Force Platform[1]

A.H. Ismail

Purpose

The purpose of the study was to analyze the nature of normal gaits among an adult population in terms of patterns and magnitude of forces; and to investigate the suitability of the force-platform data for predicting physiological costs during walking at various speeds.

The above purpose was fulfilled through:

1. Making an analysis of gaits using 'normal' adult men of different ages and body builds in terms of patterns and magnitude of forces exerted.

2. Determining the predictive power of various force-platform data for estimating oxygen consumption of individuals walking on the force-platform.

Methods and Procedures

Instrumentation for Recording Forces

The instrumentation consists of a pressure sensitive force-platform capable of measuring in the three orthogonal planes the forces exerted during any bodily movement. The platform is mounted under the belt of a specially constructed treadmill. Thus, continuous assessment can be obtained for a subject walking on the treadmill. A four channel recorder is used for obtaining the pattern of the forces. Three channels are used for recording the orthogonal components of the exerted forces while the fourth channel records the composite force consisting of the

[1] Prepared under Contract GM 10434–03 for the National Institute of Health.

vector sum of the independent components by means of an analog computer. Integration of the magnitude of the force traces over time is accomplished by means of voltage-to-frequency converters and high speed totalizers. The method of integration permits the separate recording of plus and minus voltages in relation to the zero activity level. Thus, direction as well as magnitude of forces can be analyzed with respect to pattern.

The apparatus for continuous assessment of gait has been constructed and validated experimentally with respect to static and dynamic forces. Furthermore, the data output from the platform coupled with the treadmill were validated by means of static weights moving dynamically across the belt. The pen deflections were found to be linearly proportional to the weights used. The calibration constants associated with each of the orthogonal forces were obtained from the validation procedures and were checked periodically to insure the accuracy of the pen deflections. These constants were used to derive the equation for calculating the composite force by the analog computer.

Subjects

In order to fulfill the first purpose of the study, 36 sedentary subjects were selected from students, faculty and staff at Purdue University. Nine different categories in terms of body build according to height and weight were selected. The categories of body build were: tall-heavy, tall-medium, tall-light, medium-heavy, medium-medium, medium-light, short-heavy, short-medium, and short-light. Originally, six men of different age groups were planned for each category (two young men between 20–45 years of age, two middle-aged men between 40–45 years of age and two old men between 60–65 years of age).

In order to fulfill the second purpose dealing with the predictive power of the force-platform data for estimating oxygen consumption during gait, 20 subjects were selected from the faculty and staff at Purdue University. They ranged in age from 24 to 43 years, in weight from 140 to 217 and in height from 65 to 75 inches.

Methods of Collecting Data

Relative to the first purpose, subjects were instructed to walk naturally on the treadmill at four different speeds (0.5, 1.0, 1.5, 2.0 mph). In order to secure stability and consistency of the data, a trial run for each speed was provided for each individual, thereby familiarizing the subject with the equipment and the environmental conditions. After a rest period, three trials of 20 seconds' duration were obtained on the four different speeds. The weight of each subject was corrected electronically. The four different speeds were randomized for the subjects.

Relative to the second purpose, when a subject reported to the laboratory, his age, height and weight were recorded. After resting for 5 minutes, his heart rate was recorded and checked periodically until two similar consecutive determinations were obtained. This value was recorded as the resting heart rate. Then, the subject was instructed to walk on the treadmill at the center. A two-way-J-valve was adjusted to the height of the subject and the moth piece was inserted. A nose clip was then placed over the subject's nostrils.

The subject was given a 5 minute warm-up period, consisting of walking for one minute intervals at each of five speeds (0.5, 1.0, 1.5, 2, 3 mph). The purpose of this practice was to familiarize the subject with the experimental set-up before starting the actual collection of data. Then, the subject was seated until the resting heart rate was obtained. During that time the force-platform as well as the equipment involved were calibrated.

The order of the five speeds was randomized for each subject. Then the subject mounted the treadmill and walked for 3 minutes at each of the assigned speeds during which time his weight was centered electronically on the recorder at the null or zero activity point. The purpose of this step was to zero out the effect of weight for each subject. From the beginning of the fourth minute till the seventh minute, three twenty second samples were collected dealing with mechanical data. Also, at the beginning of the fifth minute till the end of the seventh minute, the physiological data were collected. The O_2 uptake was obtained based on the average CO_2 and O_2 percentages from two samples of the expired air. The same procedure was repeated for each speed after a resting period to allow the heart rate to come back to the resting value.

At each of the five speeds, three random twenty second samples of force data were recorded and divided by the number of steps to obtain the measure of force per step in the three orthogonal directions, namely vertical, lateral, and frontal. The average of the three samples for a given force component was computed and recorded as the variable of interest. The sum of the vertical, lateral, and frontal forces was designated as the total force. Furthermore, the vector sum of the three orthogonal forces

$$\left(F = \sqrt{C_1F_v^2 + C_2F_L^2 + C_3F_f^2} \right)$$

was obtained from the analog computer which gave an estimate of the composite force. Therefore, at each speed, the following force data were obtained for each subject.

1. Composite force/step (C/S)
2. Composite force/time (C/T)
3. Vertical force/step (V/S)
4. Vertical force/time (V/T)
5. Lateral force/step (L/S)
6. Lateral force/time (L/T)
7. Frontal force/step (F/S)
8. Frontal force/time (F/T)
9. Total force/step (T/S)
10. Total force/time (T/T)

In addition to the above measures, age, height, and weight for each subject were obtained. Thus at each speed, 13 measures were considered for each subject.

Statistical Procedures

The t-test was applied to the data associated with the first purpose. As to the data associated with the second purpose, the Pearson Product Moment of Correlation was used to determine the relationship between the variables of interest. Furthermore, the multiple correlation technique was employed in order to determine the best predictors for estimating energy cost using force variable data as well as physique measures as independent variables.

Findings: Results of Gait Analysis of 'Normal Adults'

A. Analysis in Terms of Pattern

Three patterns were obtained, namely, the vertical, frontal and lateral patterns. The traces associated with the three orthogonal forces at four different speeds were found to be different for individuals of different ages and body builds. In particular, the vertical force traces discriminated among the various individuals. In terms of the gait patterns, the following conclusions were drawn:

1. Regardless of body build, the force traces for the left and right foot is not identical. In other words, subjects with 'normal' gait favor one foot over the other.

2. The patterns of gait are affected by the speed of walking.

3. In general, the patterns associated with the different body builds at any one speed are not the same. Hence, patterns should be developed according to body build, age, and speed of gait.

B. Analysis in Terms of Magnitude of Forces

The magnitude of forces was analyzed in terms of age, height and weight, The findings are listed as follows:

1. There were significant differences at the 1% level between the young and old subjects in terms of composite scores at the four different speeds. However, no significant differences were observed between either the young and the middle aged or between the middle aged and old subjects. Similar results were observed relative to the total and vertical forces, except for the speed of 0.5 mph in the total force and the speed of 0.5 and 1.00 mph in the vertical force. As to the frontal and lateral forces there were no significant differences between the age groups at any of the observed speeds.

2. There were no significant differences between the tall, medium and short subjects in terms of the five kinds of forces at the different observed speeds.

3. There were significant differences between the heavy and light subjects in terms of the five kinds of forces at the four different speeds. The heavy subjects tended to exert more force than either the medium or light subjects relative to the measured forces.

Conclusions

1. Age and weight more than height affect magnitude of forces exerted.
2. The gaits of the subjects became more efficient with increasing speed.

3. The total force followed by the vertical and the composite discriminate between subjects of different ages, heights and weights in that order.

2. Determining the Predictive Power of Various Force-platform Data.

The predictive power of the independent items for estimating oxygen consumption was analyzed and from the findings it was concluded that:

1. Oxygen consumption could be predicted by force-platform and physique data especially at higher speed.
2. When eliminating individual difference by estimating each individual oxygen consumption by force-platform data the relationships tended to be high.

Tables are available upon request.

Author's address: A.H. ISMAIL, Professor of Physical Education and Director of Research, Purdue University, *Lafayette, Ind.* (U.S.A.).

Biomechanics I, 1st Int. Seminar Zurich 1967
pp. 96–101 (Karger, Basel/New York 1968)

The Scientific Research Center of CNEFS, Bucharest

Measurement Apparatus and Analysis Methods of the Biomotor Process of Sport Movements

I. MAIER

In order to study the biomotor process which happens in sport movements we elaborated and used several measurement apparatuses as well as different methods of exploration. Some of these are briefly described as follows.

For the recording of movement we particularly employed the chronophotographic method which owing to the parametric record, presents some technical and economical advantages in comparison with the usual methods.

As far back as 1956 we used a perfectioned apparatus called 'photocyclograph' (Fig.1) which permits one to realise records in various conditions, both in the laboratory and outdoors.

Fig. 1. The photocyclograph—for records in the laboratory and outdoors.

The utilisation methods of this instrument can be multiple. They can be changed as well in function of the specific character of the movements as in conformity with the problems concerned, during the experiment, or the methodic process of sportsmen's training.

In this way we employed the following recording methods:

1. Records realised in the laboratory with a black background and white clothing (Fig. 2).

In this case the number of pictures employed can be adjusted in accordance with the control requirements of the partial movement changes of the body—brought about during the execution of the movement—or for the determination of the speed variations occurring in the course of the movement.

Fig. 2. Record realised in the laboratory with black background and white clothing. Shows succession of body movements in space and determines the speed variations occurring during the course of movement.

For the control of segments displaced with great velocity we also used—with good results—records realised with a black background, black clothing and application of white reference points. When employing sport instruments, for the supervision of succession in space being covered by the instrument at the appointed time, we used records in similar conditions with reference points applied to the instruments.

2. Records realised without a special background in conditions of training. In that case it is sufficient to choose the place where one realises the record; the background should be in the shade and the subject lighted. Very unfavourable record conditions are obtained when the background is light and the clothes of the subject are of a similar colour, whereas the contrast difference is achieved by the repeated impressions of the negative by the fact that the background is in the shade.

Because the records do not directly represent, in general, the factors determining the accomplishment of a better performance, and do not entirely clear up the problems in question, it is necessary to effectuate records under special conditions corresponding to certain requirements.

As the improvement of the performance is bound to factors in many cases unknown, and in order to create investigation possibilities for such situations, we realised records in execution conditions in which we gradually varied the charge.

By means of these records we succeeded in establishing the interdependence existing between the variation of the results obtained and the variation of the motor actions of the subject. The said method not only specifies the changes of the profile of the movements but also the imperfections of the motor capacity of the subject in conformity with the requirements of better results.

Further on we mention the record obtained of movements having an angular displacement executed in conditions having identical deformations of perspective for all the positions of the body. In these particular cases we created the possibility of superposition with graphic reference points which permits one to determine during the execution of the movement, the place, duration and amplitude of motor partial actions upon which the success and the quality of the movement execution depend.

These investigations also contributed to define the particular characteristics of the partial motor actions for angular movements. These form the object of a study we shall present in a future report.

From what we said about the study and the analysis of the kinematic process it results that these factors are representing an important part of the movement course in time and space. The fact that the displacement of the body is a consequence of the neuromuscular power—for a better knowledge of the latter—it is necessary to investigate the functional biomotor characteristics of man.

And because the exploration of the biomotor functions contains multiple aspects we had to elaborate and construct different measuring instruments in accordance with the record requirements of the motor actions. Some of these are also required for specific work conditions.

Since in sport movements the characteristic values of force are continually changing, the recording of the whole duration of the movement course is especially important as well for the variation of the proportions of the intensity of the force as for the direction and speed realised under those conditions.

In accordance we present an apparatus fulfilling all requirements specified above, the 'biodynamograph' used in our research department since 1953.

The *'biodynamograph'* effectuates complex biomotor measurements as it can record the forces applied to horizontal bars in gymnastics by vectorial inscription on a plan analogous to the real plan of the movements' display, which also permits one to establish the positions of the body on the whole trajectory of the movement. (Fig. 3). For this purpose one of the bar ends (Fig. 3/1) is prolonged and articulated (Fig. 3/3–4) by means of a lever system (Fig. 3/6–7) coupled with the inscription pen support (Fig. 3/5) which is provided with special gears for time registering and pen commands. In this manner the curves of the bar realised during the execution of the movements are transferred to the pen (Fig. 3/11) and recorded on a chart (Fig. 3/12) placed in front of the pen on a fixed pedestal (Fig. 3/9–10–13) which is set up on the pillar supporting the bar (Fig. 3/2).

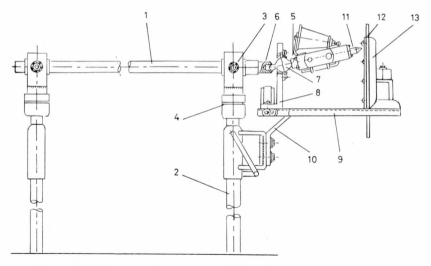

Fig. 3. The biodynamograph—for biomotor measurements. Records the forces applied to horizontal bars in gymnastics; notes positions of the body during execution of the movement.

The commands of the recorder are started electrically at a distance. The whole system is calibrated from 0 to 400 kg.

The recording is effected on current paper; it stops with the execution of the movement.

Because the curve recorded with this instrument represents the axis of time itself the speed variations as well as the movement components effect can be read directly on the chart.

By the change of the pen colour and owing to the fact that a record can be introduced several times in the instrument by means of superposition of the inscribed curves, one obtains immediately the differences existing between the correct execution and the deficient one.

Besides its technical and economical advantages, the biodynamograph also satisfies quickly analysis requirements in accordance with the particularities of the training process.

Since the size and the variations of developed forces in time result from the records obtained as well as the positions of the body, practical possibilities occur which determine—on the base of said data—the capacity of the muscular groups required for the accomplishment of the activity corresponding to the respective situation.

The fact that the whole system (bar and biodynamograph) also permits the use of some inert elements in the same movement conditions, makes it possible to realise a record which can differentiate the external effects of forces from the organic actions.

By the simultaneous use of a second instrument composed of elements which present the principal passive mechanical characteristics of the human body, we cleared up the graphic inscription and the effects of the analysis of the external forces which determine partial passive movements occurring in complex movements.

Figure 4 shows on the one hand the character of the charge developed during an entire course of movement and, on the other hand, establishes for movements of angular display the relations existing between efficiency of actions and their execution difficulty in all the phases of the movement.

We have to mention that recording of charge development on a distance covered by movements of different sport activities cannot be realised with the same equipment. For this reason we have constructed, in the past 15 years, several apparatuses adequate for the investigation requirements of the physical training department, used in our laboratories dedicated to biomotor measurements and research.

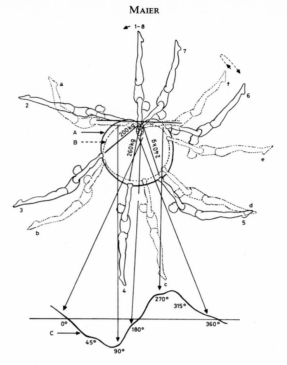

Fig. 4. Record of charge display during the whole course of movement; for movements of angular display it shows relation existing between action efficiency and execution difficulty.

With these apparatuses we realised measurements and kinematic records in the laboratory and out-of-doors. We also effected measurements of muscular capacity in isometric, isotonic, half-specific and specific activity conditions both in the laboratory and during training. In conclusion we want to specify that the results of the different investigation methods are only forming precursory data. Their efficiency will depend on their contribution to the clearing up of theoretical and practical problems which are related to the methodical process of the training. This process trends towards realisations in the physical training department which also tests their utility.

Author's address: Dr. Iosif Maier, Vasile Conta Nr. 16, *Bucarest* (S.R. Romania).

Biomechanics I, 1st Int. Seminar Zurich 1967
pp. 102–105 (Karger, Basel/New York 1968)

Instituut voor Perceptie Onderzoek, Eindhoven

Measurements on electrical and mechanical activity of the elbow flexors

J. Vredenbregt and W.G. Koster

Most of the research in muscle has been carried out on isolated muscles. The information obtained under these conditions cannot often be used to predict muscle behaviour and limb movement, since the isolated muscle is not stimulated by its own nerve system. Moreover, its natural feedback loops are cut off.

The aim of our investigations is to find a description of the mechanical behaviour of muscle contraction *in vivo* under two conditions, namely the static condition, under which the muscle contracts at constant length, and the dynamic condition under which a muscle shortens during the contraction, causing a movement of the limb.

We have carried out extensive experiments, of some of which a short description is given.

The phenomena measured simultaneously at the wrist of the forearm are:

— the force, exerted by the muscle
— the acceleration
— the degree of shortening and
— the rate of shortening.

All these phenomena were measured parallel to the longitudinal direction of the biceps muscle. Moreover, during all experiments the electromyogram as well as the integrated electromyogram were determined by a specially designed high quality electromyograph.

These phenomena were visualized simultaneously by a recorder.

Figure 1 shows the experimental set-up.

The frame work consists of a support to keep the subject's upperarm in a fixed horizontal position. A double segment, which can pivot in the vertical plane, is fixed to this support. A metal cuff encloses the wrist, while the subject keeps his forearm within the two segments, causing the axis of rotation of the segments to coincide with that of the elbow joint.

To create the static situation the forearm can be set in any position by fixing the segments. For the dynamic situation the segments enable us to load the forearm by fastening various kinds of load to the segments.

The force exerted is measured by a dynamometer, suspended in the apparatus between two rigid horizontal metal strips and connected to the metal cuff by a pair of rods, so as to detect the force acting parallel to the longitudinal direction of the muscles. The position of the wrist, which is related to the muscle length, is determined by a displacement meter, while the rate of shortening as well as the acceleration are measured directly by a speedometer and an accelerometer respectively.

In the static experiments the forearm is fixed at different angles between forearm and upper arm. In this position the subject has also to contract his forearm flexors as fast as possible from zero to maximum effort. A comparison between the mechanical response and the EMG as well as the integrated EMG shows that: 1. the electromyographic activity is almost immediately at a constant value, 2. the force

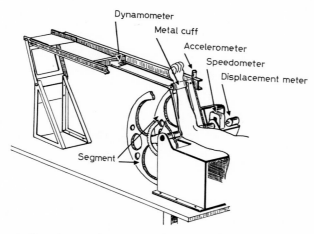

Fig. 1. General view of the apparatus for measuring simultaneously the degree and rate of contraction, the acceleration and the force of the muscle at the wrist.

builds up about twenty milliseconds later, compared with the EMG
and rises slowly in contrast with the electromyographic activity.

The force-time curve is of the same shape as found by HILL (1949)
and WILKIE (1950). The shape of the force-time curve clearly shows the
existence of elastic and damping properties of the total system.

Comparing the results obtained at different muscle lengths, it
appears that the maximum force exerted decreases with smaller muscle
length, which is in agreement with data of Wilkie. Moreover, the rate
of increase of the force is smaller for a shorter muscle. The EMG,
however, shows under maximum effort the same value and shape, in
spite of changes in muscle length.

In the dynamic experiments the forearm is moved during contraction.

It was found that the shape and value of the EMG do not differ
from those under static conditions. However, by comparing the force-
time curves obtained under static and dynamic conditions a great
difference is found. Also a considerable difference remains between
points on the dynamic force-time curve and those of the static one at
corresponding muscle lengths and points of time. This is due to
properties of the contracting mechanism. Among these an important
one is the friction in the system itself. Besides we ascertain activity
of the forearm extensors during their passive extension as a consequence
of the contraction of the flexor muscles. This extension will produce
a resistive force.

As pointed out already by BUCHTHAL (1951) friction has to be taken
in account. This friction is necessary for damping, and our investigations in this field, which are now in progress, give rise to the pre-
sumption that the system is nearly critical damped.

To evaluate the amount of resistive force from the electrical activity
of the muscle the relation between force at the wrist and the value of
the EMG has been determined for the flexor as well as for the extensor
muscles under static conditions at steady state levels of activity and at
different muscle lenghts. Plotting the level of electrical activity as a
function of the exerted force, different convex curves are found for
different muscle lengths.

Plotting the electrical activity as a function of the ratio between
the force exerted at different levels of activity and the maximum force
at the same muscle length all these curves appear to coincide without
increasing standard deviation. This shows again that the electrical

activity is independent of the muscle length. The corresponding relation for the triceps muscles shows the same shape at different absolute values.

In contrast with a linear relation found by LIPPOLD (1952), a non linear one has been found. This non-linear relation is in agreement with those of BUCHTHAL (1942) and BOTTOMLY (1964). Beside the properties already mentioned, the elasticity behaviour is equally important. Also on this subject experiments are going on and maybe the results will contribute to an understanding of the mechanical behaviour of the flexors and the movement pattern of the forearm.

References

BOTTOMLY, A.H.: The control of muscle. Progr. in Biocybern. I, 124–131, (Elsevier, Amsterdam 1964).
BUCHTHAL, F. and KAISER, E.: The rheology of the cross striated muscle fibre. Dan. Biol. Med. *21:* 1–318 (1951).
BUCHTAL, F.: Bestemmelse af "Muskelaktionspotentialernes effektivspaending" som undersøgelsesmetodik. Ugeskrift for Læger *104:* 14 (1942).
HILL, A.V.: The abrupt transition from rest to activity in muscle. Proc. Roy. Soc. B., *136:* 399–420 (1949).
LIPPOLD, O.C.J.: The relation between integrated action potentials in a human muscle and its isometric tension. J. Physiol., Lond. *117:* 492–499 (1952).
WILKIE, R.D.: The relation between force and velocity in human muscle. J. Physiol., Lond. *110,* 249–280 (1950).

Author's address: J. VREDENBREGT and W.G. KOSTER, Instituut voor Perceptie Onderzoek, Insulindelaan 2, *Eindhoven* (The Netherlands).

Biomechanics I, 1st Int. Seminar Zurich 1967
pp. 106–109 (Karger, Basel/New York 1968)

Laboratoire de Physiologie Générale, Faculté des Sciences, Lille

Experimental Determination of the Moment of Inertia of Limb Segments

S. Bouisset and E. Pertuzon

The quantitative biomechanical study of body movements demands that the moments of inertia of moving segments in relation to their axis of rotation should be known. As is usual for any solid, their experimental determination can be dynamically obtained by means of either the *compound pendulum* or the *quick release* technique (see Drillis *et al.*, 1964). The latter has been previously described by Fenn *et al.*, (1931) for the leg. It is extended here to the upper limb. The purpose of this study is: i) to determine the mass moment of inertia in relation to the humero-ulnar joint of the combined forearm and hand, this does not seem to have ever been systematically studied in the *living man*, and ii) to discuss the validity of the method. Preliminary results were published recently (Pertuzon and Bouisset, 1967).

Technique and Procedure

The subjects are seated. The right arm is placed on a horizontal cradle-shaped splint situated in a sagittal plane. The forearm is vertical, the hand in a semi-prone position with the wrist immobilized by a splint made of plastic material. The shoulder is held stable by means of a broad back rest (see Fig. 1).

The forearm is linked to a dynamometer by a horizontal cable the tension of which corresponds to the effort exerted by the extensor muscles. It is also connected to a hinged system which is regulated to reproduce its movement and which is provided with a tangential accelerometer containing a device allowing compensation for the effect of gravity.

Every subject is asked to exert a pull, F, on the cable approaching as precisely as possible a given value. The agreement between the exerted force and the imposed one can be verified on the dial of a galvanometer, both by the subject and the experimenter. Then the connection between the arm and the dynamometer is suddenly interrupted, unknown to the subject, by switching on an electromagnet. The forearm is then brought forward, with a tangential acceleration at its maximal value, Θ''. Recording simultaneously the electromyogram from the biceps, using surface electrodes, enables the experimenter to ascertain that there is no antagonistic activity in the biceps at the beginning of the movement, i.e. at the moment when Θ'' is measured.

It is easy to calculate the moment of inertia, I, if the distance d from the point of application of the force to the forearm axis of rotation is known, since $I = \frac{F.\,d}{\Theta''}$. A correction is

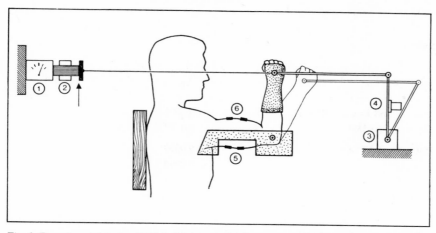

Fig. 1. Experimental device. 1) Dial of the control galvanometer. 2) Electromagnet. 3) Gonio-meter. 4) Tangential accelerometer. 5) Surface electrodes (triceps). 6) Surface electrodes (biceps). The arrow points to where the connection is interrupted.

made for the moment of inertia of the hinged system and the plastic splint which is deter-mined by the same method.

Eleven subjects, male adults, were used in the experiments; nine of them underwent two tests each. Pull forces of 2, 3 and 5 kg in the first test and 3,5 and 7 kg in the second one were considered; the order in presenting the weight was permuted from one test to the other. For each force five measures were made, the three central values being kept to calculate an average value.

Results and Discussion

The individual moments of inertia, which are taken into account for the statistics, are the average results of the two tests, that is of eighteen experimental values for each subject.

As can been seen in table I, where they are underlined, the present results agree with those of BRAUNE and FISCHER (1892) and of DEMPSTER (1955) which were obtained by means of the pendulum technique on cadaver separated segments. They also agree with those obtained from the living man by FENN (see FENN *et al.,* 1931, or FENN, 1938) using the quick release method and by WILKIE (1950) from static measures of the total volume of each 2 cm segment of the forearm. Thus, as far as it is possible to make an inference from the above data, the

Table I. Moments of inertia of the right forearm plus hand obtained both on the living man (**) and from the dismembered cadaver (*).

Reference	Number of subjects	Mean (kg · m²)	Standard Deviation (kg · m²)	Range (kg · m²)
Braune and Fischer (1892)*	2	0.0505		
Dempster (1955)*	8	0.0577	0.0152	0.0397–0.0852
Bouisset and Pertuzon (1968)**	*11*	*0.0599*	*0.0118*	*0.0430–0.0797*
Fenn (1938)**	1	0.0590		
Hill (1940)**	1	0.0277		
Wilkie (1950)**	1	0.0530		

quick release method, applied to the living man, seems to be rather accurate as compared to the results on cadaver separated segments.

However, Hill's results (1940) also obtained from the living man, and by means of the pendulum technique, are very different from the other ones. The difficulty in getting a complete muscular relaxation probably limits the use of the free oscillation technique to the study of cadaver separated segments.

Moreover, the quick release method also seems to be reliable: the average values obtained for 3 and 5 kg pulls during the first and second test show only very slight inter-test differences (3 and 1 percent) which are in no way significant.

In conclusion, this simple, rather accurate and reliable method seems to be the best in the case of limb segments.

References

Braune, W. und Fischer, O.: Abh. D. Math. Phys. Kl. d. Sachs. Akad. d. Wiss. *18:* 407–492 (1892).

Dempster, W.T.: Space requirements of the seated operator. W.A.D.C. Techn. Rpt. 55–159, pp. 254 (Wright Patterson Air Force Base, Ohio 1955).

Drillis, R.; Contini, R. and Bluestein, M.: Body segments parameters. A survey of measurement technique. Artificial Limbs *8:* 44–66 (1964).

Fenn, W.O.: The mechanics of muscular contraction in man. J. appl. Physics *9:* 165–177 (1938).

FENN, W.O.; BRODY, H. and PETRILLI, A.: The tension developed by human muscles at different velocities of shortening. Amer. J. Physiol. *97:* 1–14 (1931).

HILL, A.V.: The dynamic constants of human muscle. Proc. roy. Soc. B. *128:* 263–274 (1940).

PERTUZON, E. et BOUISSET, S.: Determination du moment d'inertie d'un segment corporel par une méthode de quick release. J. Physiol., Paris *59:* 470, 1967.

WILKIE, D.R.: The relation between force and velocity in human muscle. J. Physiol., Lond. *110:* 249–280 (1950).

Authors' address: S. BOUISSET and E. PERTUZON, Laboratoire de Physiologie Générale, Faculté des Sciences. B.P. 36 – *59 Lille* (France).

III. Technique of Motion Studies:
Electromyographic Kinesiology

Biomechanics I, 1st Int. Seminar Zurich 1967
pp. 110–122 (Karger, Basel/New York 1968)

Department of Anatomy, Queen's University, Kingston, Ont.

The Present Status of Electromyographic Kinesiology

J.V. BASMAJIAN

Electromyography has emerged in the past twenty years as an essential research tool in kinesiology. Combined with other techniques, the simultaneous recording of action potentials from various individual muscles provides the best information on the exact rôle of muscles in simple and complex movements and postures.

The new investigations have illuminated and supported some classical concepts while destroying others. Most important, they have enlarged our knowledge in areas which could not be explored by techniques that depended heavily on deduction and inference. For the first time, electromyography reveals what a muscle actually does in any particular function rather than what it might do.

As its name proclaims, electromyography is the recording of electrical discharges from muscle—more particularly, skeletal muscles. Although, in a sense, it dates back to the work of Galvani at the end of the 18th century, the real beginnings of modern electromyography coincided with the birth of the electronic age. The development of electronic circuitry, recording equipment and the cathode-ray oscilloscope gave electromyography its main impetus. Thus its history extends back less than two generations.

Almost from the beginning of its development, electromyography has been used for studies in kinesiology. Most of the early work was quite primitive; but in 1944 an important detailed study was done by INMAN, SAUNDERS, and ABBOTT of San Francisco on the rôle of specific muscles during movements of the shoulder region. Since then and during the decades of the 1950's and 60's, electromyographic kinesiology has come of age. Frequent reports and several substantial books have appeared on the subject. Even the ultimate has happened: an organization known as the International Society of Electromyographic Kinesiology (ISEK) was organized in 1965. With a membership of several hundred scientists from around the world, ISEK is a growing influence in this special branch of science.

Basis of Electromyography

The Motor Unit

Although the structural unit of a gross contraction is the muscle fibre, the functional unit (for the purpose of electromyography) is the motor unit, which is a group of fibres supplied by a single nerve cell. A contraction of a motor unit is a twitch lasting a few milliseconds. Immediately after each twitch the fibres of the motor unit relax completely and they only twitch again when an impulse arrives along the nerve fibre.

Individual muscles of the body consist of many hundreds of such motor units and it is their activity that develops the tension in the whole muscle. When one feels an intact normal muscle during a contraction, one might think that the muscle fibres are in some sort of continuous smooth shortening. Actually the motor units are repetitively twitching and this repetitive twitching of different motor units is completely asynchronous. It is this very randomized activity of different motor units that causes the smooth tension of the whole muscle rather than a jerky one.

The amount of work produced by single motor unit is rather small. In a living human being it is usually insufficient to show any movement of a joint spanned by the whole muscle of which it is a part. Even in the case of small joints, such as those of the thumb, at least two or three motor units are needed to give a visible movement. Indeed, the electromyographer can reveal normal activity of motor units even when clinical examination fails completely to detect its presence.

Under normal conditions small motor units are recruited early and, as the force is automatically or consciously increased, larger and larger motor units are recruited, while all the motor units also increase their frequency of twitching. The upper limit in man is about 50 per second, but rates much slower than this are the rule. As indicated above there is no single, set frequency; individual motor units can fire very slowly and will increase their frequency of response on demand.

Motor Unit Potentials

With appropriate equipment one can demonstrate that each twitch of
a motor unit is accompanied by a tiny electrical potential which is
dissipated into the surrounding tissues. This motor unit potential has
a brief duration (with a median of 9 msec) and a total amplitude
measured in microvolts or millivolts. When displayed on a cathode-ray
oscilloscope, most motor units recorded by conventional techniques are
sharp triphasic or biphasic spikes. Generally the larger the motor unit
potential involved the larger is the motor unit that produced it. However, distance from the electrode, the type of electrodes and equipment
used (and many other factors) influence the final size.

Equipment and Techniques

Electrodes

Probably the greatest disagreement in electromyography since its beginnings has centered around the types of electrodes. There are a multitude
of special electrodes (wires or needles). In any case, the electrodes must
be relatively harmless, and they must be brought close enough to the
motor units within the muscle to pick up its electrical changes with
fidelity.

Surface Electrodes

Because kinesiology is often performed by investigators who are not
medically qualified, surface electrodes have been used widely. Unfortunately, they have seriously curtailed the scope of many investigations.
Indeed, for excellent recordings, the difficulties rising from surface
electrodes are prohibitive. Their chief virtue is the ease with which any
novice can apply them and obtain—or appear to obtain—reasonable
success; this also is the root of their drawbacks.

Perhaps the chief usefulness of surface electrodes in kinesiology is
seen with investigations of the interplay between large, widely separated, muscles under conditions where palpation is impossible and
especially where the investigators are performing preliminary studies.
Thus, substantial progress can be made with skin electrodes in such

uncomplicated, general investigations; but their routine continued use should be avoided.

Inserted Electrodes

The renaissance of electromyography in this decade is largely due to the improvement of electrodes. Inserted electrodes are no longer as forbidding to kinesiologists as they once were and they are preferred for most scientifically sound studies. In the past, when inserted electrodes meant the large and often cumbersome bipolar hypodermic needles used in clinical investigations, it is not surprising that non-medical investigators avoided their use. Nowadays, fine-wire electrodes are conceded to be as easy to use and as easy to tolerate as are skin electrodes. This condemns the exclusive use of surface electrodes in studies of fine movements, deep muscles, the presence or absence of activity in various postures and, in short, in any circumstance where scientific precision is desirable.

For routine multi-electrode studies the best inserted electrode is our fine-wire bipolar electrode. These electrodes are (1) extremely fine and therefore, painless, (2) easily injected and withdrawn, (3) as broad in pick-up from a specific muscle as the best surface electrodes, and (4) give excellent sharp motor-unit spikes with fidelity. With one millimeter of their tip exposed, such electrodes record the voltage from a muscle much better than surface electrodes (SUTTON, 1962). Bipolar fine-wire electrodes isolate their pick-up either to the whole muscle being studied or to the confines of the compartment within a muscle if it has a multipennate structure. Barriers of fibrous connective tissue within a muscle or around it act as insulation. Thus one can record all the activity as far as such a barrier without interfering pick-up from beyond the barrier (such as there always is with surface electrodes). In the case of muscle without internal partitions, the fine-wire electrodes reflect the activity of the whole muscle as broadly as the best surface electrodes.

Our bipolar fine-wire electrodes are made from a nylon-insulated Karma alloy wire only 25 microns in diameter. They are very simple to make and their preparation is discussed in detail elsewhere (BASMAJIAN and STECKO, 1962; BASMAJIAN, FORREST and SHINE, 1966; BASMAJIAN, 1967).

Apparatus

Electromyographs (either commercial or self-constructed) are high-gain amplifiers with a preference for frequencies from about 10 to several thousand cycles per sec. An upper limit of 1,000 cycles per sec is satisfactory. For kinesiological studies, the best instruments are multi-channel. This leads to difficulties. The multi-channel equipment most readily available to the novice is ink-writing electroencephalographic equipment, and except for certain special studies, such equipment is not satisfactory. However, some of the newer types have appropriate switching devices for the recording of EMG potentials, i.e., the operator can choose a frequency response with a wider range than that which is standard for EEG's. Even then, the obvious deficiency of ink-writing equipment is that the pens are too slow to record faster frequencies. This is overcome in some laboratories by the integration of potentials (a sort of electronic summation of activity); but the use of integrated potentials without concurrent monitoring of raw EMG potentials must be condemned because the integrator does not discriminate against artifacts.

Ideally the recording device should either be photographic or employ electromagnetic taperecording. With multiple channels one may photograph a row of cathode-ray traces on photographic film in a variety of ways. Most convenient is the recording of multiple traces from ultra-violet galvanometers on bromide recording paper. Several widely distributed direct recorders are on the market; one has as many as 36 channels. The miniature galvanometers provide frequency responses suitable for electromyography and because the special paper requires no developing, there is an immediate display. (Unfortunately this paper darkens with continued exposure to light and the recording is spoiled unless the chemical process is stopped by fixation.) In recent years, multi-track taperecorders have provided a relatively cheap method of storing EMG signals. Elsewhere these matters are discussed in detail (BASMAJIAN, 1967).

General Survey of EMG Kinesiology

In a brief review of this kind, no attempt can be made to touch upon the thousands of studies reported in the literature, especially on the individual actions of specific muscles in specific movements. These have been dealt with in detail elsewhere (BASMAJIAN, 1967). Instead, three special areas will be discussed: locomotion, posture, and motor unit training.

Human Locomotion

Although until recently its contribution has not been as great as it might have been, electromyography has added a new dimension in the latest studies on locomotion. The main reason for this slow start seems to have been that multi-factorial studies are difficult and time-consuming. Only recently has equipment improved to the point where electromyography gives especially useful results. A series of large-scale studies in the author's laboratory will not be described here but are the source of a number of papers to be published almost concurrently with this article. Limitation of space allows the review of only a few highlights from previously published works.

RADCLIFFE (1962) showed that in walking there is a very fine sequence of activity in various groups of muscles in the lower limb as follows:

As the heel strikes the ground the hamstrings and pretibial muscles reach their peak of activity.

Thereafter the quadriceps increase in activity as the torso is carried forward over the limb, apparently to maintain stability of the knee.

At heel-off the calf group of muscles build up a crescendo of activity which ceases with the toe-off. Before and during toe-off, quadriceps and sometimes the hamstrings reach another (but smaller) peak of activity.

The pretibial muscles maintain some activity all through the cycle, rising to a peak at heel-contact and a smaller peak at toe-off.

Radcliffe postulated that during the stance phase the stabilizing function of the ankle plantar-flexors at the knee is most important. This was confirmed by SUTHERLAND (1966) by means of combined EMG's and motion pictures of gait. The period of activity in the calf muscles corresponds with knee extension and dorsiflexion of the foot. Only at the end of plantar-flexion of the ankle does plantar-flexion of the foot occur. A bizarre finding was that knee extension occurs after quadriceps activity has ceased. This is related to the fact that full extension of the knee never occurs during walking in the way that it does in standing (MURRAY *et al.,* 1964).

SUTHERLAND believes that knee extension in the stance phase is brought about by the force of the plantar-flexors of the ankle resisting the dorsiflexion of the ankle; this dorsiflexion is in turn the resultant of extrinsic forces—kinetic forces, gravity, and the reaction of the floor. Because the resultant of extrinsic forces proves to be greater, increased dorsiflexion of the foot continues until heel-off begins. The restraining function of the ankle plantar-flexors in decelerating forward rotation of the tibia on the talus proves to be the key to their stabilizing action.

Combining the techniques of motion picture photography, accelerograms, electrogoniograms, myograms and EMG's, LIBERSON (1965) reported the following correlation of activity during walking on the level:

1. Contraction of the triceps surae is followed by that of gluteus maximus of the opposite side.

2. Contraction of iliopsoas occurs simultaneously with that of gluteus maximus of the opposite side.

3. Dorsiflexion of the foot begins at the time of maximum acceleration of the lower leg.

4. Extension of the knee begins at the time of maximum velocity of the leg.

5. Contraction of the triceps surae corresponds to the first hump of the vertical accelerogram.

6. Contraction of the gluteus maximus on the opposite side corresponds to the second hump of the vertical accelerogram.

7. In many cases, two-joint muscles show an increase of tension without EMG potentials because they act as simple ligaments during the contraction of the antagonists.

BATTYE and JOSEPH (1966) find that:

Tibialis anterior is usually biphasic in activity, but sometimes it is active for a short time after the foot is flat on the ground—perhaps 'to pull the body over the foot in the early part of the supporting phase'.

Soleus begins to contract before it lifts the heel from the ground; it stops before the great toe leaves the ground. Apparently these are supportive rather than propulsive functions.

Quadriceps femoris contracts as extension of the knee is being completed, not during the earlier part of extension when the action is probably a passive swing. Quadriceps continues to act during the early part of the supporting phase (when the knee is flexed and the centre of gravity falls behind it). Quadriceps activity occurs at the end of the supporting phase to fix the knee in extension, probably counteracting the tendency toward flexion imparted by gastrocnemius.

The hamstrings contract at the end of flexion and during the early extension of the thigh apparently to prevent flexion of the thigh before the heel is on the ground and to assist the movement of the body over the supporting limb. In some persons, the hamstrings also contract a second time in the cycle during the end of the supporting phase; this may prevent hip flexion.

Gluteus medius and gluteus minimus are active at the time that one would predict, i.e., during the supporting phase; however, some subjects show activity in the swing phase too.

Gluteus maximus shows activity at the end of the swing and at the beginning of the supporting phase. This is contrary to the general belief that its activity is not needed for ordinary walking. Perhaps gluteus maximus contracts to prevent or to control flexion at the hip joint.

Trunk Muscles During Gait. Erector spinae shows two periods of activity, according to Battye and Joseph (as noted before by other investigators). They occur 'at intervals of half a stride when the hip is fully flexed and fully extended at the beginning and end of the supporting phase'. Apparently the bilateral activity of the erectores spinae prevents falling forward of the body and also rotation and lateral flexion of the trunk. SHEFFIELD (1962) found the abdominal muscles inactive during walking on a horizontal level. Very little investigation of gait has been done otherwise in this part of the body.

Posture

Lower Limb

The function of the large muscles of the leg and thigh in relationship to posture has been widely studied. For example, JOSEPH and NIGHTINGALE (1952) showed that the soleus of all persons and the gastrocnemius of many have well-marked activity when the subject is standing at ease while the thigh muscles remain inactive.

We found that the posterior calf muscles are generally much more active than the tibialis anterior (BASMAJIAN and BENTZON, 1954). Further, there is frequently a periodicity to the activity related to an almost imperceptible forward-and-backward swaying of the body (FLOYD AND SILVER, 1950). Deliberate leaning forward or backward produces compensatory activity in the muscle to prevent the occurrence of a complete imbalance. A very finely regulated mechanism is in control and the slightest shift causes a reflex postural adjustments. Wearing of high heels increases the activity of the calf muscles of individual subjects, apparently due to a shifting forward of the centre of gravity (BASMAJIAN and BENTZON, 1954; JOSEPH and NIGHTINGALE, 1956).

The postural function of the muscles of the foot has always posed a question of some fundamental interest in relation to the normal support and the abnormal flattening of the arches. We have shown that the intrinsic muscles are generally quiescent during normal standing, but they become extremely active when the subject rises on tip-toes and during the take-off stage of walking (BASMAJIAN, 1967).

Although the peroneal and tibial muscles have often been considered to play an important rôle in maintaining the longitudinal arches of the foot in standing, this theory seems to have been discredited by our findings and by the indirect contributory evidence of other investigators. During standing these muscles are generally quiescent. Furthermore, they remain inactive even when a subject suddenly lowers himself to a normal standing position from an elevated seated position. More recently, we showed that even enormous weights superimposed on the plantigrade foot result in little if any activity in tibialis anterior, tibialis posterior, flexor hallucis longus, peroneus longus, abductor hallucis and flexor digitorum brevis (BASMAJIAN and STECKO, 1963). During locomotion, however, peroneal and tibial muscles show marked activity. Apparently, the first line of defence against flat feet is a ligamentous one, but the added stresses of walking require special mechanisms.

Posture of Trunk

While standing erect, most human subjects require very slight postural activity and sometimes only intermittent reflex activity of the intrinsic muscles of the back, according to various investigators (see BASMAJIAN, 1967, for references). During forward flexion there is marked activity until flexion is extreme, at which time the ligamentous structures assume the load and the muscles become silent. In the extreme-flexed position of the back, the erector spinae remains relaxed in the initial stages of heavy weight-lifting. This stresses the dangers to the vertebral ligaments and joints of lifting 'with the back' rather than with the muscles of the lower limb.

During relaxed standing, only slight activity has been recorded in the abdominal muscles by FLOYD and SILVER (1950) and by CAMPBELL and GREEN (1955) who proved that the activity is greatest in the internal oblique to provide the protection against hernia that the muscle affords to the inguinal canal in the upright posture.

JONES, BEARGIE and PAULY (1953) were the first to suggest that the intercostal muscles play a part in posture, or at least, in the maintenance of certain flexed postures and adjustments of position. Certainly worthy of further study is their interesting proposal that the intercostals have as their chief function the maintenance of a proper distance between the ribs while the rib cage is actively elevated by the neck muscles during inspiration.

Upper Limb

Not surprisingly, low-grade postural activity occurs in the upper fibres of trapezius in supporting the shoulder girdle. But this falls off after a minute or two and often disappears completely, according to BEARN (1961). Minimal postural activity occurs in the serratus anterior.

At the shoulder joint, the main muscular activity in resisting downward dislocation occurs in the supraspinatus and to a slight extent in the posterior, horizontal-running fibres of the deltoid (BASMAJIAN and BAZANT, 1959). The bulk of the deltoid, and the biceps and triceps show no activity in spite of their vertical direction. Surprisingly, this is true even when heavy weights are suspended from the arm. The function of supraspinatus is apparently associated with a previously undescribed locking mechanism dependent upon the slope of the glenoid fossa. The horizontal pull of the muscle, along with an extreme tightening of the superior part of the capsule only when the arm hangs vertically, prevents downward subluxation of the humeral head.

At the elbow joint, without an added load, there is no activity in the muscles, suggesting that the ligaments carry the weight. The addition of a small or moderate load does not produce any activity in biceps, triceps, brachioradialis or pronator teres. Moreover, brachio-radialis shows little if any activity in maintaning flexed postures even against added loads because it is an excellent example of a 'shunt' muscle as first postulated by MACCONAILL (1949). A shunt muscle is one that acts chiefly during rapid movement along the long axis of the moving bone to provide centripetal force. Spurt muscles, in contrast, are those that produce the acceleration along the curve of motion (e.g., brachialis and biceps). (See BASMAJIAN, 1967, for a fuller discussion.)

Motor Unit Training

In recent years, we have been studying the control that conscious man can exert over individual motor units. Our experiments on motor unit controls and training have been applied to a number of different muscles, especially muscles of the thumb and little finger, various muscles of the forearm, arm and back, and the tibialis anterior. Given a clear response of their motor unit activity on a cathode-ray oscilloscope and loudspeaker, and though completely unaware of any movement in the muscle, everyone can achieve notably better wilful control over tiny muscle contractions within half an hour. In this time, almost all can learn to relax the whole muscle instantly on command and to recruit the activity of a single motor unit, also instantly, keeping it active for as many minutes as desired (BASMAJIAN, 1963).

Most persons are able to switch to and gain mastery over other new units in a matter of minutes. More than half of all people can repeat the performance with a third new unit within a few minutes. A few persons can recruit a fourth or a fifth isolated unit; some can do even more.

Once a person has gained isolation and control of any spinal motor neuron (for that is the essence of motor unit training) he can learn to vary its rate of firing. This rate can be deliberately changed in im-mediate response to a command. The lowest limit of the range of frequencies is zero, i.e., one can start from neuromuscular silence and then give single isolated contractions at regular rates as low as one per second and at increasingly faster rates.

Most persons also can be trained in the production of specific rhythms. Almost all can reduce and increase the frequency of a well-controlled unit with ease and immediately on command.

Persons with the finest control may be trained to learn various special tricks. Many can learn to recall specific units into activity in the absence of the aural and visual feedbacks but they are unable to explain how (BASMAJIAN, BAEZA and FABRIGAR, 1965).

After testing several hundred people we have failed to find any clear-cut personal characteristics that reveal reasons for the quality of their performance. Fewer than ten per cent of our subjects have given poor performances. We have found both poor and excellent performers at different ages, among both sexes, and among both the manually skilled and unskilled, the educated and uneducated, and the bright and the dull personalities. Some 'nervous' persons do not perform well, but neither do some very calm persons.

The explanation of how a person trains individual motor units is still not clear. CARLSÖÖ and EDFELDT (1963) believe that: 'Proprioception can be assisted greatly by exteroceptive auxiliary stimuly in achieving motor precision'. WAGMAN, PIERCE and BURGER (1965) greatly emphasize the rôle of proprioception, believing that certain positions of a joint must be either held or imagined for success in activating desired motor units in isolation. On the other hand, our subjects have expressed bewilderment when asked to give their formula for success.

We have found that moving nearby joints while a motor unit is firing is a distracting influence, yet most subjects can keep right on firing the unit in isolation in spite of such distraction (BASMAJIAN and SIMARD, 1967). With Wagman and his colleagues we agree that subjects must first receive our form of motor unit training before they can maintain the activity while the limb or joints are moved into varying positions. This apparently is a form of proprioceptive memory and almost certainly is the basis of motor learning and of kinesiology. Studies now in progress promise to add fundamental knowledge to this important field.

References

BASMAJIAN, J.V.: Control and training of individual motor units. Science *141:* 440–441 (1963).

BASMAJIAN, J.V.: (1967) *Muscles Alive: Their Functions Revealed by Electromyography.* 2nd Ed. (Williams & Wilkins, Baltimore 1967).

BASMAJIAN, J.V. and BAZANT, F.J.: Factors preventing downward dislocation of the adducted shoulder joint: an electromyographic and morphological study. J. Bone J. Surg. *41:* 1182–1186 (1959).

BASMAJIAN, J.V. and BENTZON, J.W.: An electromyographic study of certain muscles of
    the leg and foot in the standing position. Surg. Gynec. Obstet. *98:* 662–666 (1954).
BASMAJIAN, J.V.; FORREST, W.J. and SHINE, G.: A simple connector for fine-wire electrodes.
    J. appl. Physiol. *21:* 1680 (1966).
BASMAJIAN, J.V. and SIMARD, T.G.: Effects of distracting movements on the control of
    trained motor units. Amer. J. phys. Med. *46:* 1427–1449 (1967).
BASMAJIAN, J.V. and STECKO, GEO.: A new bipolar indwelling electrode for electromyo-
    graphy. J. appl. Physiol. *17:* 894 (1962).
BATTYE, C.K. and JOSEPH, J.: An investigation by telemetering of the activity of some
    muscles in walking. Med. biol. Eng. *4:* 125–135 (1966).
BEARN, J.G.: An electromyographic study of the trapezius, deltoid, pectoralis major,
    biceps and triceps muscles, during static loading of the upper limb. Anat. Rec. *140:*
    103–108 (1961).
CAMPBELL, E.J.M. and GREEN, J.H.: The expiratory function of the abdominal muscles
    in man. An electromyographic study. J. Physiol. *120:* 409–418 (1953).
CARLSÖÖ, S. and EDFELDT, Å.W.: Attempts at muscle control with visual and auditory
    impulses as auxiliary stimuli. Scand. J. Psychol. *4:* 231–235 (1963).
FLOYD, W.F. and SILVER, P.H.S. Electromyographic study of patterns of activity of the
    anterior abdominal wall muscles in man. J. Anat., Lond. *84:* 132–145 (1950).
INMAN, V.T., SAUNDERS, J.B. DEC. M. and ABBOTT, L.C.: Observations on the function
    of the shoulder joint. J. Bone J. Surg. *26:* 1–30 (1944).
JONES, D.S., BEARGIE, R.J. and PAULY, J.E.: An electromyographic study on muscles of
    costal respiration in man. Anat. Rec. *128:* 733–746 (1953).
JOSEPH, J. and NIGHTINGALE, A.: Electromyography of muscles of posture: leg muscles in
    males. J. Physiol., Lond. *117:* 484–491 (1952).
JOSEPH, J. and NIGHTINGALE, A.: Electromyography of muscles of posture: leg and thigh
    muscles in women, including the effects of high heels. J. Physiol., Lond. *132:* 465–468
    (1956).
LIBERSON, W.T.: Biomechanics of gait: a method of study. Arch. phys. Med. *46:* 37–48
    (1965).
MACCONAILL, M.A.: The movements of bones and joints. 2. Function of the musculature.
    J. Bone J. Surg. *31:* 100–104 (1949).
MURRAY, P.M.; DROUGHT, A.B. and KORY, R.C.: Walking patterns of normal men. J.
    Bone J. Surg. *46:* 335–360 (1964).
RADCLIFFE, C.W.: The Biomechanics of below-knee prostheses in normal, level, bipedal
    walking. Artif. Limbs. *6:* 16–24 (1962).
SHEFFIELD, F.J.: Electromyographic study of the abdominal muscles in walking and other
    movements. Amer. J. phys. Med. *41:* 142–147 (1962).
SUTHERLAND, D.H.: An electromyographic study of the plantar flexors of the ankle in
    normal walking on the level. J. Bone J. Surg. *48:* 66–71 (1966).
SUTTON, D.L.: Surface and needle electrodes in electromyography. Dent. Progr. *2:* 127–131
    (1962).
WAGMAN, I.H.; PIERCE, D.S. and BURGER, R.E.: Proprioceptive influence in volitional
    control of individual motor units. Nature, Lond. *207:* 957–958 (1965).

Author's address: J.V. BASMAJIAN, M.D., Department of Anatomy, Queen's University,
Kingston, Ont. (Canada).

Biomechanics I, 1st Int. Seminar Zurich 1967
pp. 123–127 (Karger, Basel/New York 1968)

Department of Human Anatomy, University of Göteborg, Sweden
Head: (Professor Bo E. Ingelmark, M.D.)

Wire Electrodes in Electromyographic Kinesiology

B. Jonsson

Introduction

Wire electrodes have been used in kinesiologic EMG investigations for at least 15 years (Inman et al., 1952). Being intramuscular, these electrodes can be used for the study of most muscles, even those that are small and deep, and hence beyond the reach of surface electrodes. As wire electrodes usually cause little or no discomfort they are suitable for kinesiologic investigations.

Several different techniques for using wire electrodes have been published, especially during the last decade (inter alia Long et al., 1960; Morris et al., 1961; Basmajian and Stecko, 1962; Long and Brown, 1964; Scott, 1965; Sumitsuji et al., 1965; Ahlgren, 1966; Basmajian et al., 1966; Keagy et al., 1966; Pauly, 1966). The differences concern such factors as the material and diameter of the wire, the length of the intramuscular uninsulated end of the wire, the distance between the uninsulated wire ends in bipolar wire electrodes, the mode of insertion and the way of connecting the wires to the EMG apparatus.

The present investigation aims at studying some of the technical requirements for an adequate use of intramuscularly placed bipolar wire electrodes for kinesiologic EMG experiments. A preliminary report of some of the results will be given here.

The Effect of the Length of the Intramuscular Uninsulated Wire Ends and of the Interelectrode Distance on the Mean Voltage of the EMG

The mean voltage of the EMG was recorded from the brachioradialis muscle during a standardized isometric contraction. Three or four pairs

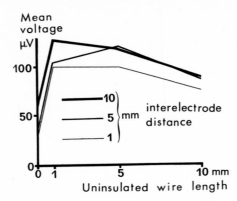

Fig. 1. The effect on the EMG mean voltage of using different lengths for the uninsulated distal ends of the wires (0 stands for square-cut wires) and different distances between the uninsulated parts of the wires. Each plot represents the mean of at least 7 different observations.

of wire electrodes of different constructions were placed near each other in the muscle. It was found that, largely independently of the interelectrode distance, the highest mean voltage was obtained with uninsulated distal wire ends 1 to 5 mm long (Fig. 1). It is interesting that the activity obtained with square-cut wires was mostly an interference pattern, though with a relatively low voltage.

Displacement of Wire Electrodes During an Experiment

Measurements showed that the part of the wires which projects outside the skin is usually shorter after an experiment than before. Detailed studies indicated that most of this displacement occurs during the first few contractions of the muscle.

It is usually found that the wires are somewhat deformed after an experiment involving movements. What is perhaps surprising is that the greatest deformation often seems to have occurred in the part that has been situated between the muscle and the skin. A probable explanation is that, during the first contractions, additional wire is drawn in beneath the skin. After this the part of the wire between the skin and the muscle is alternately bent and stretched by the muscle movements during the experiment. This problem is to be investigated further with roentgenologic techniques.

Intramuscular Fracturing of Wire Electrodes

Wire electrodes located in the lateral head of the gastrocnemius muscle during 20 minutes walking fractured during the experiment or when they were extracted in 25 per cent of the cases when using KARMA alloy wires with a diameter of 25 microns and in 3 per cent when using wires with a diameter of 50 microns. The length of the wire fragments ranged from 1 to 40 mm. Apparently the fragments did not usually cause more discomfort than in cases without fractures. When wire electrodes were inserted into a relaxed muscle and then immediately extracted, fractures never occurred.

It should be pointed out that the electromyographic effect of such a fracture during an experiment is probably very slight and may be interpreted erroneously as a normal change in the degree of muscular contraction.

Short-circuiting of Wire Electrodes

The wire electrodes may sometimes short-circuit due to direct contact between the uninsulated ends of the two wires, especially when the interelectrode distance is small. Such short-circuiting may occur during part of a movement only and thus simulate the effect of a muscle relaxation.

Combined Electromyographic and Radiographic Location of Wire Electrodes

When inserting intramuscular electrodes into small and/or deep muscles it may be difficult to determine whether they have been placed in the correct muscle or not. Furthermore, wire electrodes cannot be moved once the insertion needle has been withdrawn.

It is, however, possible to introduce the wires with a coated hypodermic needle which is used as a monopolar EMG electrode during the insertion (Fig. 2). If only the tip of the needle is uninsulated and if the bent wire ends are small, the needle electrode can at least show when the wire electrode ends are intramuscularly placed.

When the final position of the wire electrodes has been decided, but before the insertion needle is withdrawn, a gaseous contrast medium, carbon dioxide, can be injected into the muscle. The carbon dioxide stays within the muscle fascia and can be visualized by standard roentgen techniques (Fig. 3). The effect of the injected carbon dioxide on the electromyogram lasts only a few minutes.

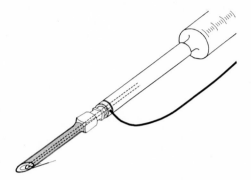

Fig. 2. The wire electrodes can be introduced with a coated hypodermic needle; this is used as a monopolar EMG electrode during the insertion and, after this, for the injection of carbon dioxide.

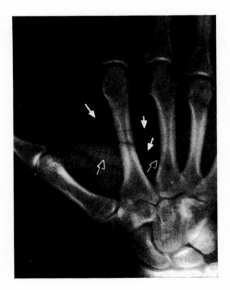

Fig. 3. The transverse head of the adductor pollicis muscle after injection of 16 ml carbon dioxide. The gas is seen as fine streaks between the fibre bundles.

References

AHLGREN, J.: Mechanism of mastication. A quantitative cinematographic and electromyographic study of masticatory movements in children, with special reference to occlusion of the teeth. Acta odont. scand. *24:* suppl. 44 (1966).

BASMAJIAN, J.V.; FORREST, W.J. and SHINE, G.: A simple connector for fine-wire EMG electrodes. J. appl. Physiol. *21:* 1680 (1966).

BASMAJIAN, J.V. and STECKO, G.: A new bipolar electrode for electromyography. J. appl. Physiol. *17:* 849 (1962).

INMAN, V.T.; RALSTONE, H.J.; SAUNDERS, J.B. DE C.M.; FEINSTEIN, B. and WRIGHT, E.W.: Relation of human electromyogram to muscular tension. Electroenceph. clin. Neurophysiol. *4:* 187–194 (1952).

KEAGY, R.D.; BRUMLIK, J. and BERGAN, J.J.: Direct electromyography of the psoas major muscle in man. J. Bone Jt. Surg. *48-A:* 1377–1382 (1966).

LONG, C. II; BROWN, M.E. and WEISS, G.: An electromyographic study of the extrinsic-intrinsic kinesiology of the hand: Preliminary report. Arch. phys. Med. *41:* 175–181 (1960).

LONG, C. II. and BROWN, M.E.: Electromyographic kinesiology of the hand: muscles moving the long finger. J. Bone Jt. Surg. *46-A:* 1683–1706 (1964).

MORRIS, J.M.; LUCAS, D.B. and BRESLER, B.: Role of trunk in stability of the spine. J. Bone Jt. Surg. *43-A:* 327–351 (1961).

PAULY, J.E.: An electromyographic analysis of certain movements and exercises. I. Some deep muscles of the back. Anat. Rec. *155:* 223–234 (1966).

SCOTT, R.N.: A method of inserting wire electrodes for electromyography. IEEE Trans. Bio-Med. Engin. *12:* 46–47 (1965).

SUMITSUJI, N.; MATSUMOTO, K. and KANEKO, Z.: A new method to study facial expression using electromyography. Electromyography *5:* 269–272 (1965).

Author's address: BENGT JONSSON, M.D., Department of Human Anatomy, Medicinaregatan 3, Fack, S-40 033 Göteborg 33 (Sweden).

Biomechanics I, 1st Int. Seminar Zurich 1967
pp. 128–131 (Karger, Basel/New York 1968)

Boston University, Sargent College of Allied Health Professions, Boston, Mass.

A Simple Method of Synchronizing
Cinematographic-Electromyographic Data

A.L. O'CONNELL

Unless electromyograms (EMGs) are objectively correlated with the course of the movement being performed, they are of little value. It is impossible to determine at which point during the action each muscle begins or ends its activity. To insure accuracy, a cinematographic record should be synchronized with the EMG. We have developed a simple, inexpensive, and highly satisfactory method which allows the subject freedom of movement, facilitates study of results, and assures accuracy of interpretation of the EMG. We make use of a $3\frac{1}{2}$ inch electric timer with a one second sweep hand, such as is used in physics laboratories, which is placed at a right angle (90°) to the camera on the track of a specially designed pan-head (Fig. 1). The track is sufficiently elevated to bring the center of the timer level with the center of the camera lens. We use a Bolex Rex H16 16 mm reflex camera with a wide angle lens. A 3-inch biconvex lens is placed facing the timer with its center at the same level as that of the clock. This lens focuses the timer dial into a $48 \times 48 \times 54$ mm beam splitter which reflects a frame-filling image of the timer into the camera. The beam splitter rests directly in front of the camera lens on a small platform so that its center is on a line with the other centers. With adequate lighting the reverse image of the timer dial appears on each frame of the film superposed over the figure of the performing subject (Fig. 2). (N.B. The beam splitter's top and the side away from the camera must be shielded from the light focused on the timer face. Black construction paper is adequate.)

A pushbutton device, described in O'CONNELL, A.L. and GARDNER, E.B., (Res. Quart. Amer. Ass. Hlth. Phys. Educ. *34:* 166, 1963), instantaneously activates a small neon light set in a 6-inch reflector and drops the baseline of one channel of the EMG, thus simultaneously marking both film and EMG. The time in the first photographic frame in which the light appears (Fig. 2a) is also the exact time of the baseline

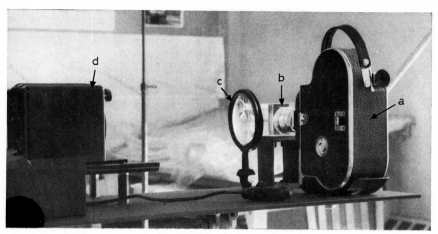

Fig. 1. Special pan head on tripod set up for photography. A, Bolex reflex camera; B, beam splitter; C, biconvex lens; D, electric timer, See text.

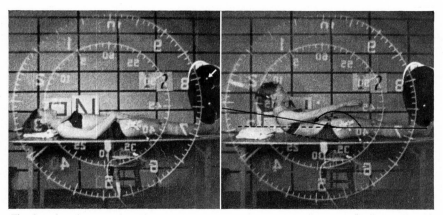

Fig. 2a   *Fig. 2b*

Fig. 2. Enlargements from 16 mm film of sit-up while EMG is being recorded from hip flexor muscles. A, frame in which neon light first appears, see arrow. Time, 30.53 seconds, read from timer dial. B, Time, 31.22 seconds, when tensor fascia lata begins contracting. See Figure 3. Horizontal line drawn through hip and knee axes makes ventral angel of 171° with line through lower trunk axis.

drop on the EMG[1]. Any frame in the film can be accurately correlated with the EMG by reading the time on the frame and counting forward on the EMG record from the time marker (baseline drop). Six centimeters per second is a convenient paper speed since each vertical section of the paper is traversed in 0.1 second. To simplify the process even more, the author uses a strip of EMG paper at least equal in length to the record and marked off in seconds beginning with the first even second which appears on the filmed record (Fig. 3). By indicating the time of the first 'light' frame on this guide sheet and placing this point immediately below the baseline drop on the EMG, the portion of the EMG coincident with any significant frame may be pinpointed directly

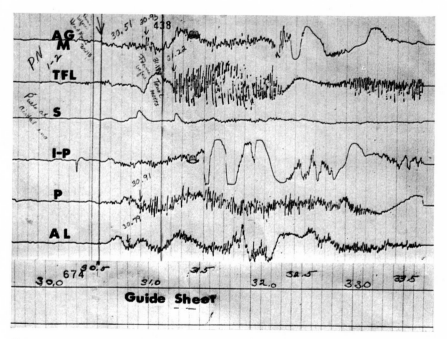

Fig. 3. EMG of the sit-up illustrated in Figure 2. Note guide sheet used to read off times of initiation of activity. AGM, anterior gluteus medius; TFL, tensor fascia lata; S, sartorius; I-P, iliopsoas; P, pectineus; AL, adductor longus. Records of gracilis and rectus femoris covered by guide sheet.

[1]To synchronize several cameras photographing in different planes, the reader is referred to BLIEVERNICHT, D.L. (Res. Quart. Amer. Ass. Hlth. Phys. Educ. *38:* 146, 1967) for a description of a cone device.

from the paper guide. Thus it becomes possible to determine objectively the muscle activity accompanying any part of the overt movement pattern, or, by measuring joint angles on the film (Fig. 2b), the exact range over which a specific muscle is active. The high degree of accuracy afforded by this method also provides a basis for reasonable speculation concerning the operation of reflex mechanisms.

The procedure described above has been used successfully in our kinesiological research laboratory for several years. For example, in connection with one of our recent studies where we are concerned with the roles of various muscles in flexing the hip under a variety of circumstances (such as the starting position, the weight of the lever, and the length of its moment arm), electrical activity appears in the tensor fascia lata on the EMG at 31.22 seconds as read from the guide sheet (Fig. 3). The film frame with this time on it (Fig. 2b) shows the coincident point in the movement. When lines are drawn through the long axes of the thigh and lower trunk, the ventral angle is found to be 171 degrees, indicating 9 degrees of hip flexion (180 minus 171) as the point where this muscle becomes active.

A Few Cautions

The Timer: a) The timer should have a black dial face with white numbers; manufacturer's legends, zeros, and all but the last centimeter of the two hands should be painted out with a dark paint. b) To avoid undesirable reflections, the glass over the dial must be removed and the case, if shiny, sprayed with a light absorbing black paint.
Lighting: a) The light on the timer face must be at a minimum, i.e., just sufficient to make the dial visible in the viewfinder over the fully lit subject. b) Because the beam splitter absorbs 50 to 75% of the light that would otherwise reach the camera, the lighting on the subject must be increased by a factor of 2 to 4 over ordinary requirements. Use of a very sensitive film (ASA No. 400 or more) is recommended.
The Neon Light: a) A neon light is used rather than a carbon filament lamp because the latter requires several frames (filmed at 64 frames/second) to reach full intensity or to die out. The neon lamp is instantly on, instantly off. b) The position of the neon light must be checked through the reflex viewfinder before each run to be sure it is not obscured by the numbers or hands of the reflected timer face.

Author's address: ALICE L. O'CONNELL, Ph. D., Associate Professor, Boston University, Sargent College of Allied Health Professions, University Road, *Boston*, Mass. 02215–USA.

Biomechanics I, 1st Int. Seminar Zurich 1967
pp. 132–137 (Karger, Basel/New York 1968)

University of California, Santa Barbara, Cal.

Photo-Recording Electromyography in Clinical Kinesiological Studies [1]

M.M. FLINT

Introduction

A frequent problem among researchers using electromyography in movement studies has been the synchronizing of gross motor activities with the recording of muscle activity.

The purpose of this study was to investigate the function of the hip extensor muscles during selected movement patterns by using a photo-recording electromyographic procedure.

The gluteus maximus and the three hamstring muscles, the semimembranosus, semitendinosus and biceps femoris, are generally ascribed the function of thigh extension at the hip joint. How much effort each contributes to the total movement of hip extension and the phase during which each is working has not been determined.

Method

Equipment

Instruments. A Meditron electromyograph, Model 302, with a dual channel cathode ray oscilloscope, was used to record the data for this study.

Permanent records of the electromyograms were obtained by use of a Bolex sixteen millimeter reflex camera equipped with an optical beam-splitting device situated in such a way as to simultaneously record the traces on the oscilloscope, the data board mounted above the oscilloscope and the subject. Thus, an exact reading of the subject's movements and the corresponding muscle responses were obtained on a permanent record.

[1] Study supported by University of California, Grant 140.

The physical arrangement of the instruments and apparatus is shown in Figure 1. The camera was placed 18.5 inches from the oscilloscope; the subject was located at a ninety degree angle and approximately eight to twelve feet from the lens aperture. Behind the subject was a grid board with a vertical reference line and angles outlined in tape to determine the position of the extremity during all movements. A data board for recording the operator's notes was mounted above the oscilloscope and illuminated by a spot light with a long tubular shield. Photo floods were used to illuminate the subject and grid board. The cameras, electromyograph, and lights were incorporated into one unit on a dolly, which permitted a single adjustment for changing height and position in order to keep the subject at right angles to the camera at all times.

Optical Assembly. A ninety degree prism was held in a matte box which was attached to the camera five inches in front of the lens. The prism was adjusted so that the left half of the camera field of view was deflected at right angles to view the subject and the grid board. The right half of the camera-field did not intercept the prism and had normal forward vision placing the face of the cathode ray tube on the lower right quadrant of the aperture and the data board on the upper right quadrant. This same picture could be viewed through the camera viewer

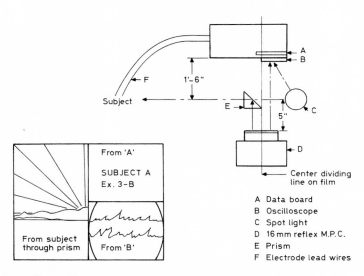

Fig. 1. Recording method and duplicate of 16 mm film frame.

during filming. A copy of one frame of the film has been duplicated in Figure 1. In order to obtain satisfactory focus for the three areas, subject, oscilloscope and data board, a wide angle lens (15 mm) and Tri-X reversal film were used. This combination allowed sufficient depth of field to cover the required focus range. The reflected light levels for each of the three areas were equalized by first determining the exposure needed for the traces on the cathode ray tube and then adjusting the light levels in the other areas to this value.

Electronics. Monopolar needle electrodes were used to pick up the action potentials of the semitendinosus, long head of the biceps femoris and the gluteus maximus. The active electrodes were placed approximately in the center of the muscle belly and the reference needles were placed subcutaneously one inch distal to the active electrode. The ground, a small metal plate, was attached firmly to the skin on the lower aspects of the thigh. All three leads were connected by phone tips to a compact Marinacci cable head which was taped securely to the leg. A fifteen foot shielded cable connected the cable head with the machine. This arrangement required short lead wires thus reducing motion and potential interference.

Subjects. Seven University of California students, five women and two men, served as subjects for this study.

Movements. The basic movements were:

1. Extension of the thigh, knee extended, while the body and left leg were supported in a prone position. The right leg, free to swing, was flexed at the hip to approximately 60 degrees, foot touching floor. The subject extended the right thigh upward from 60° flexion to minus forty degrees hyperextension and then was slowly returned to the initial position.

2. Exercise 1 repeated with knee held in flexion.

3. Extension of thigh against a wall pulley. A leather cuff, placed around the thigh just above the knee, was attached by a rope to the floor attachment of the pulley. The subject stood facing the pulley as he moved his thigh from forward flexion to hyperextension. Adequate support was provided for balance.

Treatment of Data

The cinematographic recordings were analyzed on a 16 mm. Kodoscope Analyst projector modified for stop and interval readings, and a Recordak microfilm reader. Amplitude and frequency of the action potential response were the parameters used for measuring the magnitude of muscle activity. The electrical activity was then given a rating

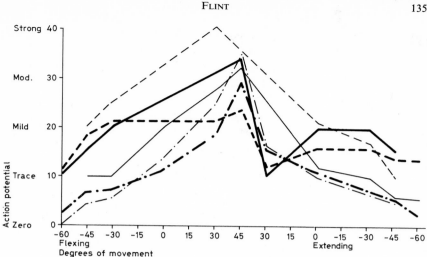

Fig. 2. Mean readings in extension, knee extended (———) biceps femoris, (— · —) gluteus maximus, (— — —) semitendinosus.
Mean readings in extension, knee flexed (———) biceps femoris, (— · —) gluteus maximus, (– – –) semitendinosus.
0°, leg is in extension; negative degrees, leg is in flexion; positive degrees, leg is in hyperextension.

of zero, trace, mild, moderate, or strong for each phase of the exercise. Subsequently, arbitrary values were awarded these ratings. The arc of rotation was divided into phases of 15° each.

From the subjects' tabulated scores, means were determined for each phase of the movement and plotted with the phase as shown in Figures 2 and 3.

Analysis of the Data

The potential recordings for the three muscles investigated followed a similar pattern (Fig. 2) through the total range of extension from 90° flexion through the 0 or neutral position to 40° hyperextension. The potential activity for each of the muscles gradually increased from a low intensity at 90° flexion to a strong intensity at 40° hyperextension. A reverse pattern was evident on the lowering or final phase of the exercises. In each case the intensity of the potentials was less on the lowering phase of the exercise or during eccentric contraction of the extensor muscles.

It was apparent that the harmstring muscles initiate and control backward extension when the thigh is held forward of the neutral position. Not until the leg was in 5° to 10° hyperextension did the gluteus maximus show involvement, which gradually increased to a moderate reading at 30° and a very strong reading at 40°. Hyperextension beyond approximately 10° is known to take place in the lumbar articulations. The high potential activity might possibly result from the effort to overcome the resisting pull of antagonistic structures.

Hip extension against a resistance supplied by a wall pulley (Fig. 3), shared a similar pattern of potential activity to the exercises performed without resistance. The intensity readings on the resistance exercise failed to reach the same magnitude for any of the muscles except the biceps femoris.

Whether the knee is flexed or extended does not substantially effect the activity of the hamstrings (Fig. 2 and 3). The semitendinosus did show stronger potential activity when the knee was held in extension.

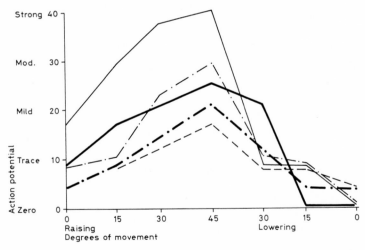

Fig. 3. Mean readings in extension, knee extended while standing, facing wall pulley (———) biceps femoris, (— · —) gluteus maximus, (— — —) semitendinosus.
Mean readings in extension, knee flexed, standing, pulley resistance (———) biceps femoris, (— · —) gluteus maximus.
Raising phase includes extension from 0° or neutral position to 45 degrees of hyperextension. Lowering phase includes the return of leg from hyperextension to neutral position.

Conversely, the biceps recorded slightly stronger potential activity when the knee was held in flexion.

Discussion

The photo recording electromyography procedure used in this study appears to be a very accurate and efficient means of analyzing movement patterns while correlating them with muscle activity. A telemetry monitoring device would permit the subject greater freedom as well as reduce interference from cable movement. Wire electrodes might prove more comfortable for the subject. With these modifications the technique described here should be highly desirable for kinesiological evaluations.

Summary and Conclusions

Electromyographic recordings of the gluteus maximus, semitendinosus, and biceps femoris were recorded simultaneously with motion picture studies of subjects performing extension movements of the hip joint. An evaluation of the activity of the three muscles was made for the various phases of the movements and revealed that the gluteus maximus worked most effectively as a thigh extensor when the thigh moves into hyperextension. During exercise, the hamstrings initiate and control backward extension of the thigh when forward of the normal standing position. As a technique for kinesiological studies, the procedure as described appears to be efficient and accurate. A telemetry monitor and wire electrodes might be desirable modifications for consideration.

Author's address: M. MARILYN FLINT, Department of Physical Education, University of California, *Santa Barbara,* Cal. 93 106 (USA).

IV. Telemetry

Biomechanics I, 1st Int. Seminar Zurich 1967
pp. 138–146 (Karger, Basel/New York 1968)

Departement of Physiology, School of Health Sciences, University of Tokyo

Application of Telemetry to Sports Activities

T. Ishiko

Telemetry is a measure to obtain information of the subject apart from the observer. It has mainly been developed for the necessity of studying rockets. But now we have many phases in applying telemetry to sports activities, as they are performed with rapid movements and in various places including water, snow and ice.

Some outdoor sports may be introduced into the laboratory by utilizing a treadmill, bicycle ergometer, and rowing machine, etc. But there are not many such activities and they may be misrepresented to some extent. Most sports cannot be realized in the laboratory.

Formerly movie technique was applied to analyse human motion. This method is indeed excellent due to the fact that movements of the subject are not disturbed at all. But a movie can neither catch the movements behind an object nor record various physiological phenomena occurring in the body. Compensating these defects, telemetry is really a powerful weapon for researchers of sports activities.

Telemeter for Sports

In order to apply a telemeter to the scientific study of sports, some requirements are necessary:

1. Information should be easily changed into electrical events, whether the phenomena are physiological or mechanical. Measurement of cardiac output is, in this sense, not adequate for telemetering.

2. The transmitter should possibly be small and light in order not to disturb sports activities of its carrier. The recent development of transistors has contributed a great deal to the field of telemetry.

3. The apparatus should stand up to violent movements, and signals should be free from noises occurring from impulses and vibrations of the carrier.

4. The apparatus can record the signals of oscillatory phenomena ranging from DC to hundreds of cps.

5. Simultaneous observation of various information is to be desired. Thus, a multichannel apparatus of easy use is required. Main phenomena to be observed in sports activities are the following:

physiological: ECG, respiration, EMG, EEG, temperature
mechanical: force, acceleration, velocity.

Electrocardiogram

Since HOLTER [4] observed the ECG during exercise, the main utilization of telemetry in sports activities has been directed to this field [1, 2, 7–10]. For the recording of ECG, electrodes are ordinarily applied on the chest of the subject in order to avoid noises from EMG. An accurate recording of ECG will be obtained by an apparatus having a time-constant longer than 1.5 sec. If researchers are interested in getting the heart rate only, the time-constant will be smaller, which gives more stability in recording. Telemeters, which are popular in Japan have a time-constant of 0.8–1.5 sec.

Figure 1 shows the change in heart rate of two long-distance runners during and after 5000 m running. In the first minute of running the heart rate of the subjects increased to 160–180/min and it reached its maximum of 190–200/min. After the exercise, it decreased below 100 beats per minute in a few minutes in one subject, but it remained at 120 beats/min even after 5 min rest in the other subject. Thus, telemetry gives us information about personal differences in cardiac function of sportsmen.

Heart rate is frequently considered in prescribing training schedules for athletes. Figure 2 is the diagram showing heart rate change during and after 40 strokes of rowing. At the end of this exercise, the heart rate amounted to 168–192 beats per minute and decreased to 140–163

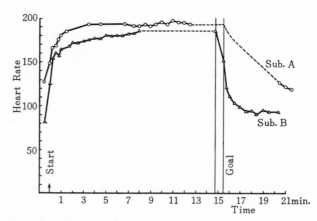

Fig. 1. Heart rate during and after 5000 meters running. Sub. A and sub. B ran in 15′ 38″ 2 and 14′ 50″ 2 respectively.

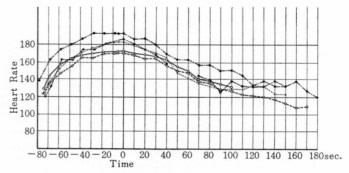

Fig. 2. Heart rate during and after 40 strokes of rowing. Heart rate was studied in 5 oarsmen. Time is recorded as zero when the subjects finished rowing.

in a minute's rest and 121–133 in two minutes. Thus, on prescribing an interval training, the interval should be 90–120 sec. The telemetering of ECG is also utilized in medical examinations. WOLFFE [11] reported heart-block during running with telemetry.

Respiration

Respiration is of great importance in the study of physical activities. A pneumograph, which is a device to record changes in chest girth, is inadequate for our purpose, because it may be affected by the movements of upper limbs and the body. Pneumotachography may restrict free respiration by expiring through a small space. So the author prefers to set a thermistor at the opening of the nose cavity. This device does not restrict free movement of the subject.

Figure 3 shows a simultaneous recording of respiration and ECG during a 100 m run. This subject was non-athlete; his respiration was inhibited during the first half of running; respiration occurred after the

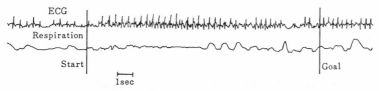

Fig. 3. Telemetric Recording of ECG (chest lead) and respiration during 100 meter sprint (untrained). Respiration was inhibited in the first half of the course.

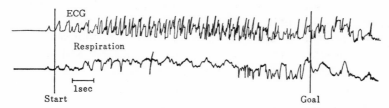

Fig. 4. Telemetric recording of ECG and respiration during 100 meters sprint (trained). Respiration was not stopped.

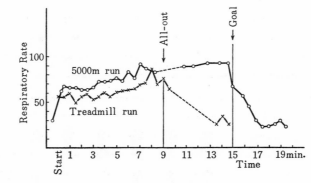

Fig. 5. Comparison of respiratory rate between running of 500 m and treadmill in the same subject. Mean speed of 5000 m running was 316 m/min. Treadmill test was performed at 240 m/min, 5 degrees for 5 min and at 260 m/min, 5 degrees to exhaustion.

subject ran about 50 meters. On the contrary, the athletic sprinter breathed from the beginning of a 100 m sprint as shown in Figure 4.

In the middle- and long-distance runs, breath-holding was not observed throughout the course. Respiratory rate increased to 80–90 per minute in a few minutes of running. On observing respiratory rate of running on a treadmill in the same subject, it did not reach such a rapid rate as obtained in real running, although the load of the treadmill was so heavy that the subject became exhausted in a few minutes (Fig. 5). Thus, the treadmill test does not inform real respiratory rate during running.

Electromyogram

EMG is the important evidence of muscular activities. In order to avoid the pain of the subject, surface electrodes are usually used. To understand the movements as a whole, a simultaneous recorder of several EMG, that is, a multichannel apparatus (over 4 channels) is desirable. In this respect the author prefers wire telemetering rather than radio telemetering with a few channels.

Figure 6 shows EMG recording of 9 channels and mechanical elements of 2 channels during rowing. In this experiment the subject

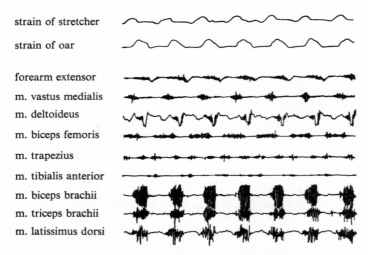

Fig. 6. EMG during rowing. EMG of the arm and shoulder corresponds to strain of oar. EMG of m. vastus med. and m. biceps femoris corresponds to strain of stretcher.

rowed in the water of a pool, sitting on a sliding seat at the side of the pool. The EMG was led with wires to the laboratory near the pool. The EMG with mechanical signals in Figure 6 can explain the activities of muscles corresponding to the phase of stroke. The EMG during swimming was studied with the same method by IKAI *et al.* [5]. In this case shielding of the electrodes against water is important.

Electroencephalogram and Temperature

The voltage of EEG being several μV, clear recordings of EEG by telemetering are more difficult but not impossible [3]. Body temperature can also be recorded by using a thermistor. But from the standpoint of biomechanics, EEG and body temperature are not important.

Force

As force is the source of movements, continuous recording of dynamic force was desired. Due to the development of a strain gauge, we can easily observe dynamic force with a telemeter. For instance, the author

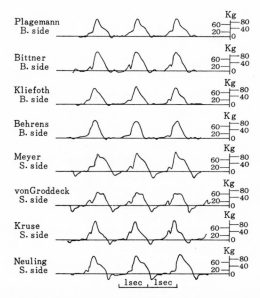

Fig. 7. Strain of oars during 3 strokes of rowing obtained from Ratzeburg crew (German).

applied a strain gauge for the analysis of rowing movements [6]; the strain gauge was placed on the inboard part of the test oar. With this device rowing force was studied.

Figure 7 is the curve of strain in the oar performed by eight oarsmen. Strain was calibrated into kg at the grip of the oar by hanging standard weights there. From Figure 7, we can observe the change of muscular strength during a stroke. Curious to say, the curve obtained from the eight oarsmen showed quite different patterns in spite of the fact that they were world famous champions. The movement of oar in the air was of course uniform and synchronous. Nevertheless, the

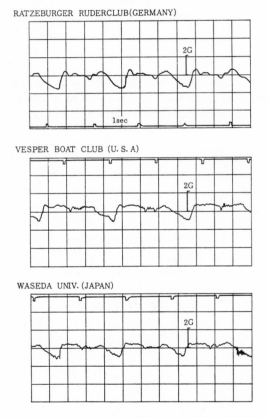

Fig. 8. Acceleration curves of rowing in Ratzeburg (German), Vesper (American) and Waseda (Japanese) crews.

movement in water was not uniform: they rowed in their own style. By improving their rowing technique, even this excellent crew is expected to obtain a better performance.

Acceleration and Velocity

Acceleration can also be recorded with telemetering. The author used an apparatus constructed with a strain gauge; acceleration towards the bow-stern direction of a test-boat was recorded with it.

Figure 8 is the curve of acceleration of a boat (shell eight) during rowing. After the oar touched the water, acceleration increased rapidly until it began to decrease by finishing the stroke. But acceleration showed a slight increase again, which could be explained as the result due to reaction of the boat against the sternward movement of the body. The acceleration curve showed its own pattern according to the style of rowing as shown in Figure 8. Velocity can also be recorded by integrating the acceleration.

Conclusion

As a modern technique, telemetry has various utilizations in the study of sports activities, especially of body mechanics. By scientific use of telemetry, we can obtain new knowledge, which otherwise cannot be detected. The author has shown a few examples in this respect. As more frequent utilizations of telemetering is expected, the author will lay stress upon the combined recordings of physiological and mechanical events in order to obtain better information.

References

1. GOODWIN, A.B. and CUMMING, G.R.: Radio telemetry of the electromyogram, fitness tests, and oxygen uptake of waterpolo players. Canad. med. Ass. J. 95: 402–406 (1966).
2. HANSON, J.S. and TABKIN, B.S.: Electrocardiographic telemetry in skiers. New Engl. J. Med. 271: 181–185 (1964).
3. HAMBRECHT, F.T.; DONAHUE, P.D. and R. MELZACK: A multiple channel EEG telemetry system. Electroenceph. clin. Neurophysiol. 15: 323–326 (1963).
4. HOLTER, N.J.: Radioelectrocardiography: A new technique for cardiovascular studies. Ann. N.Y. Acad. Sci. 65: 913–923 (1957).
5. IKAI, M.; ISHII, E. and MIYASHITA, M.: An electromyographic study of swimming. Res. J. phys. Educ. 7: 47–54 (1964).

6. ISHIKO, T. and ITO, S.: Kinesiological study of rowing. Proc. Int. Congr. Sport Sci. 420–422 (1964).
7. MATSUI, H.: The application of radio-telemeter in the study of physical activity. Res. J. phys. Educ. 7: 55–67 (1964).
8. MORIO, Y. and SUGI, S.: On the record of the bioelectric phenomenon by wireless inductor. Jap. J. phys. Fitness 7: 15 (1958).
9. NOMURA, S.: Adaptation of radiotelemetry to equestrian games and horse racing. Jap. J. vet. Sci. 28: 191–203 (1966).
10. OKA, Y., UTSUNOMIYA, N.; SEKINE, T. and NODA, K.: On the short wave wireless carriage of ECG during muscular exercise. Jap. J. phys. Fitness 7: 16 (1958).
11. WOLFFE, J.B.: Intermittent heart block in athletes. XVI. Weltkongr. Sportmed. 213–220 (1966).

Author's address: TOSHIHIRO ISHIKO, Department of Physiology School of Health Sciences, University of Tokyo, 3-1, 7-chome, Hongo Bunkyo-ku, *Tokyo* (Japan).

Biomechanics I, 1st Int. Seminar Zurich 1967
pp. 147–149 (Karger, Basel/New York 1968)

Université Libre de Bruxelles
Laboratoire de l'Effort (Dir. Prof. M. Segers)

Telemetrical Analysis of the Electromyogram

L. Lewillie

We tried to define the possibilities of telemetry in electromyography, choosing as our major subject the swimmer.

The electromyographic analysis of different swimming styles has been reported by Ikai [3, 4], using a conventional wire apparatus by means of a trolley.

Other writers [2] used telemetry to follow the cardiac frequency of water polo players during the normal conditions of a competition, but in that case the proper variations of the signal were without significance.

Recently Battye and Joseph [1] presented a telemetrical analysis of walking.

The experiments were conducted in a community swimming pool. No particular precautions were taken. In some cases, the pool was even occupied by other swimmers.

The characteristics of the transmitter are as follows: dimensions $30 \times 20 \times 15$ mm; weight 20 g; frequency band 82 to 108 Mc.

The receiver is of a common commercial type. It is connected to a tape recorder.

The amplifier was built in our laboratory according to the following diagram.

Its volume is about the same as the transmitter. The over-all dimensions of the apparatus allow the doubling of the system so as to obtain a simultaneous recording on two channels.

When using the system on the ground, belt-type antennae proved themselves entirely satisfactory. However, for the swimmer, we prefered a tuned vertical antenna supported by a balloon. That system allowed complete freedom for the swimmer while maintaining the antenna vertically.

The apparatus was simply placed in a water-tight bag, fixed dorsally by the belt of the swimming suit. The electrodes were placed on the skin, along the muscular fibres, at a distance of 3 cm and fixed by an adhesive tape, itself covered by plastic varnish.

The electrodes are constituted by little rasps, 5 by 5 mm. The one connected to the earth is bigger and fixed on the sternal manubrium.

The receiver stands along the pool, the distance between the antennae of receiver and swimmer varying from 5 to 20 m. No signal modification was observed.

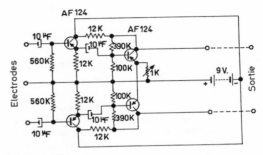

Fig. 1. Diagram of the amplifier.

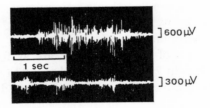

Fig. 2. Simultaneous recording of the brachial triceps (A) and of the femoral quatriceps (B) of a free-style swimmer.

Different muscles were tested on a free style swimmer. Many characteristics were found to be the same as in the works of IKAI *and coll.* [3].

The brachial triceps seems, however, particularly characteristic and leads to special consideration. A typical aspect appears to be:

The double belly of the contraction corresponding to the actual technique of the free-style swimmers completing the usual movement by pushing the hand along the thigh.

References

1. BATTYE, C.K. and JOSEPH, J.: An investigation by telemetering of the activity of some muscles in walking. Med. Biol. *4:* 125–135 (1966).
2. GOODWIN, A.B. and CUMMING, G.R.: Radio telemetry of the electrocardiogram tests and oxygen uptake of water polo players. Canad. med. Ass. J. *95:* 402–406 (1966).
3. IKAI, M.: Etude électromyographique de la natation. Rev. Phys. *11:* 124–126 (1962).
4. IKAI, M.; ISHII, K. and MIYASHITA, M.: An electromyographic study of swimming. Jap. Res. J. Physic. Ed. *7:* 55–67 (1964).

Author's address: L. LEWILLIE, Université Libre de Bruxelles, Laboratoire de l'Effort, *Bruxelles* (Belgique).

BOGNOR REGIS
COLL. of EDUCN.
LIBRARY

V. Principles of Human Motion: General Aspects of Coordination

Biomechanics I, 1st Int. Seminar Zurich 1967
pp. 150–154 (Karger, Basel/New York 1968)

Zentralinstitut für Körperkultur, Moskau

Bewegungsprinzipien der Biomechanik im Sport

D. DONSKOI

Prinzipien und Gesetze

Der Entwicklungsprozeß jeder Wissenschaft wird in hohem Maße durch die Ausnützung von Prinzipien als wissenschaftlichen Leitideen bestimmt.

Prinzipien stellen die verallgemeinerten Grundsätze eines Fachgebietes dar, Gesetze bestimmen die wissenschaftlich faßbaren Zusammenhänge in den einzelnen vorgezeichneten Situationen. So stellen zum Beispiel die bekannten biomechanischen ,Prinzipien des rationellen Krafteinsatzes' G. HOCHMUTHS (1960) von unserem Standpunkt aus sehr wichtige Gesetze der Biomechanik dar, aber keine Prinzipien. Einzelne Gesetze der Bewegungen wurden im weitern von G. SCOTT (1942) J. WARTENWEILER (1965) und anderen dargestellt.

Die Wirksamkeit der Bewegungen im Sport wird weniger durch Gesetze der Mechanik und Physiologie bestimmt, die für Tiere und Menschen gemeinsam gelten, als durch die für den Menschen spezifische Steuerung bei der Gestaltung und Entwicklung der Bewegungssysteme. Die Biomechanik des Sports muß sich in ihrer Entwicklung nach den Prinzipien orientieren, welche die heutigen Erkenntnisse zum Ausdruck bringen und die Richtung der weiteren Forschungsarbeiten bestimmen. Als Prinzipien können wir das ,Prinzip der Bewegungsstruktur' und das ,Prinzip der progressiven Umgestaltung des Bewegungssystems' bezeichnen.

Das Prinzip der Bewegungsstruktur

Das Prinzip der Bewegungsstruktur besagt, daß jede Bewegung ein organisches Ganzes ist, in einem Bewegungssystem, welches aus Bewegungen vieler kinematischer Kettenglieder des menschlichen Körpers besteht, bei einer großen Anzahl von Bewegungsmöglichkeiten in den Gelenken. Bewegungen kommen jeweils unter dem Einfluß von veränderlichen Kräften (Muskel- und Außenkräften) in einem stets wechselnden Milieu zustande. Der Aufbau des Bewegungssystems aus einzelnen Komponenten wird als Struktur bezeichnet.

Die Struktur wird gekennzeichnet:

a) durch die Vereinigung von Bewegungselementen und Gruppen von Elementen in hierarchischer Ordnung; kleinere Einheiten (Untersysteme) unterstehen den größeren Untersystemen.

b) durch eine Vielfalt von Wechselbeziehungen zwischen den verschiedenen Bewegungseinheiten.

Diese Systematik ermöglicht die zielgerichtete Untersuchung von *Hauptstrukturen* (kinematischen, dynamischen und informatorischen) und *Einzelstrukturen* (muskeltopographischen, neurologischen, sensorischen, psychologischen usw.). Stellung und Rolle jeder Struktur ist nur unter dem Gesichtspunkt ihrer Wechselwirkung mit den anderen Strukturen, sowie im Hinblick auf das System als Ganzes zu verstehen.

Die Verhältnisse sind in biomechanischer Hinsicht sehr verwickelt; Wechselwirkungen nach dem Kraftverlauf sind nicht voraussehbar, und die Beziehung zwischen den Bewegungsimpulsen des Gehirns und den von ihnen gesteuerten Bewegungen können nicht immer eindeutig belegt werden (N. BERNSTEIN, 1947).

Das Prinzip der progressiven Umgestaltung des Bewegungssystems

Das Prinzip der progressiven Umgestaltung des Bewegungssystems bringt eine Reihe von komplizierten Prozessen zum Ausdruck:

1. Anpassung der von früheren Aufgaben anders bestimmten Untersystemen an die neuen Aufgaben;

2. Unterdrückung ungeeigneter Untersysteme;

3. Einbau neuer Untersysteme, die den neuen Anforderungen entsprechen, und

4. Einsatz des neuen Gesamtsystems, das auf der Basis aller Untersysteme in gegenseitiger Anpassung und Abstimmung zustande kommt.

Die progressive Entwicklung besteht also in der Umgestaltung und Veränderung einer Gesamtstruktur in ihren gesetzmäßigen Wechselbeziehungen und Wechselwirkungen, sowie deren Untersystemen und Elemente. Dies geschieht im Sport bei planmäßiger und zielgerichteter Tätigkeit des Trainers und des Sportlers.

Es passen sich Größe, Richtung, Wirkungszeit, Angriffspunkte und das Verhältnis der Kräfte neu an im Sinne der Optimierung. Äußere und innere Kräfte werden besser ausgenützt. Es bildet sich das Können heraus, Kräfte bewußt einzusetzen.

Im Verlauf des Umgestaltungsprozesses verändert sich das Verhältnis (die führende Rolle) von paarigen, dialektisch gegensätzlichen
Entwicklungstendenzen im System: Integrierung – Differenzierung, Stabilisierung – Variabilität, Standardisierung – Individualisierung.

Die äußeren Faktoren, darunter auch das Einwirken des Trainers,
sowie die Aktivität des Sportlers selbst im Umgestaltungsprozeß des
Bewegungssystems, spielen eine wichtige Rolle. Aber die Hauptquelle
der Entwicklung, des ,Selbstvorwärtsschreitens' des Systems, liegt im
Kampf, in der Entfaltung von Gegensätzen, und zwar in den erwähn-
ten gegensätzlichen Entwicklungstendenzen. Die Kenntnis dieser
Tendenzen, sowie die Kunst, sie richtig einzusetzen, bilden die Grund-
lage für die schöpferische Tätigkeit des Trainers.

Das Prinzip der Bewegungsstruktur und das Prinzip der progressiven Umgestaltung des Bewegungssystems sind die theoretischen Grundlagen jedes Bewegungsgeschehens. Sie lassen sich im folgenden weiter
erläutern.

Integrierung – Differenzierung

Der Etappenaufbau des Bewegungssystems in der Sporttechnik erfolgt
auf Grund zweier gegensätzlicher Tendenzen, der Integrierung und
der Differenzierung.

Die Integrierung (Ganzheit) gewährleistet das einheitliche Zusammenspiel von Systemkomponenten (Ausscheiden des Überflüssigen,
Gestaltung des Besten) bei ihrer Vereinigung zu einem zielgerichteten
sportlichen Verfahren. Durch Integrierung ordnen sich die Systemteile
dem Bewegungssystem als Ganzem ein.

Die Differenzierung (Gliederung) besteht im Aussondern von einzelnen Bestandteilen des Systems (theoretisch und praktisch) als wichtigen Merkmalen für die Trainingsgestaltung des Sportlers (Verlagerung
der Aufmerksamkeit, Betonung einzelner Untersysteme). In den höchsten Stufen der technischen Meisterschaft soll man alle Besonderheiten
der Technik genau verstehen und nach Bedarf beachten.

Bei der Vervollkommnung der Technik ist individuell vorzugehen,
indem je nach Notwendigkeit die Integrierung, oder die Differenzierung
in den Vordergrund gestellt werden, was dann zur synthetischen oder
analytischen Trainingsmethode führt.

Stabilisierung – Variabilität

Erste Bedingung zur Konsolidierung des Bewegungssystems ist die Vereinheitlichung (Stabilisierung) der Bedingungen, unter welchen eine Bewegung erfolgt.

Bei vorgerücktem Können führen auch veränderliche Bedingungen (Variabilität) zur Konsolidierung, wobei störende Wirkungen sowohl der Umwelt des Sportlers als auch der zufälligen Änderungen der Untersysteme ausgeglichen werden, und eine erhöhte Störungsfestigkeit entsteht.

Normalerweise entsteht Variabilität durch zufällig sich verändernde Ausführungsbedingungen, die von nachfolgenden Korrekturen begleitet sind (sensorische Korrekturen, N. BERNSTEIN, 1947).

Besonders wertvoll ist die vorbeugende Regulation als Blockierung von Störungen (nach dem Mechanismus der ‚zuvorkommenden Widerspiegelung‘, P.K. ANOCHIN, 1935). Diese Art der Variabilität hat ausgleichende Variationen der Bewegungen zur Folge.

So führt also auch Veränderung zur Sicherstellung des Effekts in der Sporttechnik.

Wir wiederholen: Variabilität jeder beliebigen Charakteristik ist mehr oder weniger unvermeidlich; die absolute Wiederholung in allen Details kommt nie vor. Im Training sollten ungünstige Abweichungen reduziert und der Diapason von adaptierenden Abweichungen verbreitert werden. Aus diesem Grund ist bei der progressiven Umgestaltung des Bewegungssystems zwischen Stabilisierung und Variabilität abzuwechseln.

Standardisierung – Individualisierung

Die heutige Sporttechnik ist soweit fortgeschritten, daß man beim Systemaufbau von gutbekannten Normen ausgehen kann (Standardisierung). Musterbewegungen dienen jederzeit als Vorbild und werden durch praktische Demonstrationen, Film und Erklärungen eingeführt.

Andererseits verlangen die konstitutionellen Besonderheiten jedes Sportlers gewisse Anpassungen (Individualisierung). Über das Ausmaß der zulässigen Abweichung ist noch verhältnismäßig wenig bekannt, vor allem fehlt es an wissenschaftlicher Fundierung.

Weitere Erforschung der Bewegungsstruktur und der progressiven Umgestaltung des Bewegungssystems, sowie eine vertiefte Erkenntnis der Bewegungsgesetze wird die klassische Biomechanik erweitern und ihr Anwendungsgebiet in der sportlichen Leistungsschulung finden.

Literatur

ANOCHIN, P.: Problema wsaimootnoschenija centra i periferii (Gis, Gorkij 1935).

BERNSTEIN, N.: O postroenii dwischenij (Medgis, Moskwa 1947).

HOCHMUTH, G.: Biomechanische Prinzipien des rationellen Krafteinsatzes. Theorie und Praxis der Körperkultur 2 (1960).

SCOTT, G.: Analysis of human motion (Crafts, New York 1942).

WARTENWEILER, J. und WETTSTEIN, A.: Biomechanische Grundprinzipien für schwunghafte Bewegungen. Die Körpererziehung 7: 149–160 (1965).

Adresse des Autors: Prof. Dr. D. DONSKOI, Zentralinstitut für Körperkultur, Sojuzsport, Skaterny per. 4, *Moskau 69* (UdSSR).

Biomechanics I, 1st Int. Seminar Zurich 1967
pp. 155–160 (Karger, Basel/New York 1968)

Deutsche Hochschule für Körperkultur, Leipzig

Biomechanische Prinzipien

G. Hochmuth

Ende der 50er Jahre hielten wir die Entwicklung für herangereift, die biomechanischen Erkenntnisse über die zweckmäßigsten sportlichen Techniken für die Lehrarbeit im Fach Biomechanik zu verallgemeinern und zu systematisieren. Die zu diesem Zeitpunkt vorliegenden Erkenntnisse veranlaßten uns, sechs biomechanische Prinzipien zu formulieren [1]. Inzwischen erfolgte eine Reduzierung auf fünf, indem die Prinzipien der 'Anfangskraft' und der 'günstigen Lage des Kraftmaximums' zu einem Prinzip vereinigt wurden (Abb. 1). Außerdem wurde das Prinzip des 'langen und geradlinigen Beschleunigungsweges' auf Grund neuerer Forschungsergebnisse in ein Prinzip des 'optimalen Beschleunigungsweges' umgewandelt [2, 3].

Im folgenden werden zwei Prinzipien näher vorgestellt[1] und Probleme aufgezeigt, die weitere Forschungen erfordern.

Entwicklung der biomechanischen Prinzipien:

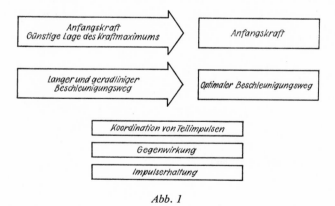

Abb. 1

[1] Vgl. auch den Beitrag: Marhold, G.: Zum Problem des optimal langen Beschleunigungsweges bei sportlichen Hochsprüngen.

Prinzip der Anfangskraft

Dieses Prinzip kennzeichnet den Sachverhalt, daß durch eine einleitende Gegenbewegung bei einem Sprung, Wurf, Stoß oder einer ähnlichen Körperbewegung ein größerer Beschleunigungsstoß erreicht werden kann. Durch das Abbremsen der Gegenbewegung ist zu Beginn des Beschleunigungsstoßes, falls sich der Übergang flüssig vollzieht, bereits eine positive Kraft vorhanden. Durch Reihenuntersuchungen konnte bei Sprüngen ein optimales Verhältnis von Brems- zu Beschleunigungsstoß ($\varkappa$-Wert) gefunden werden (Abb. 2). Das Optimum liegt bei $\varkappa = 0{,}3$ bis $0{,}4$. Es ist aber noch vom Beschleunigungsweg abhängig.

Die Kraft-Zeit-Kurven der dynamographischen Messungen weisen bei Sprüngen vielfach zwei Kraftmaxima auf (Abb. 3). Es lassen sich mehrere Ursachen hierfür angeben. Eine mechanische Ursache ist in

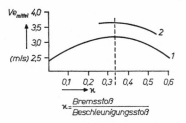

Abb. 2. Optimales Verhältnis von Brems- zu Beschleunigungsstoß beim beidbeinigen Strecksprung: 1 = jugendliche Sportler (nach HOCHMUTH); 2 = Leistungssportler (nach MARHOLD).

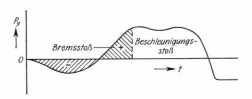

Abb. 3. Welliger Kraft-Zeit-Verlauf.

den sich überlagernden Schwungbewegungen (Arme und Schwungbein beim einbeinigen Sprung) zu sehen. Auch motorische und muskelphysiologische Einflüsse können den welligen Kraftverlauf bewirken.

Es ist deshalb durch komplexe Untersuchungen der Biomechanik mit der Muskelphysiologie und der Motorik zu klären, ob der wellige Verlauf vorteilhaft ist oder nicht.

Prinzip der Koordination von Teilimpulsen

Das Prinzip der Koordination von Teilimpulsen gilt für sportliche Bewegungsabläufe, bei denen durch mehrere gleichzeitige Kraftwirkungen entweder ein Endglied der kinematischen Kette des Bewegungsapparates oder der Schwerpunkt des gesamten Körpers eine größtmögliche Geschwindigkeit erhalten soll.

Im ersten Fall wird die größtmögliche Geschwindigkeit dann erreicht, wenn die Geschwindigkeitsmaxima des Endgliedes und des übrigen Körpers zum gleichen Zeitpunkt auftreten. Es versteht sich von selbst, daß bei dieser Superposition nur die Geschwindigkeitskomponenten in der interessierenden Richtung in Betracht gezogen werden dürfen.

Für den zweiten Fall, bei dem der Schwerpunkt des gesamten Körpers eine größtmögliche Geschwindigkeit erhalten soll, ist das Koordinationsprinzip wegen der mechanischen Gegenwirkungen zwischen den inneren Kräften und der funktionalen muskelphysiologischen und motorischen Abhängigkeiten nicht so ohne weiteres zu übersehen. Zur Klärung des Einflusses der mechanischen Gegenwirkung der inneren Kräfte wird ein Federmodell herangezogen (Abb. 4). Die beiden Federn und Massen sind miteinander fest gekoppelt. Die untere Feder liegt auf dem Widerlager aber nur auf, so daß sie sich nach der Entspannung wieder dort lösen kann. Zum Problem der richtigen zeitlichen Koordination erlaubt das Modell folgende Aussage: Wenn die obere Masse m_2 ihr Geschwindigkeitsmaximum später erreicht als die untere m_1, entsteht ein Verlust am Gesamtimpuls, weil sich die Masse m_1 mit dem Erreichen des Geschwindigkeitsmaximums vom Widerlager löst. Im umgekehrten Fall wird durch die feste Koppelung der Masse m_2 mit der oberen Feder die Geschwindigkeit durch Federkraft abgebremst. Die Reaktion auf diese Impulsverminderung bewirkt eine dementsprechende Impulsvergrößerung der Masse m_1. Nach actio et reactio heben sich beide Wirkungen auf.

Das Abbremsen der Geschwindigkeit erfolgt aber nicht nur durch elastische innere Kräfte, sondern außerdem durch die Schwerkraft und bei sportlichen Bewegungen durch innere Reibung. Diese Ge-

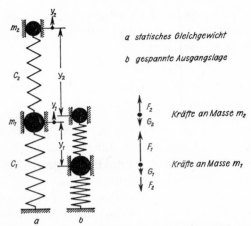

Abb. 4. Federmodell zur Veranschaulichung der mechanischen Gegenwirkung der inneren Kräfte:

Federkräfte:

$F_1 = -c_1 (f_1 + y_1)$

$F_2 = -c_2 (f_2 + y_2 - y_1)$

Schwerkräfte:

$G_1 = -c_1 f_1 + c_2 f_2$

$G_2 = -c_2 f_2$

Beschleunigungskräfte:

$m_1 \ddot{y}_1 = F_1 - G_1 - F_2 = -c_1 y_1 + c_2 (y_2 - y_1)$

$m_2 \ddot{y}_2 = F_2 - G_2 = -c_2 (y_2 - y_1)$

schwindigkeitsverluste werden nicht ausgeglichen. Wegen ihnen muß man fordern, daß die Geschwindigkeitsmaxima zum gleichen Zeitpunkt erreicht werden.

Zur Zeit liegen erst wenige experimentelle Ergebnisse über den Einfluß der funktionalen muskelphysiologischen und motorischen Abhängigkeiten auf die Koordination vor. Im Falle des beidbeinigen Strecksprunges konnte beobachtet werden, daß bei einem kräftigen Armeinsatz und bei einer bewußten Orientierung auf diesen die Körperstreckung meist nachteilig beeinflußt wird. Die Zeitdauer für die positive Beschleunigung des Armschwungs ist rund nur halb so groß wie die der Körperstreckung. Der Sportler, der bewußt einen kräftigen Armschwung ausführen will, verringert dabei unbewußt die Zeitdauer der Körperstreckung, indem er einen kleineren Beschleunigungsweg des Körperschwerpunktes ausnutzt. Der Verlust am Beschleunigungsstoß der Körperstreckung ist dann meist größer als der Gewinn infolge eines kräftigeren Armschwungs. Aus diesem Grunde muß bei der Koordination von Teilimpulsen stets darauf geachtet werden, daß derjenige Kraftstoß, den die stärksten Muskelgruppen hervorbringen und der demzufolge am größten ist, durch die Koordination nicht beeinträchtigt wird.

Man muß insgesamt mit einer starken gegenseitigen Abhängigkeit der einzelnen Kraftwirkungen rechnen, die muskelphysiologisch und motorisch bedingt ist und über die einfachen mechanischen Beziehungen von actio et reactio hinausgeht. Es liegt die Vermutung nahe, daß entgegen dem Federmodell beim menschlichen Bewegungsapparat auf das Widerlager größere Kräfte übertragen werden können, als die Sprungmuskulatur ohne die zusätzlichen Kraftwirkungen infolge der Schwungbewegungen entwickeln kann. Wir kommen zu dieser Hypothese, weil die Muskeln unter äußerem Zwang, z.B. beim Abbremsen eines Niedersprunges, den größten Kraftstoß hervorbringen.

Die hier aufgezeigten, noch ungelösten Probleme verlangen umfangreiche experimentelle Untersuchungen. Erst danach können die optimalen biomechanischen Bedingungen exakt erfaßt und das Prinzip eindeutig und allgemeingültig formuliert werden.

Ausblick auf weitere biomechanische Prinzipien

Das Studium der sportlichen Praxis weist auf weitere Probleme hin, die eine Verallgemeinerung der biomechanischen Erkenntnisse fordern. Zwei Richtungen zeichnen sich dabei schon deutlich ab.

1. Ausnutzen von Federkräften

Es ist eine bekannte Erfahrungstatsache, daß man mit einem Federbrett höher und weiter springen kann. Mit Hilfe einer federnden Unterlage wird offensichtlich die Muskelarbeit besser in Bewegungsenergie umgesetzt, weil die Bremsarbeit der einleitenden Gegenbewegung nicht verlorengeht. Bekannt ist aber auch, daß die Schwingung der federnden Unterlage mit der Körperbewegung in Phase liegen muß, wenn man einen optimalen Effekt erzielen will.

Beim Reckturnen treten Drehschwingungen der Reckstange auf, die der Turner für das Gelingen der Übung geschickt ausnutzt. Auch hier liegen bestimmte Phasenbeziehungen zwischen Körperbewegung und Drehschwingung vor. Wir halten es deshalb für erforderlich, das Problem der Ausnutzung von Federkräften systematisch zu erforschen und die Erkenntnisse zu einem neuen biomechanischen Prinzip zu verallgemeinern.

2. Bewegungsökonomie

Dis bisher formulierten biomechanischen Prinzipien wurden fast ausschließlich aus den Kennlinien der zweckmäßigsten Technik von Kraft-, Schnellkraft- und technischen Disziplinen verallgemeinert. In Ausdauerdisziplinen besteht demgegenüber aber eine andere biomechanische Zielstellung. Es soll nicht eine maximale Geschwindigkeit während eines Bewegungszyklus oder während weniger Zyklen, sondern eine maximale mittlere Geschwindigkeit auf einer längeren Wegstrecke erreicht werden. Infolgedessen übt die Ökonomie des Krafteinsatzes, der Wirkungsgrad von ausgenutzter und aufgewandter Muskelarbeit, den entscheidenden Einfluß aus.

Beim leichtathletischen Mittel- und Langstreckenlauf, beim Skilanglauf, Rudern, Schwimmen, Radsport usw. ist dieser biomechanische Wirkungsgrad wahrscheinlich vom Verhältnis der positiven zur negativen Kraftstoßsumme, von Verhältnis der Bewegungs- amplitude zur Bewegungsfrequenz, von der Stetigkeit des Krafteinsatzes und von der zweckmäßigen Richtung der Kraftvektoren wesentlich abhängig.

Viel stärker als in den anderen Sportdisziplinen beeinflussen hier Kreislauf und Stoff- wechsel den Krafteinsatz. Aus diesem Grunde sind die biomechanischen Untersuchungen zur Erforschung der aufgezeigten Problematik nur dann sinnvoll, wenn sie im Komplex mit den entsprechenden sportbiologischen Disziplinen in Angriff genommen werden.

Das Anliegen des Vortrages war es gewesen, zur Mitarbeit an der Vervollkomm- nung der biomechanischen Prinzipien der zweckmäßigsten sportlichen Technik anzuregen. Ein weiterer wesentlicher Fortschritt wird dann zu erzielen sein, wenn zu dieser Proble- matik in vielen Ländern und möglichst in Kooperation systematische Forschungen betrie- ben werden.

Literatur

1.   HOCHMUTH, G.: Das biomechanische Prinzip der Anfangskraft. Theorie und Praxis der Körperkultur 2: 126 (1960). – Das biomechanische Prinzip der günstigsten Lage des Kraftmaximums. Theorie und Praxis der Körperkultur 3: 212 (1960). – Das biomecha- nische Prinzip des langen und geradlinigen Beschleunigungsweges. Theorie und Praxis der Körperkultur 4: 320 (1960). – Das biomechanische Prinzip der Koordination von Teilimpulsen. Theorie und Praxis der Körperkultur 5: 409 (1960). – Das biomecha- nische Prinzip der Gegenwirkung. Theorie und Praxis der Körperkultur 6: 500 (1960). – Das biomechanische Prinzip der Impulserhaltung. Theorie und Praxis der Körper- kultur 8: 680 (1960).
2.   HOCHMUTH, G.: Biomechanik sportlicher Bewegungen; 1. Aufl., pp. 187–209 (Sport- verlag, Berlin 1967).
3.   MARHOLD, G.: Biomechanische Untersuchungen sportlicher Hochsprünge; paed. Diss. Leipzig (1963).

Adresse des Autors: Prof. Dr. G. HOCHMUTH, Deutsche Hochschule für Körperkultur, Institut für Biomechanik, Friedrich-Ludwig-Jahn-Allee 59, *701 Leipzig* (DDR).

Biomechanics I, 1st Int. Seminar Zurich 1967
pp. 161–164 (Karger, Basel/New York 1968)

Abteilung Biomechanik an der Forschungsstelle der Deutschen Hochschule für
Körperkultur, Leipzig

Zum Problem des optimalen Beschleunigungsweges bei sportlichen Hochsprüngen

G. Marhold

Sportliche Hochsprünge nehmen einen großen Raum in vielen Sportarten
ein. Die unterschiedlichen biomechanischen Bedingungen der Bewegungsformen und die individuellen Voraussetzungen bewirken erhebliche
Unterschiede. Damit werden theoretisch wie praktisch interessierende
Fragen aufgeworfen:

Welchen Einfluß hat die Länge des ausgenutzten vertikalen Beschleunigungsweges auf die Sprunghöhe?

Wie wirkt die Intensität der einleitenden Anlauf-, Schwung- und
Beugebewegungen auf die Sprunghöhe ein?

In welchem Zusammenhang stehen die ermittelten Abhängigkeiten?
Eine energetische Betrachtung stützt die mechanische Forderung, maximale Beschleunigungskräfte längs eines maximal langen Weges einzusetzen. Es wäre also zu fordern, eine möglichst tiefe Ausgangslage ein-
zunehmen.

Dagegen erheben sich Bedenken, «weil eine sehr starke Beugung der
unteren Gliedmaßen einen Teil der für den Absprung aufgespeicherten
Kraft für die Aufrichtung des Körpers aus der tiefen Hocke bean-
sprucht». Es wird geraten, «den Absprung aus einer mittleren Knie-
beuge durchzuführen» [7]. Dieser pauschalen Ansicht begegnet man in
der Literatur mehrfach [1, 4]. Die Bedenken verstärken sich durch die
Überlegung, daß mit zunehmender Beugestellung die Schwerkraft der
Körpermasse in größerem Abstand von den Gelenken als den Dreh-
punkten angreift. Die Ergebnisse muskelphysiologischer Untersuchungen [5, 6] lassen auf einen optimalen Beugebereich schließen, der von
der Schwerkraft und den Hebelverhältnissen beeinflußt wird.

Zur Klärung waren Untersuchungen nötig. Die Messungen lassen
sich mit kinematographischen und dynamographischen Methoden

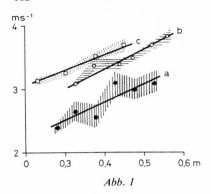 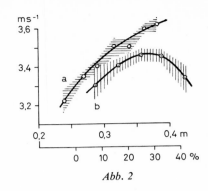

Abb. 1   Abb. 2

Abb. 1. Die vertikale Abfluggeschwindigkeit als Funktion des vertikalen Beschleunigungsweges. Kurve a: Schlußsprung aus dem Stand (nach HOCHMUTH). Kurve b: Schlußsprung
aus dem Stand. Kurve c: Schlußsprung aus dem Anlauf. (Die Schraffur kennzeichnet die
mittlere Abweichung des Mittelwertes).
Abb. 2. Die vertikale Abfluggeschwindigkeit als Funktion des vertikalen Beschleunigungsweges (a) und des $\varkappa$-Verhältnisses (b) beim leichtathletischen Hochsprung. (Die Schraffur
kennzeichnet die mittlere Abweichung des Mittelwertes).

wettkampfnah durchführen. Die interessierenden Größen können aus
den Kraft-Zeit-Funktionen errechnet werden.

HOCHMUTH [2] stellte fest, «daß der Gewinn durch einen längeren
Beschleunigungsweg größer ist als der Verlust infolge erschwerter Bedingungen für das Herausbilden großer Muskelkräfte». Das konnte an
trainierten Volleyball- und Basketballspielern bei erhöhtem Muskel-
kraftniveau in ähnlichen Grenzen bestätigt werden.

(Abb. 1) Im Falle des beidbeinigen Absprunges aus dem Anlauf
sind die Beschleunigungswege geringer. Der zu erwartende bogenför-
mige Verlauf zeigt sich experimentell bei den umfangreicheren Ergebnissen des leichtathletischen Hochsprungs. (Abb. 2 – Kurve a) Die
Betrachtung des Beschleunigungsweges darf jedoch nicht losgelöst
von anderen Faktoren erfolgen, zu denen u.a. die Intensität der einleitenden Anlauf-, Schwung- und Beugebewegungen im Verhältnis zur
Streckbewegung zählt (vgl. Abb. 2 – Kurve b). Dieses $\varkappa$-Verhältnis[1] steht
in Beziehung zum Beschleunigungsweg. Im Hochsprung nimmt das
$\varkappa$-Verhältnis bei gleichbleibender technischer Ausführung des Anlaufs
und Übergangs zum Absprung mit wachsender Anlaufgeschwindigkeit

[1] $\varkappa$ (in %) $= \dfrac{\text{Bremsstoß}}{\text{Beschleunigungsstoß}} \cdot 100$

zu. Das ergibt eine optimale Anlaufgeschwindigkeit für einen technisch ausgebildeten Athleten in einem bestimmten Entwicklungsstand seiner Sprungkraft. Die dargelegten theoretischen Erkenntnisse und praktischen Ergebnisse weisen auf das starke gegenseitige Beeinflussen der Faktoren Sprungkraft, Bewegungsfertigkeiten, Beschleunigungsweg und $\varkappa$-Verhältnis hin. So kann das Optimum des $\varkappa$-Verhältnisses wegen der sich verändernden Verhältnisse bei unterschiedlichen Beschleunigungswegen nicht gleich bleiben. Es liegt nahe, für größere Beschleunigungswege kleinere Optima anzunehmen. Die experimentellen Befunde stimmten mit dieser Hypothese überein.

Die Zusammenhänge lassen sich in einem Modell räumlich darstellen. (Abb. 3) Sie weisen aus, daß der Beschleunigungsweg maßgeblich die Sprunghöhe bestimmt. Seine optimale Länge hängt bei den

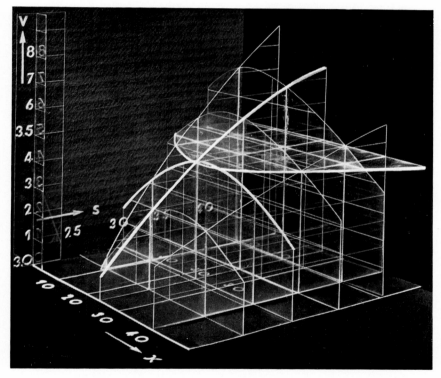

Abb. 3. Die Abhäṅgigkeiten zwischen der vertikalen Abfluggeschwindigkeit v (ms⁻¹), dem vertikalen Beschleunigungsweg s (cm) und dem Verhältnis zwischen Brems- und Beschleunigungsstoß $\varkappa$ (%).

Hochsprüngen neben dem technischen Können von der Größe der Sprungkraft ab. Die Intensität der einleitenden Anlauf-, Schwung- und Beugebewegungen muß sich optimal diesen Bedingungen anpassen.

Literatur

1. DUFOUR, X.: Die menschliche Bewegung und zweibeinige Fortbewegung; Gymnast. educat. *4:* 127–164 (Brüssel 1959).
2. HOCHMUTH, G.: Untersuchungen über den Einfluß der Absprungbewegung auf die Sprungweite beim Skispringen; S. 105–106, Diss. Fak. für Maschinenbau TU (Dresden 1958).
3. MARHOLD, G.: Biomechanische Untersuchungen sportlicher Hochsprünge; Diss. DHfK (Leipzig 1963).
4. NAGORNY, X.: Fußnote zur russischen Übersetzung von Hochmuth, G.: Über die Absprungtechnik beim Skispringen; Teorxa i parktika fizičeskoj kultury. *1:* 71 (Moskau 1956).
5. PAERISCH, M.: Die Physiologie der somato-motorischen Systeme; S. 84 (VEB Deutscher Verlag der Wissenschaften, Berlin 1959).
6. REIN, H.: Physiologie des Menschen; 12. ber. Auflage, S. 384 (Springer, Berlin, Göttingen, Heidelberg 1956).
7. TITTEL, K.: Beschreibende und funktionelle Anatomie; 2. Auflage, S. 246 (VEB Verlag der Wissenschaften, Berlin 1958).

Adresse des Autors: Dr. G. MARHOLD, Abteilung Biomechanik an der Forschungsstelle der Deutschen Hochschule für Körperkultur *701 Leipzig* (DDR).

Biomechanics I, 1st Int. Seminar Zurich 1967
pp. 165–171 (Karger, Basel/New York 1968)

Zentralinstitut für Sportmedizin, Budapest

Der binäre, antagonistische Mechanismus der Bewegungssteuerung

M. Nemessuri

Vom Standpunkt der Bewegungsschulung und Trainingslehre in der Sportmedizin, Arbeitsmedizin und Lehre des Leistungssportes aus erwartet man von den Forschern der Bewegungslehre, daß die Resultate ihrer wissenschaftlichen Arbeiten in der Praxis ohne weiteres anwendbar sein sollen.

Auch meine Arbeitsgruppe verfolgt praktische Ziele, weil wir unsere Ergebnisse zur Optimierung der Arbeit- und Sportbewegung benützen wollen. Unsere Bewegungsstudien zeigten aber, daß zuerst grundlegende motorische Mechanismen geklärt werden müssen.

Die einheitliche Beurteilung der komplizierten, vielseitigen Bewegungseffekte benötigt einen physiologisch gemeinsamen Gesichtspunkt und eine Methodik, mit der die verschiedenen motorischen Vorgänge quantitativ auswertbar und vergleichbar sind.

Wir untersuchten deshalb in erster Linie die Muskelsteuerung

1. der gut definierbaren Bewegungen, die sich in *einem* Gelenk abspielen.

2. der einfachen, gut definierbaren Bewegungen *mehrerer* Gelenke. Zur Analyse der Vorgänge zerlegten wir die motorischen Prozesse in kleine, 1–15 ms große Zeiteinheiten, Mikroperioden, und aus deren Messungen konnten wir auf die charakteristischen physiologischen Eigenschaften des ganzen Bewegungsaktes folgern.

Wir bestimmten die Mikroperioden des motorischen Effekts mit zwei Methoden:

1. der Filmanalyse mit Hilfe der von uns erarbeiteten Methode der Fotokinographie (Nemessuri) und des von uns konstruierten Fotokino-testers (Nemessuri-Vaday-Várady).

2. der elektromyographischen Aufzeichnung der aktivierten – statische und dynamische Arbeit leistenden – Muskeln.

Mit den genannten Methoden untersuchten wir elementares Heben und Senken der Arme und Beine, Kniebeugen, Spreizhochsprung, Einnahme der Spagatstellung und komplexe Bewegungsprozesse, wie Wegstoßen, Köpfeln, Fangen des Balles, Ballwurf, Gewichtheben, Laufen, usw.

Die Ergebnisse unserer langjährigen Untersuchungsserien können wir wie folgt zusammenfassen:

1. Die von uns untersuchten Bewegungen, die gleichmäßig, gleichmäßig beschleunigt oder verlangsamt wurden, weichen immer ab von der Programmierung, weil sie nicht gleichmäßig und auch nicht ununterbrochen ablaufen. Die Körperteile bewegen sich rhythmisch alternierend, stoßweise, in beschleunigten und verlangsamten Mikroperioden, und von Zeit zu Zeit finden wir Mikroperioden ohne Bewegung. Die Frequenz des Alternierens ist nach unseren fotokinographischen und elektromyographischen Untersuchungen: 30–40/sec (Abb. 1–2).

Aus diesen Daten folgerten wir, daß sich der Effekt der motorischen Innervation nicht fließend, sondern stoßweise, in quantitativ bestimmbaren Impulsquanten manifestiert. Unsere Bewegungen sind deshalb nur scheinbar gleichmäßig, und diese Täuschung – ähnlich der

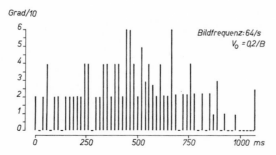

Abb. 1. Das Fotokinogramm des Fußhebens zeigt den rhythmisch alternierenden Ablauf des Bewegungswinkels.

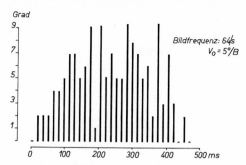

Abb. 2. Das Fotokinogramm zeigt eine 25mal schnellere Bewegung, wie in Abbildung 1. Der Fuß bewegt sich auch hier stoßweise.

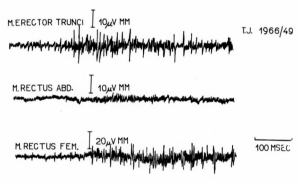

Abb. 3. EMG des Kniebeugens. Der Fixator (m. erector trunci) wird zuerst aktiviert, 80 ms nachher folgt die Aktivierung des Antifixators (m. rectus abdominis).

Bewegungsillusion im Kinofilm – hängt mit der Fusionseigenschaft unseres optischen Analysators (Auge) zusammen.

2. Bei jeder Bewegung werden auch die Antagonisten aktiviert. Der Grad ihrer Aktivität verstärkt sich im Verhältnis zur Bewegungsintensität. Das Verhältnis der Dynamik der Agonisten-Antagonisten-Arbeit zeigt gewisse asynchrone Eigenschaften. Oft aktiviert sich die antagonistische Muskulatur später und desaktiviert sich früher, als die agonistische. Die Amplituden der bioelektrischen Potentiale der Antagonisten sind kleiner.

3. Bei habituierten Bewegungen in Antigravitationsrichtung ist die antagonistische Aktivität geringfügig. Wir sind der Ansicht, daß in solchen Fällen die bremsende, regulierende Rolle der Antagonisten durch die Gravitationskraft ersetzt wird.

4. Das physiologische Grundelement der Bewegung ist also eine Doppelkraft mit einander gegengestellter Richtung der Komponenten. Der Bewegungseffekt wird durch eine – teilweise asynchrone – agonistisch-antagonistische Muskelaktivität hervorgerufen. Die Wirkung der Muskeltätigkeit wird aber teilweise auch durch die Gravitationskraft, die Gelenkhalteeinrichtungen und andere Gewebe modifiziert, bzw. ersetzt (Abb. 3–5).

5. Die Muskelsteuerung der Bewegung wird nicht aus einem einzigen Kräftepaar, sondern aus je 3 Muskelgruppenpaaren aufgebaut. Drei Muskelgruppen üben mit den je zu ihnen gehörigen Antagonisten eine sechsfache Aktivität aus:

a) *Stabilisierung*. Die Fixator-Muskelgruppe stabilisiert durch statische Arbeit Gelenke und Gelenkreihen über kürzere oder längere Zeit. Die Aktivierung des Antifixators hält das Gleichgewicht und kontrolliert die Tätigkeit des Fixators (Abb. 3).

b) *Hauptrichtung der dynamischen Arbeit*. Die Kinetor-Muskelgruppe wirkt in der Hauptrichtung der Bewegung. Die Antikinetoren kontrollieren diese Tätigkeit durch Bremsen (Abb. 4).

c) *Modulation*. Die Modulator-Muskelgruppe steuert den bewegten Körperteil in die Ebene der Fortbewegung, verhindert die Abweichung von der programmierten Richtung, unterstützt also die Kinetor-

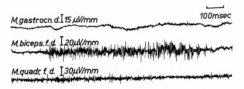

Abb. 4. Die starke Kinetor-Aktivität des m. biceps femoris bei Kniebeugen ist mit einer kleineren, sich früher beendenden Antikinetor-Aktivität des m. quadriceps femoris gekoppelt.

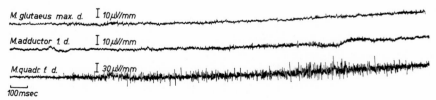

Abb. 5. Die Modulator- (Adductor-Gruppe) und Antimodulator- (Abductor-Gruppe) Aktivität zeigt eine leichte Steigerung bei Kniebeugen.

Aktivität. Das ist meist notwendig, weil die Tätigkeit der Kinetoren allein den bewegten Körperteil nicht genau in der geplanten Richtung leitet. Die Antimodulator-Muskelgruppe bremst, d.h. kontrolliert ähnlicherweise wie die oben geschilderten Antagonisten-Kräfte (Abb. 5 und 7).

Die Regelung des Bewegungsprozesses durch den von uns beschriebenen drei antagonistischen Muskelgruppenpaaren, einer Trias der Fixator-Kinetor-Modulator Kräftepaare, führt durch periodische Aktivierung und ständige Rückmeldungsprozesse zu alternierenden motorischen Effekten und verursacht damit den stoßartigen Ablauf der Bewegungen.

Wir können also unseren Bewegungsapparat als eine Maschinenreihe modellieren, bei welcher im gegebenen Zeitpunkt eine Maschine die Stabilisierung einiger Gelenke und andere Maschinen die Bewegungen verursachen. Zu jeder Maschine gehört dann jeweils eine antagonistisch wirkende – bremsende – Maschine. Die beschriebenen sechs Kräftespender werden nicht ständig von denselben Muskelgruppen repräsentiert, sondern ihre Funktion wird, von der Bewegungssituation abhängend, von verschiedenen Muskelgruppen übernommen. So spielt ein Muskel in einem bestimmten Zeitpunkt des Bewegungsablaufes eine gewisse Rolle von den sechs beschriebenen Möglichkeiten, kann aber in der Folge – der motorischen Programmierung entsprechend – eine andere Funktion übernehmen.

Durch diese Beschreibung der elementaren Bewegungseffekte wollen wir Anhaltspunkte für die Analyse des mechanischen Ablaufs der menschlichen Bewegungsformen gewinnen und mit unseren Ergebnissen an die Arbeiten anderer Forscher anknüpfen. Dabei stimmen wir mit WARTENWEILER überein, wenn er sagt: «Leider ist die diesbezügliche Forschung nicht sehr weit gediehen. Außer den klassischen Untersuchungen von MAREY, DUBOIS-REYMOND, BRAUNE-FISCHER, F.A. SCHMIDT und einigen weiteren Autoren des ausgehenden 19. und beginnenden 20. Jahrhunderts liegt nicht manche wissenschaftliche Arbeit zur Bewegungslehre vor».

Die Bestimmung des Prinzipes der Aktion-Reaktion in der Bewegungslehre von BORELLI, die Konzeption der kinetischen Kette von BAYER, die Einführung der Foto- und Filmmethode von MUYBRIDGE, BERNSTEIN, KNOLL und anderen, die Analyse der Muskelschlingen von TITTEL, Adaptierung der modernen elektro-physiologischen-kybernetischen Methoden in der Bewegungslehre durch MARGARIA, MITOLO,

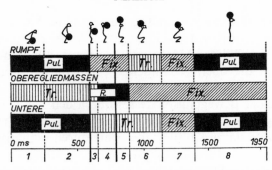

Abb. 6. Die Körperteile zeigen beim Gewichtheben am Grunde der fotokinografischen Analyse eine gut meßbare Dynamik der Fixierung, Pulsion, Traktion und Rotation.

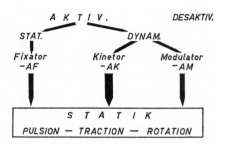

Abb. 7. Die 6 motorischen Operatoren (Fixator-Antifixator, Kinetor-Antikinetor und Modulator-Antimodulator) regeln die Kräfte der Statik und Dynamik (Pulsion, Traktion und Rotation) des bewegten Körpers.

WARTENWEILER, HEBBELINCK, BASMAJIAN, GROH und Mitarbeiter und andere, sind jedoch heute schon wertvolle Bauelemente, die zu einer biologisch gut begründeten Konzeption des motorischen Aktes führen können.

In Berücksichtigung der heutigen Ergebnisse der genannten Arbeiten und unserer Konzeption der binären, antagonistischen motorischen Regelung haben wir versucht aus den alltäglichen Bewegungen, wie Gehen, Laufen, Springen, Werfen, Ziehen, Schlagen, Schwimmen usw., gemeinsame motorische Elemente hervorzuheben.

Als Beispiel stehe hier die Bewegungsanalyse des *Gewichthebens:* Wir machten 40 Filmaufnahmen mit 64/sec und 96/sec Bildfrequenz vom 50 kp Gewichtheben, die nach unserer Fotokinografie-Methode bewertet wurden, außerdem EMG-Untersuchungen. Dabei fanden wir die folgenden motorischen Perioden:

1. Langsamer Zug in den oberen Gliedmaßen, Stoßen in Rumpf und unteren Gliedmassen, dann ca. 50 ms Pause (im ganzen durchschnittlich 250 ms).

2. Schneller Zug im Arm, Stoßen in Rumpf und Bein (350 ms).

3. Zug und Drehung im Arm, Stabilisierung des Rumpfes und Zug im Bein. Das war die kürzeste Periode (70 ms) und die schnellste Bewegung (Endgeschwindigkeit: 5,65/ms).

4. Drehen und Stoßen im Arm, Fixation des Körpers und Ziehen im Bein (130 ms).

5. Stoßen in den oberen, Zug in den unteren Gliedmaßen, Fixation des Rumpfes (200 ms).

6. In den folgenden Perioden waren die Arme fixiert, am Bein und Rumpf fanden wir Zug (200 ms).

7. Rumpf und Bein fixiert (200 ms).

8. Stoßen in Rumpf und Bein (500 ms) (Abb. 6).

Abb. 7 zeigt ein Schema des Operator-Systems und der elementaren motorischen Effekte.

Literatur

BASMAJIAN, J.V. and LATIF, A.: Integrated actions and functions of the chief flexors of the elbow. J. Bone Jt. Surg. *39:* 1106–1118 (1957).

BUCHTHAL, F.: The functional organisation of the motor unit. Amer. J. phys. Med. *38:* 125–128 (1959).

GROH, H., KUBETH, A. und BAUMANN, W.: Zur Kinetik und Dynamik schneller menschlicher Körperbewegung. XVI. Weltkongr. Sportmed. pp. 268–282 (1966).

JOKL, E.: Physiologie des Laufens und Hürdenlaufens. Z. Arbeitsphysiol. *1:* 296 (1929).

JOKL, E.: Alter und Leistung (Springer, Berlin-Göttingen-Heidelberg 1954).

MARGARIA, R., CAVAGNA, G.A. and ARCELLI, E.: External mechanical power in sprint running. XVI. Weltkongr. f. Sportmed. pp. 268–282 (1966).

MITOLO, M.: Fisiologia dell'apparato motore, 2. ed. Libr. Scient. editr. Napoli (1967).

NEMESSÚRI, M.: Funktionelle Sportanatomie. Budapest (Akadémiai Kiadó 1963).

NEMESSÚRI, M.: L'applicazione dell'analisi mediante la cinematografia ultrarapida del movimento nel vari sports. Ungh. d'oggi. *6:* 46–54 (1965).

NEMESSÚRI, M.: Gli elementi cinetici del tiro a rete. Med. Sport. *6:* 348–360 (1966).

SZENDE, O. and NEMESSÚRI, M.: Studies on the relations of muscle co-ordination in the isolated movements of the finger. Acta physiol. Acad. Sci. hung. *25:* 375–387 (1964).

TITTEL, K.: Beschreibende und funktionelle Anatomie des Menschen (DHfK., Leipzig 1956).

VERZÁR, F.: Theorie der Muskelkontraktion (Schwabe, Basel 1943).

WARTENWEILER, J. und WETTSTEIN, A.: Charakteristik schwunghafter Bewegungen nach biomechanischen Gesichtspunkten. XVI. Weltkongr. Sportmed. Hannover, pp. 702–706 (1966).

Adresse des Autors: Dr MIHÁLY NEMESSÚRI, Alkotás-u. 48, *Budapest XII* (Ungarn).

Biomechanics I, 1st Int. Seminar Zurich 1967
pp. 172–177 (Karger, Basel/New York 1968)

Academy of Physical Education, Warsaw

Some Biomechanical Principles of Muscle Cooperation in the Upper Extremities

K. Fidelus

The aim of the present work is to determine the biomechanical parameters, decisive for the volume of the moment of force developed by the individual muscles, and to establish on this basis the degree of their participation in the given movement. The measurements and calculations were carried out on the flexors and extensors of the elbow and wrist joint. These data can be used for analysing the coordination of movements, and in the construction of bioprostheses and their control.

Relationship Between the Biomechanical Parameters of Muscles and their Moment of Force

It was assumed, on the basis of literature and our own investigations, that the moment of force developed by the individual muscles is composed of a number of parameters interconnected by the following equation:

$$M_e = \delta \sum_{i=1}^{n} r_i(\alpha)\, p_i \left[\frac{F}{F_o}\left(\frac{1}{1_o}\right)\right]_i (\alpha)\, \frac{U_i(\alpha)}{U_{i\,max}} \quad [kGm]$$

where:

M_e	external moment of force developed by the muscles during their active tension, [kGm]
σ	stress of the muscle, $\left[\dfrac{kG}{cm^2}\right]$
r_i	radius of the force of the i muscle, [m]
α	angle of the joint,
p_i	physiological square section area of the muscle, [cm²]
$\left[\dfrac{F}{F_o}\left(\dfrac{1}{1_o}\right)\right]_i$	relationship between force (F) and length (1) developed by the i muscle,
U_i	current value of the myopotential, [μV]
$U_{i\,max}$	value of U_i registered under given experimental conditions during maximum effort of the muscle [μV]

The above mathematical equation is a modification of the equation established by a team composed of: J. EKIEL; K. FIDELUS; A. MORECKI and K. NAZARCZUK [2].

The length-tension relationship is a complex value, which is affected by the structure of the myofibrils and the system of muscle fibres of the given muscle. It differs for fusiform and penniform muscles. The maximum stress of a muscle is a sort of characteristic indicator of its strength capacity per unit of the muscular section. It depends on the kind of fibres (white and red), as well as on the degree to which they are fatigued. In our case σ also plays the role of a certain proportionality coefficient. It depends also on the difference between the values obtained on anatomical preparations (p_i), skeletal models ($r_i[a]$, $\frac{l_i}{l_o}[a]$) and rabbit muscles $\frac{F}{F_o}$ $\left(\frac{l}{l_o}\right)$, and real values found in the subject investigated.

The integrated value of the electromyogram U depends mainly on the quantity of activated muscle fibres and on a number of factors connected with it: the pick up, amplification, integration and registration of EMG in the course of the investigation. In order to eliminate measurement factors, the obtained U values were compared to U_{max}, assuming that U_{max} is obtained during the tension of all the muscle fibres making up the physiological section area p. In this manner $\frac{U_i}{U_{i\,max}}$ characterizes the quantity of active fibres of a given muscle, that is, it determines what part of p is actually being used for the development of force by the muscle.

Results and Discussion

In the elbow joint we examined musculi: pronator teres—PT, biceps brachi, caput longum—BBCL, caput breve—BBCB, brachialis—B, brachio-radialis—BR, triceps brachii, caput longum—TBCLong, caput laterale—TBCLat and caput mediale—TBCM. Data concerning these muscles: r_i (a), p_i and $\frac{l_i}{l_o}$ (a) were published in previous papers [2,5].

In the wrist joint we investigated the following musculi[1]: extensor carpi radialis longus—ECRL (2) and brevis—ECRB (1), extensor carpi ulnaris—ECU (2), extensor digitorum communis—EDC (4), flexor

[1] Values of physiological section areas in sq. cm are given in brackets.

carpi radialis—FCR (2,2) and ulnaris—FCU (3), flexor digitorum sublimis, fingers II and III—$FDS_{II,III}$ (2) and fingers IV and V— $FDS_{IV,V}$ (2,5).

These are not all the muscles acting on the wrist joint during flexion and extension. When calculating the moments of force of the flexors it was assumed that musculus flexor digitorum profundus—FDP develops a moment of force equal to FDS.

The values of $\frac{F}{F_o}$ as the function of $\frac{1}{1_o}$ were so far mostly investigated on isolated muscle fibres or the muscles of frogs [1, 3, 6]. As far as we know, no investigations have been carried out so far on penniform muscles.

Measuring force with a strain gauge dynamometer, we stimulated with an electric current selected muscles of anaesthetized rabbits. Figure 1 gives the values obtained for fusiform muscles and penniform muscles. The course of the function differs quite essentially in the two types of muscles [2].

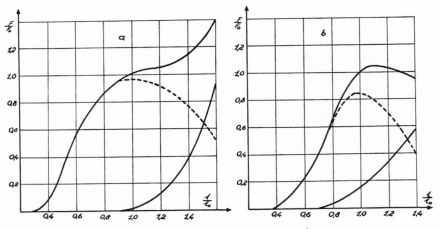

Fig. 1. Value of force $\frac{F}{F_o}$ as a function of the muscle length $\frac{1}{1_o}$. F_o is assumed as force developed by the muscle at initial length 1_o, that is with the length when the value of the active force of the muscle (broken line) was maximal. The lower continuous line indicates passive force of the muscle. The upper line indicates the measured resultant force during stimulation (a: fusiform muscle, b: penniform muscle)

[2]The experiments on rabbits were carried out with the help of the Chair of Biology of the Academy of Physical Education.

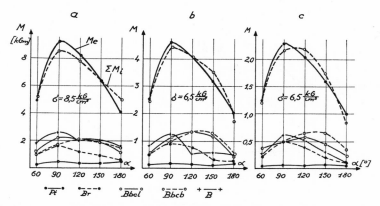

Fig. 2. Courses of calculated values of moments of force of the individual flexors of the elbow joint, their sum ΣM_i and the measured external moments M_e (a. by M_{max}, b. by 0.5 M_{max}, c. by 0.25 M_{max}, σ = stress of the muscle). Symbols of the muscle are given in the text.

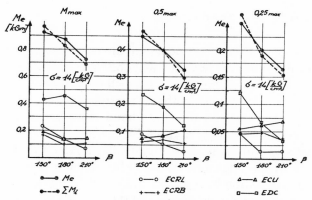

Fig. 3. Courses for calculated and measured moments of force for wrist extensors (β = wrist joint angle. Symbols as in Fig. 2).

The measurments of the external moment of force M_e and of myopotentials U were made on a specially constructed stand. The individuals were asked to develop the maximum moment of force (M_{max}) under static conditions in various positions of the elbow and wrist joint. Then they were asked to maintain moments of force equal to 0.5 M_{max} and 0.25 M_{max}.

Figure 2, 3 and 4 show the courses of the calculated moments of force of the muscles and their sums. They are compared with the moments of external forces measured with the help of a dynamometer.

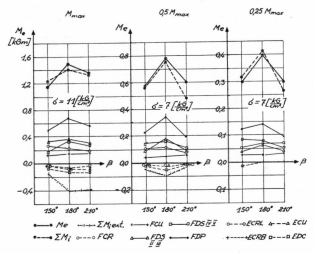

Fig. 4. Courses of calculated and measured moments of force of flexors and extensors, acting during the flexion of the wrist joint. Symbols as in Fig. 2.

The conformity between the values of direct measurements and the calculated values may be regarded as good. Worth emphasizing is the fact that the flexors and extensors of the elbow joint and the extensors of the wrist joint may work without a visible tension of their antagonists. Wrist extensors, on the other hand, always participate in the flexing of that joint by M_{max} and 0.5 M_{max} effort.

The stress of muscle is most frequently greater by M_{max} than by 0.5 and 0.25 M_{max}. The cause of this phenomenon is probably to be found in the correlation between the force and myopotentials. In static conditions in the range between 0 and 0.6–0.8 of the maximum force this correlation is a linear one. In the range of maximum force, on the other hand, force increases more rapidly than the myopotential [4]. This explanation is confirmed by the fact that for the wrist extensors σ is a constant value for all values of force (Fig. 3). In this case, by M_{max}, the mean value of myopotential does not exceed as a rule more than 0.5–0.6 of the maximum muscle tension.

Conclusion

The work presents a mathematical theory of the determination of the contribution of muscles in the achievement of the moment of force in the elbow and wrist joints. Good conformity of the theoretical calculations and measurement results means that basic biomechanical parameters of muscles have been found and determined, and that they are decisive for the moment of muscle force developed by them. The research results permit a quantitative analysis of the function of muscles and their cooperation under static conditions.

References

1. ASMUSSEN, E.: Muscular performance; in: Muscle as a tissue. Ed. by K. RODAHL and S.M. HORVATH, p. 161 (McGraw-Hill, New York 1962).
2. EKIEL, J.; FIDELUS, K.; MORECKI, A. and NAZARCZUK, K.: Niektóre zagadnienia biocybernetyki występujące przy współdziałaniu mięśni kończyny górnej w żywym organiźmie. Zeszyt jubileuszowy Katedry Teorii Maszyn i Mechanizmów P w, p.73–107, Warszawa 1966.
3. ERNST, E.: Biophysics of the striated muscle (Akadmiai Kiadò, Budapest 1963).
4. FIDELUS, K.; STACHE, H.-J. und SCHILLE, D.: Elektromyographische Untersuchungen der Beuge- und Streckmuskulatur im Kniegelenk beim Muskelkrafttraining. Med. Sport 6: 111–116 (1966).
5. MORECKI, A.; EKIEL, J. and FIDELUS, K.: The peripheral organisation of externally controlled natural and artificial limbs. IXth Automation and Instrumentation Conference and Exhibition, Milano 19.–25. XI. 1966.
6. RAMSEY, R. and STREET, S.: J. cell. comp. Physiol. 15: 11 (1940).

Author's address: Dr KAZIMIERZ FIDELUS, Academy of Physical Education, ul. Marymoncka 34, *Warsaw* (Poland).

Biomechanics I, 1st Int. Seminar Zurich 1967
pp. 178–187 (Karger, Basel/New York 1968)

Motor Learning Research Laboratory, School of Education, and the
Department of Physical Education for Women, University of Wisconsin, Madison,
Wisconsin

Integration of Movement

Autonomous–Sensory–Motor Components

J.C. WATERLAND

Teachers of motor activities are often only concerned with the movement phase that directly accomplishes the aim or purpose. The
moving part receives a place of prominence; the teacher directs little
attention to the autonomous components accompanying the willed
movement. Yet, skillful performance results from an integration of
both willed and autonomous phenomena.

The facilitatory nature of the autonomous components of movement in man is a physiological phenomenon, which is evoked by the
act willed (HELLEBRANDT and associates, 1956). The level of performance will be determined by the degree to which the body can
anticipate and support willed movement (HESS, 1954). The voluntary
phase of the motion is referred to by HESS (1954) as *'teleokinetic'* and
the autonomous phase as *'ereismatic'*. Autonomous components
provide the 'dynamic support' upon which willed movement is superimposed. Thus, muscular control depends on the integration of the
autonomous, sensory and motor components.

The work of the Motor Learning Research Laboratory at the
University of Wisconsin has been largely devoted to a study of the
autonomous components of volitional movement. The research has
been based on the concept that skillful movement is composed of three
interrelated components: 1. willed movement which may be cortically
directed; 2. autonomous components which are evoked in association
with the purposive act; and 3. sensory inputs from the external and
internal environment. It might be said that 'poor' or 'unskilled' move-

Supported in part by the Easter Seal Research Foundation, National Society for
Crippled Children and Adults and the Research Committee of the Graduate School from
funds supplied by the Wisconsin Alumni Research Foundation.

ment is dominated by 'cortical' control which largely supersedes the autonomous and integrative mechanisms while 'successful' or 'skilled' movement is a harmonic blend (WATERLAND, 1967a)[1].

In 1956 Hellebrandt and co-workers thought that autonomous head positioning might augment work out-put on the part of the subject during heavy resistive wrist exercises. WATERLAND and HELLEBRANDT (1964) found that the increased sensory input resulting from muscular stress may be directly responsible for the integration of the head and shoulder girdle, while interfacilitation with other reflex phenomena appeared to affect the body as a whole. The invariability of the head–shoulder linkage demonstrated by subjects exercising under imposed stress was so impressive that the effect of nonstressful arm and shoulder girdle movements was then analyzed by WALTERLAND and MUNSON (1964). Movements of the shoulder complex evoked changes which were in keeping with the patterning of individuals exercising under stress. The hypothesis that identifiable autonomous components 'support' a skilled performance was tested by studying the standing broad jump (WATERLAND, 1967b)[2].

Ten subjects, who represented extreme levels of skill, were randomly selected from 1,282 freshmen women at the University of Wisconsin. The five unskilled performers made six maximal distance jumps. The skilled subjects executed three all-out effort jumps and, in order to compare overt patterning, they also performed three moderate distance and three minimal distance jumps. Multiple light chronocyclegraph photography was used to record the movement traces of the arms, thighs, shoulder girdle and head during 75 experiments. In addition, stroboscopic lights were set off to record one image of the subject during each movement sequence. Objective measurements and subjective evaluation of the data showed that increased sensory input magnified autonomous movement components. The head–shoulder stereotype was an integral part of the overt patterning. Like phenomena were not as evident in the 'less good' jump performed deliberately by the skilled performers and in the maximal jumps executed by the unskilled subjects.

[1] Reprinted, in part, from WATERLAND, 1967a with permission of the *American Journal of Physical Medicine*.

[2] All but the third paragraph of this paper is reprinted in part or in toto from WATERLAND, 1967b with permission from QUEST, a publication sponsored by The National Association for Physical Education of College Women and The National College Association for Men.

Behavioral Response of the Unskilled Jumpers Performing for Maximal
Distance and Gradation of Effort by the Skilled Performers

The distance covered by the unskilled jumpers ranged from 3.6' to 5.0'.
Typical of the unskilled pattern configuration was the limited mobility
of all body segments. The integrity of the body was not to be jeop-
ardized by moving the center of gravity beyond the base of support by
a vigorous motion of the arms. The upper extremities were kept close to
the body or in a slightly abducted position which hinted at the 'wing-
ing' phenomenon observed in very young children by HELLEBRANDT
and associates (1961). There appeared to be no attempt to use the arms
as a neuromuscular facilitatory aid at take-off or during saltation;
instead the arms seemed to serve as stabilizers. As a result of the lack of
sensory bombardment, the head and shoulder girdle showed only minimal changes and the body lacked the totality of observable integration
so apparent in the skilled performer. ZIMMERMAN (1951), HALVERSON
(1958) and FELTON (1960) in bio-mechanical studies reported that the
unskilled subjects evidenced a similar degree of joint inactivity.

Inspectional analysis of body images on the photographs also displayed a *marked* asymmetrical positioning of the extremities in the
unskilled jumpers. Several of the unskilled jumpers used a one-foot
take-off similar to the pattern observed in children by HALVERSON
(1958) and HELLEBRANDT *et al.* (1961). It is of interest that vestiges
of the asymmetrical patterning were also discernible in the skilled performers jumping for maximal distance.

The moderate distance jumped by the skilled subjects changed the
overt patterning seen in all-out performance. Concern for distance
dictated the head positionings. From the time of take-off until the subject
was preparing to land, the head was held in ventroflexion. Subjective
analysis of the photographs disclosed that during saltation the subjects
fixed their attention on the mats, purposely holding their head position
in order to see their *self-imposed* landing mark. Since no practice jumps
were allowed before each series of trials calling for a decrease in energy
expenditure, there was little opportunity for the neuromuscular mechanisms to make adjustments to the changing situation. A modified
pattern evolved when inhibition of the normal head movement by cortical
intent disrupted the organization of the stimulus-response patterning as
seen in all-out performances. Requesting the skilled subjects to jump
with such little effort perhaps disrupted an integrated pattern causing

a slight disarrangement of the normal neuromuscular harmony (Fig. 1).
PAILLARD (1960) explained that the exertion of the 'will' is capable of
controlling the stream of impulses influencing the effector structures,
which determine the emerging volitional pattern. WATERLAND and

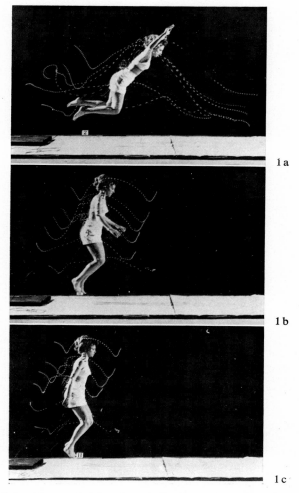

1 a

1 b

1 c

Fig. 1. a) A skilled subject performing the standing broad jump for maximal distance.
b) The same skilled subject volitionally executed a moderate distance jump. c) The subject,
pictured above, did the standing broad jump for minimal distance. The asymmetrical patterning of the limbs seemed to become less pronounced as the subject decreased her energy
expenditure. Subject images recorded on the photographs depict different phases of the jump.

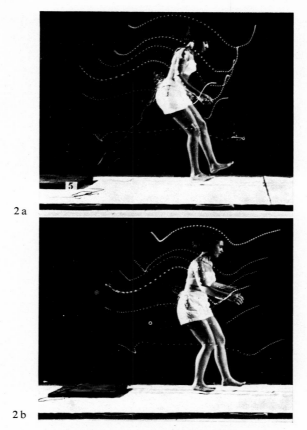

2 a

2 b

Fig. 2. a) A skilled subject expending minimal energy while she executed the standing broad jump. The performer used a one-foot take-off. b) An unskilled subject executed a maximal distance jump. Like the skilled performer, a one-foot take-off was used. a) and b) The overt patternings of the skilled and unskilled subjects were similar. However, the skilled performer exhibited a 'totality' of response not evident in the unskilled subject.

MUNSON (1964) have also reported that the mutual dependency of the head–shoulder stereotype may be interfered with by cortical intent.

To perform minimally the skilled jumpers had no concern about distance; in fact, they adapted their performance more easily to this situation than to the moderate distance. The patterning denoted a slight similarity to their maximal effort; however, range of movement was markedly decreased. The skilled subjects suppressed the autonomous components of willed movement, the unskilled could not educe them

(Fig. 2). Perhaps herein lies a clue to the success of achieving a skilled motor act. Until the unskilled become accustomed to greater stress, facilitating mechanisms cannot be utilized to attain 'high' score performances.

Behavioral Response of the Skilled Jumpers Performing for Maximal Distance

The measured distance for the skilled jumpers' maximal effort ranged from 5.9' to 7.6'. The method of executing the preparatory backswing of the arms varied among the five subjects; however, all performers elicited propulsive force with the arm swing just prior to take-off. ZIMMERMAN (1951) concluded that the vigorous arm action brought the center of gravity in front of the base of support at take-off. A diminished angle of inclination of the body with the floor caused the force to be directed forward and upward at an advantageous angle for maximal distance. While the arms may well serve this function as revealed by Zimmerman's bio-mechanical analysis it is believed by PAILLARD (1960) that volitional impulses which initiate skilled move-

Fig. 3. A skilled performer executed the standing broad jump for maximal distance. The subject was photographed during the 'preparation for landing' phase of the jump.

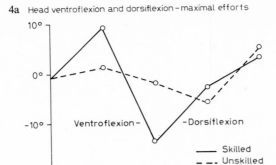

4a Head ventroflexion and dorsiflexion – maximal efforts

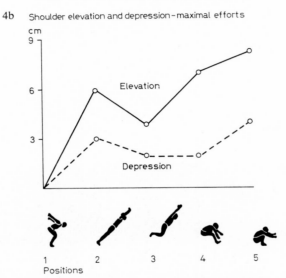

4b Shoulder elevation and depression – maximal efforts

1   2   3   4   5
Positions

Fig. 4. a) Head movements were measured in degrees for the maximal efforts of the unskilled and skilled subjects during five phases of the standing broad jump: 1) preparation for take-off; 2) take-off; 3) full flight; 4) preparation for landing and 5) landing. A zero degree reading was assigned to position 1 (preparation for take-off) so that the range of movement used by the unskilled and skilled performers would be highlighted. The position figures at the bottom of the graph were not taken from pictures used in this study. b) Shoulder girdle movements were measured in centimeters for the maximal efforts of the unskilled and skilled subjects during the five phases of the standing broad jump. A zero centimeter measurement was used to denote shoulder girdle position for the first phase of the jump (preparation for take-off). a) and b) Concomitant head and shoulder girdle movements for the unskilled and skilled subjects. Restricted mobility of the head and shoulder girdle was illustrated when the unskilled performers executed the standing broad jump for maximal distance. The diminished response was indicative of the inability to utilize supportive elements within the body. The movement of the head-shoulder complex of the unskilled jumpers followed that of the skilled performers except between phase 3 (full flight) and

ment act as a 'programmed input' which put to work the cortical
motor mechanism modulating executive impulses at the spinal level. In
the standing broad jump the arms initiate the movement and perhaps
activate the mechanism necessary to support the willed act. Hyperextension of the arms at the gleno-humeral joint during the backswing
was tied with shoulder girdle depression and head ventroflexion. Subsequent flexion of the upper extremities at the same joint complex was
linked with shoulder girdle elevation and head dorsiflexion; these motor
pattern components increased in magnitude during the time of take-
off. When the arms reversed their direction, near the high point of the
jump, shoulder depression was linked with head ventroflexion. Upon
landing the arms were brought forward, the shoulders elevated and
the head dorsiflexed. The same overt pattern configurations were found
by WATERLAND and MUNSON (1964) to be associated responses during
non-stressful sagittal arm movement. Range of motion could well
determine the degree of head–shoulder integration and in turn, total
body unification.

    Sagittal plane movements of the head, trunk and arms created an
exigency which required righting of the head in relationship to gravity
(Fig. 3). The labyrinthine and optical righting reflexes seemed to be
implicated regardless of the degree of skill (RUSHWORTH, 1961). Dorsiflexion of the head occurred in the preparation to land phase with
every subject jumping for maximal distance (Fig. 4). Perhaps this explains why a comparison of the means of the differences for ventro-
and dorsiflexion of the head revealed no significant difference between
the two skill groups upon landing for the last two figure positions
analyzed (preparation for landing and landing). A significant difference
at the 5% level was found between the skill levels for the three earlier
phases of the jump (prepararation for take-off, take-off and high
point).

Discussion

Spontaneous overt pattern configurations of the head, shoulder girdle
and upper limbs were evident in the skilled and unskilled performers

---

phase 4 (preparation for landing) of the jump. The skilled subjects used increased joint
ranges as indicated by the head and shoulder girdle movements. The 'full blown' harmony
of movement between head and shoulder girdle for the skilled subjects resulted in successful
saltation.

jumping for maximal distance. However, the unskilled jumpers failed to realize the potential of an activated and integrated neuromuscular mechanism. The autonomous components of the movement were diminished but adequate for the distance jumped. HESS (1954) explained that 'the course of a movement is nothing else but a projection to the outside of a pattern of excitation taking place in a corresponding setting in the central nervous system'. The integration of the musculature is essential for coordinated performances. Muscular action stimulates proprioceptive impulses which in turn elicit motor responses within the body. Cortical control is 'dethroned'. The executive order of the willed movement is modulated by sensory input and controlled by the lower centers.

SCHAFFER in 1954 advocated that subcortical mechanisms dominate the organism under stress. The subcortical level seems to fixate whatever pattern of behavior happens to be on-going at that time and reactivates itself in response to environmental conditions. The head–shoulder girdle components operative in the standing broad jump were first identified during wrist ergographic exercise in the overload or stressful zone. All-out performance of the standing broad jump by skilled performers was characterized by force or stress. The jumpers automatically called forth indigenous patterning which is thought to be autonomous in nature.

A point of practical importance emerges: gross differences in end-results do not necessarily indicate deficits in strength or neuromuscular coordination. The poor showings of the unskilled may be due to a defect in the precept of the act prescribed or insufficient movement experience to activate the associated pattern. There is reason to believe that exposure to a variety of significant movement experiences may facilitate performance of the act prescribed more effectively than practice of the skill *per se*.

References

FELTON, E.: A kinesiological comparison of good and poor performances in the standing broad jump. Unpublished Master's thesis, University of Wisconsin, Madison, 1960.

HALVERSON, L.E.: A comparison of performance of children in the take-off phase of the standing broad jump. Unpublished Ph. D. dissertation, University of Wisconsin, Madison, 1958.

HELLEBRANDT, F.A.; HOUTZ, S.J.; PARTRIDGE, M.J. and WALTERS, C.E.: Tonic neck reflexes in exercises of stress in man. *Amer. J. phys. Med. XXXV:* 144–159 (1956).

HELLEBRANDT, F.A.; RARICK, G.L.; GLASSOW, R.B. and CARNS, M.L.: Physiological analysis of basic motor skills, *Amer. J. phys. Med. XL:* 14–25 (1961).

HESS, W.R.: *Diencephalon—Automatic and Extrapyramidal Functions.* (Grune and Stratton, New York, 1954).

PAILLARD, J.: The Patterning of Skilled Movements, Vol. III of *Hb. Physiol.* (Chap. 67 of Section 1, Neurophysiology). Ed.: J. FIELD, H.W. MAGOUN and V.E. HALL. Washington, D.C.: Amer. phys. Soc. 1960.

RUSHWORTH, G.: On postural and righting reflexes. *Cerebr. Palsy Bull. III:* 535–543 (1961).

SCHAFFER, H.R.: Behavior under stress: A neurophysiological hypothesis. *Psychol. Rev.LX:* 323–333 (1954).

WATERLAND, J.C. and HELLEBRANDT, F.A.: Involuntary patterning associated with willed movement performed against progressively increasing resistance. *Amer. J. phys. Med. XLIII:* 13–30 (1964).

WATERLAND, J.C. and MUNSON, N.: Reflex association of head and shoulder girdle in nonstressful movements of man. *Amer. J. phys. Med. XLIII:* 98–108 (1964).

WATERLAND, J.C.: The supportive framework for willed movement. *Amer. J. phys. med. XLVI:* (1967a), 266–278. BASMAJIAN, J.V. 'Comment on Dr. Waterland's paper.' *Amer. J. phys. Med., XLVI:* 279 (1967).

WATERLAND, J.C.: The effect of force gradation on motor patterning. *Quest: VIII:* 15–25 (1967b).

ZIMMERMAN, H.M.: Characteristic likenesses and differences between skilled and non-skilled performances of the standing broad jump. Unpublished Ph. D. dissertation, University of Wisconsin, Madison, 1951.

Author's address: JOAN C. WATERLAND, Ph. D., Motor Learning Research Laboratory, 310 Lathrop Hall, University of Wisconsin, *Madison,* Wisconsin, 53706 (USA).

Biomechanics I, 1st Int. Seminar Zurich 1967
pp. 188–191 (Karger, Basel/New York 1968)

Department of Biomechanics of FTVS, Charles University, Prague

Mechanical Model of Some Functions of the Motion System of Man, and its Analysis Based on Matrix Algebra

S. Otáhal

Mechanical examinations of motions of the human body and also analysis of the proper motion system of man are usually connected with creation of a substitute mechanical system and with the mathematical expression of its motion from the points of view of kinematics and dynamics. For the solution of different problems connected with the mathematical expression the utilisation of matrix algebra is very advantageous.

The model system can be described from the kinematic point of view by the matrix equations for paths, velocities and accelerations [1]. From these equations characteristic quantities for any point of the model system can be directly determined. The equation for the path of an arbitrary point is (e.g. point M on Fig. 1): $r_{Ma} = r_{Mb} \cdot T_{ba} + r_{ba}$. By its successive differentiation with respect to time we obtain the results for the velocities and accelerations of point M: $v_{Ma} = r_{Mb} \cdot \Omega_{ba} \cdot T_{ba} + v_{ba}$; $a_{Ma} = r_{Mb} \cdot (\Psi_{ba} + \Omega_{ba}^2) \cdot T_{ba} + a_{ba}$, where r_{Ma} is the radius vector in matrix form of point M with respect to the coordinate system a; r_{Mb} is the radius vector of point M related to the coordinate system b; T_{ba} is the transformation matrix, it transforms the coordinatory system b into system a (matrix of direction cosines of the coordinates of system b and a); r_{ba} is the radius vector of the origin of coordinate system b in relation to system a; v_{Ma} is the vector of the resulting velocity of point M related to the space a; v_{ba} is the vector of the carrier velocity of point M related to a; Ω_{ba} is the matrix of the relative angular velocity of systems b and a; a_{Ma} is the vector of the resultant of the acceleration related to space a; a_{ba} is the vector of the carrier acceleration of point M related to a; Ψ_{ba} is the matrix of the angular acceleration of the motion $b : a$. Symbols b, a belong to the coordinate systems of the members b and a of the

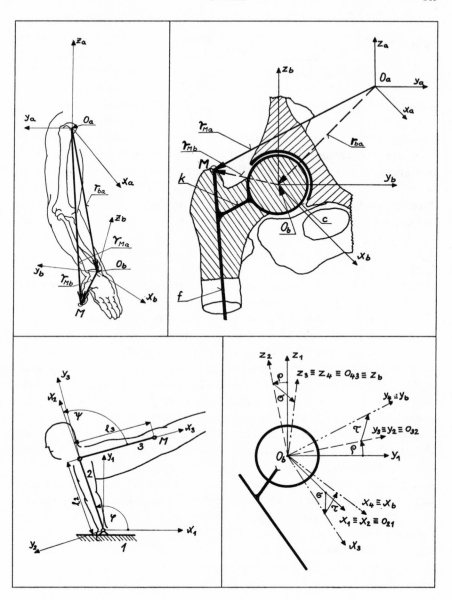

Fig. 1

mechanical system which are interconnected by a chain of further segments and kinematic pairs. The transformation matrix T_{ba} and matrices Ω_{ba}, Ψ_{ba} derived from it depend upon the partial transformation matrices of the individual pairs, connecting the whole chain from b to member a. As direction cosines of the coordinates of system b related to system a are dependent on time, T_{ba}, Ω_{ba}, Ψ_{ba} are also functions of time.

The simple example of the model of 'swing on parallel bars' (in vertical plane conception) illustrates [2] the use of this method. For the motion according to picture 2 the following equations can be written: $r_{M1} = r_{M3} \cdot T_{31} + r_{31}$; $r_{M1} = r_{M2} \cdot T_{21} + r_{21}$; $r_{M2} = r_{M3} \cdot T_{32} + r_{32}$; $r_{21} = 0$. By substitution and modification we obtain the formula for the resulting position (path) of point M: $r_{M1} = [l_2 \cdot \cos\varphi + l_3 \cdot (\cos\psi - \sin\psi \cdot \sin\varphi); l_2 \cdot \sin\varphi + l_3 \cdot (\cos\psi + \sin\psi \cdot \cos\varphi)]$, where the first member of the row matrix r_{M1} is the expression for the x-coordinate of point M related to system 1, the second member for its y-coordinate. The angles ψ and φ are time functions. By differentiation of T_{31} with respect to time we obtain Ω_{31}. In this example the considered joints of segments 3, 2, 1 (the shoulder, the wrist) were simply replaced by the rotatory plane pairs.

For the formation of a satisfactory precise model of the motion system, it is necessary to determine the type of pairs which replace the natural joints and their transformation matrices. By the mentioned method the analyses of the hip joint, which was replaced by the spheric pair [3] with three degrees of freedom, were performed (Fig. 3). The coordinate system b was fast connected with the femur. The origin of system b was placed into the center of the surface of the head O_b and the direction of the coordinates was identical or parallel to the cardinal axes of the human body, in the case of a rest position of the femur. The general resulting spherical motion was resolved into partial rotations gradually round the axes o_{21} (abduction or adduction), o_{32} (flexion or extension), o_{43} (rotation) about the angles ϱ, σ, τ (Fig. 4). The position 4 is the final position of the femur b related to position 1. By the determination of the transformation matrices for the partial rotations we can determine the resulting transformation matrix of the hip joint: $T_{ba} = T_{43} \cdot T_{32} \cdot T_{21} =$

$$= \begin{bmatrix} \cos\tau \cdot \cos\sigma; & \sin\tau \cdot \cos\varrho + \cos\tau \cdot \sin\sigma \cdot \sin\varrho; & \sin\tau \cdot \sin\varrho - \cos\tau \cdot \sin\sigma \cdot \cos\varrho \\ -\sin\tau \cdot \cos\sigma; & \cos\tau \cdot \cos\varrho - \sin\tau \cdot \cos\sigma \cdot \sin\varrho; & \cos\tau \cdot \sin\varrho + \sin\tau \cdot \sin\sigma \cdot \cos\varrho \\ \sin\sigma; & -\cos\sigma \cdot \sin\varrho; & \cos\sigma \cdot \cos\varrho \end{bmatrix}$$

By differentiation of the mentioned expression with respect to time we obtain the relation for the quantities Ω_{ba} and Ψ_{ba}.

The described method enables us to model in a clear form also the complicated spatial or plane motions of the human body or of its parts and facilitates their easy numerical analysis.

References

1. BRÁT, J.: Maticová metoda kinematického rešení prostorovych mechanismu. Rozpravy CSAV. *75:* 2 (1965).
2. KARAS, V.: Pohybové struktury a podmínky jejich určení. Sborník FTVS. *6:* 53–61 (1964).
3. WILLIAMS, M. and LISSNER, H.: Biomechanics of human motion. (Saunders, Philadelphia/London 1962).

Author's address: Dr. S. OTÁHAL, Department of Biomechanics of FTVS, Charles University, *Prague* (CSSR).

Biomechanics I, 1st Int. Seminar Zurich 1967
pp. 192–195 (Karger, Basel/New York 1968)

Department of Biomechanics of Faculty of Physical Education, Charles University, Prague

Application of the Theory of the Motion System in the Analysis of Gymnastic Motions

V. Karas and A. Stapleton

The human body forms in motion a system of bodies. The system can form an open or closed kinematic chain. In gymnastics the kinematic chain is often open. As there are many movable members of the system connected by different kinematic pairs in the human body, complicated movements can exist. It is therefore advantageous to eliminate movements of lesser importance. The set of principal movements represents the basic *movement structure* of the given gymnastic element. Single motions are the *constructive components* of the structure. The movement structure can be expressed in its geometrical image, kinematic and dynamic. By the determination of the movement structure we obtain the model, expressing the biomechanical principles of a given moving activity of a sportsman. The variants of this model are adequate in establishing the different methods of realising a specified gymnastic element.

The notation of the content of motion structure is possible by expression of the constructive components of the structure. To illustrate this we shall mention some examples which can also be applied to other gymnastical elements. The constructive components of the motion structure of swing preceding the hollow back somersault on parallel bars are used. The main constructive components of the movement are: A) *Carrying motion* of arms forwards and backwards round the wrist. B) *The relative motion* of the trunk with the legs around the shoulders. For the general motion 3,1 of the trunk and legs the disintegrated motion is valid [2]: $31 = 51 + 35$ (Fig. 1). By the appropriate adaptation of the constructive components of the motion structure a theoretical base can often be reached for the project improving the performance of the gymnast, e.g. by adaption of the velocity of the

shoulder motion in the last supporting phase of the swing before the
backwards somersault it is possible to increase the height of the flight
of the somersault (Fig. 2). For the height of the flight $h = v_h^2/2g$ by
the somersault the vertical component v_h of the velocity of the centre
of gravity v_T is decisive. With the backward shoulder motion with the
velocity $v_{51} = v_{21} = 1,3$ m/s the height of the flight of the centre of
gravity was realized at $h = 27$ cm (Fig. 2a). By arresting the backward
shoulder motion the height of flight increased by 18 cm (Fig. 2b).
Arresting of the shoulders is possible.

In the applied disintegration of the motion, the following forces are
acting on the trunk and legs: A) $F_{51} = m_{Tt} \cdot a_{51}$ – the force of carrying
traversable motion 5,1; B) $F_{35n} = m_{Tt} \cdot \omega_{35}^2 \cdot \overline{RT_t}$ – the centripetal force

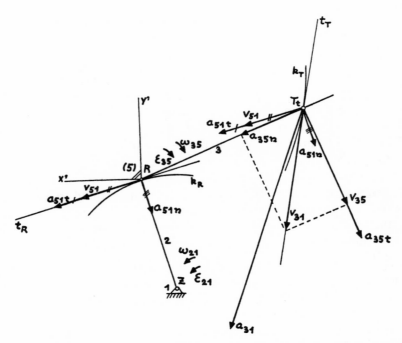

Fig. 1. An example of one possible expression of the kinematic constructive components
of the motion structure in swinging at the bars. ($v_{51} = v_{21}$, $a_{51\,n,t}$ – velocity and tangential
and centrifugal acceleration of the carrying motion of the shoulders R, a translatory
motion of an assistant space x', y' $\equiv$ (5); v_{35}, $a_{35\,t,n}$ – velocity and tangential and centrifugal
acceleration of the relative rotatory motion of the gravity centre of the trunk and legs T_t
round the shoulders R; v_{31}, a_{31} – the resultant velocity and resultant acceleration T_t).

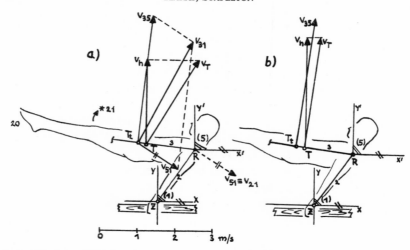

Fig. 2. Velocity relation in the last phase of the swing before the backwards somersault. a) The actual situation. b) After the shoulders are made motionless.

of motion 3,5; C) $F_{35t} = m_{Tt} \cdot \varepsilon_{35} \cdot \overline{RT_t}$ – the tangential force of motion 3,5. With the help of mentioned forces we can determine, e.g. the tension of 'the shoulder axis' in the swing. The forces from the swing before the backwards somersault had been found to reach 280 kp. Let us call attention to the following interesting question—the influencing of the motion 3,2 by the extensors or flexors of the arms. These muscles by their rotating influence upon the trunks and arms, help to balance the unstable situation of the gymnast in the support and to accelerate or slow the rotation motion of the trunk. The gravitational force affecting the trunk and legs provokes the angular acceleration ε'_{35} of the relative motion 3,5. When we use the radius of inertia according to $i = \sqrt{\frac{J}{m}}$ we can write that $\varepsilon'_{35} = \overline{RT_t} \cdot \sin\, a \cdot g / i^2$ (where $g = 9{,}81$ m/s² of gravity acceleration, i– the distance of a point with a mass m_{Tt} from the shoulders which point substitutes the trunk with legs). At the non-uniform carrying motion of shoulders with acceleration of the translatory motion a_{51} the tangential component of the inertial force D_{51} acts by the rotatory moment on the trunk with legs (Fig. 3) and gives the acceleration $\varepsilon''_{35} = -a_{51} \cdot \cos \beta \cdot \overline{RT_t}/i^2$ After the determination of senses ε'_{35} and ε''_{35} the rotatory moment of the relative motion 3,5 with the action force of gravity and force of the supporting motion 5,1 will be $M_{p35} = J_R \cdot \varepsilon_{p35} = m_{Tt} \cdot i^2 (\varepsilon'_{35} - \varepsilon''_{35})$. Besides the moment

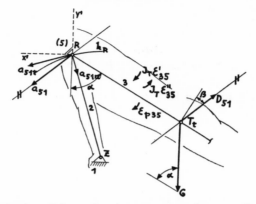

Fig. 3. The determination of the acceleration moment at the non-uniform motion of the shoulder axis R with acceleration a_{s1}.

M_{p35} the other moment of force M_{m35} of the extensors and flexors of the arm is influencing the trunk with the legs. The angular acceleration ε_{35} which can be determined from a film record of the motion is the resulting acceleration appropriate to the resulting moment M_{35}. We can write $M_{35} = M_{p35} + M_{m35}$. For example in Fig. 3 for the muscular moment can be written $M_{m35} = m_{Tt} \cdot i^2 (\varepsilon_{35} - \varepsilon'_{35} + \varepsilon''_{35})$.

As a result of our measurings, values of the moments of inertia of the trunk and legs were determined on parts of a corpse [1]. Further, the approximate relation for the calculation of the radius of the inertia of the trunk with the legs towards the transverse shoulder axis was deduced

$$i \doteq \sqrt{\frac{m_1 \cdot 0{,}44 \cdot l_1^2 + m_2 (0{,}07 \cdot l_2^2 + r_2^2)}{m_{Tt}}}$$

(where m_1–the mass of the trunk, m_2–the mass of both legs, l_1 and l_2–the length of the trunk and legs, r_2–the distance of the centre of gravity of the legs from the shoulder axis).

According to the informative solutions $i = 0{,}5$–$0{,}6$ m.

References

1. HORÁK, Z.; KRUPKA, F. and ŠINDELÁR, V.: Technická fysika (SNTL, Prague 1960).
2. ŠREJTR, J.: Technická mechanika II. Kinematika (SNTL, Prague 1955).

Authors' addresses: Ph. Dr. VLADIMÍR KARAS, Department of Biomechanics of Faculty of Physical Education, Charles University, Újezd 450, *Prague 1* (CSSR) and ANNETTE STAPLETON, 3. Milnthorpe Rd., *London W. 4* (England).

Biomechanics I, 1st Int. Seminar Zurich 1967
pp. 196–200 (Karger, Basel/New York 1968)

University of Birmingham, Edgbaston, Birmingham

Bias in Linear Hand Movements

E.N. CORLETT and P. THRUNAVUKKARASU, Birmingham

Introduction

The accurate achievement of a rapid movement requires prediction of the muscular forces needed to overcome the total resistance. It is conceivable that the accuracy of a movement performed mainly by rotating limb segments is greater than one involving translation of the centre of gravity.

Experiment

To determine whether re-orientation of a line drawing task would bring about a modification of the direction of BEGBIE's (1959) line of least error, BEGBIE's experiment was repeated but with the task centred in line with the subject's right shoulder. The task and experiments were exactly as described by BEGBIE.

The lengths of the lines (16, 20, 28 and 32 cm) were modified from those used by BEGBIE, (16, 20, 24 and 32 cm) to attempt a better assessment of whether the differences in line length suggested by him were real.

Six subjects performed a randomised block experiment, with four trials per condition.

Results

Scoring was done by measuring the perpendicular distances by which the line missed the target. *Error* was the sum of the four deviations, added regardless of which side the error occurred. *Bias* was assessed by (i) adding the number of times the subject was to one side or the other of the target, and (ii) by adding algebraically the amount of error occurring to one side or the other of the target dot. Clockwise bias was given a negative sign.

Errors

In an analysis of variance the main effects of subjects, lengths, directions and bias all showed high significance. Table I shows that subjects maintain the same rank order with eyes closed and eyes open but demonstrate greater error.

Table II illustrates the errors occurring for each length on each of the test days. The results confirm BEGBIE, that the nature of the movement changes when the length is greater than about 20 cm.

The line direction and length affected the size of the error (Fig. 1). Opposite directions are not significantly different for short lengths. Three pairs of long lengths differ (for the 'eyes closed' case). The line A–B marks the directions of least error with an additional 'easy' direction for the eyes closed case. These diagrams do not show the quadriphasic shape found by BEGBIE.

Table I. Average error per trial in mm

Subject	Average of first 6 days	7th day eyes open	8th day eyes closed
1	15.51	15.58	30.89
2	11.36	10.00	26.87
3	12.39	9.50	26.54
4	10.83	9.30	23.85
5	11.04	9.40	24.61
6	12.29	14.05	30.18

Table II. Total error of all subjects for each test day

Length	16 cm	20 cm	28 cm	32 cm
Total Error, eyes open (mm)	662.5	714.0	925.0	958.5
Total Error, eyes closed (mm)	1499.0	1734.0	2237.5	2350

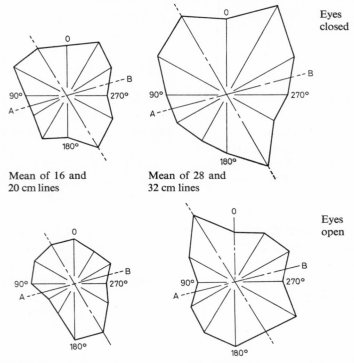

Fig. 1. Distribution of errors for 'eyes closed' and 'eyes open' tests with different lengths of line (scale for 'eyes open' diagram is twice that for 'eyes closed' diagram.

Bias

Calculating by method (i) there was no significant difference between the four lengths for each direction, 50 results were added over lengths. (Table III).

The difference between the + and — columns of Table III (Fig. 2) demonstrates the predominant bias for each direction. Many of the results are not statistically significant but with 4 exceptions are consistent.

Discussion

Where a movement is too fast for visual control the success must be verified afterwards. Correction comes from a revision of the programme, accounting for both the observed error and the experience of

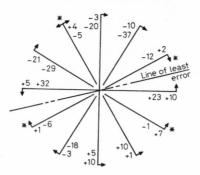

Fig. 2. Algebraic differences between clockwise and anti-clockwise misses (outer figures 'eyes open'; inner figures 'eyes closed').

Table III. Number of occasions subjects were to one side or other of the target spot

Direction		Eyes open					Eyes closed				
		—	0	+	χ_2	Sig.	—	0	+	χ_2	Sig.
0	1	43	13	40	0.05		56	4	36	3.91	5%
30	2	41	10	45	0.11		46	9	41	0.29	
60	3	53	11	32	4.70	5%	60	9	31	8.62	1%
90	4	37	17	42	0.20		28	8	60	10.9	1%
120	5	38	19	39	0.00		48	6	42	0.20	
150	6	42	15	39	0.05		64	6	26	15.20	1%
180	7	38	10	48	0.94		42	7	47	0.18	
210	8	42	11	43	0.00		41	4	51	0.88	
240	9	37	15	44	0.44		45	7	44	0.00	
270	10	36	14	46	0.99		33	7	56	5.43	5%
300	11	41	12	43	0.01		52	4	40	1.31	
330	12	44	18	34	1.04		66	1	29	14.10	1%

— = missed clockwise from target.
0 = hit.
+ = missed anti-clockwise from target.
χ_2 = chi-squared test values.

the external forces affecting the limb. Where the influence of external forces is least, the opportunity for successfully predicted movements is greatest. Also if the number of degrees of freedom can be effectively reduced the control required is simplified.

Those movements which have the least error require the smallest amount of prediction, in terms of the above argument. Other movements require additional predictions of co-ordinated muscular innervations to achieve accuracy. Under-estimation of these would cause bias in the direction of the line of least error, as shown.

Reference

BEGBIE, G.H.: Accuracy of aiming in linear hand movements. Quart. J. exp. Psych. *11:* 65–75 (1959).

Author's address: E.N. CORLETT, Ph. D., Senior Lecturer in Engineering Production, University of Birmingham, Edgbaston, *Birmingham 15* (Great Britain).

Biomechanics I, 1st Int. Seminar Zurich 1967
pp. 201–204 (Karger, Basel/New York 1968)

Deutsche Sporthochschule Köln

Bewegungsstudien in den ersten Lebensjahren

LISELOTT DIEM

Das Didaktisch-Methodische Seminar der Deutschen Sporthochschule Köln führt zur Zeit eine Untersuchung über die motorische Entwicklung in den ersten Lebensjahren durch. Dieses Forschungsvorhaben wird finanziert durch das Sportpädagogische Kuratorium des Deutschen Sportbundes.

Die Untersuchung berührt bzw. stellt auch *Fragen der Biomechanik*. Sie gehört zu der von DONSKOI bezeichneten Gruppe der «Untersuchungen der funktionellen Charakteristika der körperlichen Entwicklung, um Wege der Steigerung der funktionellen Möglichkeiten des Organismus (des Sportlers) zu finden...» (S. 10). Die Selbstbewegung des Kindes erfährt schon im ersten Lebensjahr eine «Steigerung der funktionellen Möglichkeiten» durch adäquate Situations-Reize – zwei Beispiele werden aus der Untersuchung herausgegriffen und die damit zusammenhängenden Fragen hier gestellt:

I. Erstes Beispiel

Das Kind wird – obleich es sich im Mutterleib immer in rumpfvorgebeugter Haltung verhielt – rückenkräftig, fähig zur Aufrichtung geboren. Es ist am ersten Lebenstag in der Lage, für eine oder mehrere Sekunden den schweren Kopf zu heben, der ein Drittel des Körpergewichts ausmacht. Abb. 1 zeigt die Spannkraft der Rücken- und Gesäßmuskulatur sowie die Haltefähigkeit des Kopfes.

Erste Frage: Diese bei der Geburt vorhandene Rücken-Haltekraft bleibt nur bei entsprechender Bauchlage erhalten. Müßte man darum nicht grundsätzlich für die ersten Lebensmonate vorwiegend Bauchlage im Wechsel mit Rückenlage empfehlen?

Zweite Frage: Läßt sich durch die verstärkte Beanspruchung der Rückenmuskeln in der Bauchlage bzw. durch die Hautberührung (Tastorgane), durch sensomotorische Eindrücke auch eine Funktionsverbesserung der Extremitäten feststellen? In der Bauchlage ist das Kind fähig zu tasten, drücken, klammern, stemmen, stoßen mit Fingern, Händen, Zehen und Füßen.

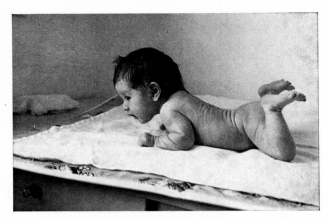

Abb. 1. Alter: 17 Tage; Länge: 52 cm; Aufnahmedatum: 13. Dezember 1966.
Foto: Did.-Meth. Seminar Köln

II. Zweites Beispiel

Die amerikanischen Untersuchungen der McGraw Klinik New York
zeigten die verbesserte Koordinationsfähigkeit schon bei Neugeborenen
«unter erschwerten Umständen» in der Wasserlage[1]. Die gleichen
Autoren weisen in ihrem Zwillingsfilm (Jimmy and Jonny) nach, daß
die Koordinationsfähigkeit abhängig ist von entsprechenden Reizsitua-
tionen im ersten Lebensjahr. Fehlen diese frühzeitigen Reize, so wird
eine Koordinationsverminderung bis zum 6. Lebensjahr festgestellt.

Unsere eigenen Untersuchungen belegen zielgerichtetes Beinstoßen
aus der Rückenlage in der Badewanne, die Schwebelage im Wasser mit
Hilfe von Schwimmblasen an den Armen und damit die günstige Voraussetzung für intensive Bein- und Armbewegungen (ab 6. Lebensmonat). Bei Sprung- und Tauchversuchen werden die Arme verstärkt
eingesetzt – obwohl es bisher so scheint, als seien die Beinbewegungen
zu Beginn besser koordiniert. Gut koordinierte Bewegungen sowohl in
Rücken- als auch in Bauchlage zeigen sich auch in schwierigen Situationen im dritten Lebensjahr, z.B. Tauchgeschicklichkeit und Atem-
beherrschung unter Wasser.

Frage: Der Säugling kann seine Doppelkoordination der Arme –
Beine am besten unbelastet – in der Schwebelage im Wasser, unterstützt durch den Wasserauftrieb – zur Entwicklung bringen. (Abb. 2
zeigt die gut koordinierte und flüssige Bewegung eines 15 Monate alten

Abb. 2
Foto: Kindergarten Los Angeles

Kindes im Wasser). Sollte Schwimmen also *vor* dem Laufen erlernt werden, und wäre damit eine Verbesserung der Koordinationsqualität zu erreichen?

Anregung: Die Tauch- und Schwimmfähigkeit ist nicht nur ein angeborener Reflex (wie die McGraw Klinik behauptet), sondern ein den ersten Lebensmonaten entsprechendes Bewegungsverhalten, das bei immer wieder angepaßten und gesteigerten Situationen laufend vom Kind selbst verbessert wird. Der Röntgenologe D. Hooker berichtet vom vierten Lebensmonat *vor* der Geburt: «... dies ist eine wichtige Entwicklungsstufe, denn nun ändert sich die Qualität der Reaktionen. Sie sind jetzt nicht mehr marionettenartig oder mechanisch... Die Bewegungen werden anmutig und gleichmäßig wie bei einem Neugeborenen...»[2]. Um die Schwimmöglichkeit vom ersten Lebensmonat an zu finden, sollten nach Größe und Form geeignete Badebecken gebaut werden.

[1] *Filme:* Reflex Behaviour of the newborn Infant, International Film Bureau, Chicago/Ill./USA – Jimmy and Jonny, International Film Bureau, Chicago/Ill./USA.
[2] s. Flanagan, L.: Die ersten neun Monate des Lebens. Rowohlt, Reinbek 1963.

Literatur

BUYTENDIJK, F.J.J.: Allgemeine Theorie der menschlichen Haltung und Bewegung (Springer, Berlin-Göttingen 1956).
DONSKOI, D.D.: Biomechanik der Körperübungen (Sportverlag, Berlin 1961).
FLANAGAN, L.: Die ersten neun Monate des Lebens (Rowohlt, Reinbek 1963).
HOOKER, D.: Early Human Fetal Behaviour, Baltimore 1954).
MEINEL, K.: Bewegungslehre (Volk und Wissen, Berlin 1960).
STRAUS, E.: Vom Sinn der Sinne, 2. Aufl. (Springer, Berlin-Göttingen 1956).

Adresse der Autorin: Prof. LISELOTT DIEM, Hum. D., Deutsche Sporthochschule Köln, *D-5 Köln* (Deutschland).

Biomechanics I, 1st Int. Seminar Zurich 1967
pp. 205–208 (Karger, Basel/New York 1968)

Centre for Educational Research, University of Jyväskylä, Finland

On the Relationship Between a Simple Movement Pattern and Physical Fitness

J. KIRJONEN

Introduction

It was my aim to study the characteristics of gross motor performance and their connections with certain factors of physical fitness. At the same time I tried to find out how stroboscopic photography techniques can be used for the registration of movement (JONES and O'CONNELL 1958, 1119). In addition I wanted to study what kind of changes physical exertion produces in the performance of the movement on subjects with different levels of endurance. According to some reports, muscular activity increases activation (e.g. DUFFY 1957, 268 and 1962, 17 and 140) and decreases the negative influences of sleep deprivation in the performance of a skilled task (WILKINSON in EDHOLM and BACHARACH 1965, 418–419). According to DEESE (GLASER 1962, 199–222), muscular exertion may produce stress, the effect of which is to increase the velocity of motor performance, whereas coordination decreases (variability increases and precision decreases).

Problems

1. I was trying to study by means of factor analysis whether it is possible to explain the inter-individual differences in the performance scores of a movement on the basis of the measurements of physical fitness (body constitution and motor fitness).
2. I tried to study what kind of changes in the performance measures of the movement can be observed after muscular work lasting for about six minutes in persons of three different levels of endurance.

For the computing of the main effects and interactions of the muscular work and the endurance variance analysis was used.

Methods

For the registration of the scores a stroboflash apparatus, a photography camera and reflecting tapes attached to the subject tested were used. In principle the method was the same as that introduced by JONES and O'CONNELL in 1958. On each of the film frames a series of marks is produced by the reflections from stroboflash apparatus emitting flashes at a certain frequency (here 10/sec) and these reflections correspond to certain changes of velocity of the movement and the movement paths of the different parts of the body. A rotating filter disc situated in front of the camera objective gives a different colour to the successive reflections and so it becomes possible to study e.g. the timing of the performance.

86 Jyväskylä University male students of an average age of 26 years and 3 months were used as subjects. During the first meeting they were given a motor fitness test battery covering 6 items (e.g. chinning, standing broad jump, grip dynamometer, etc.). During the second meeting their weights and heights were registered and photorecordings were made.

The experimental movement was a simple stereotype gross body pattern which was not supposed to be affected by learning. The tested subjects had to rise from a sitting position and stand on a chair 50 cm high (Fig. 1). This movement was photographed eight times.

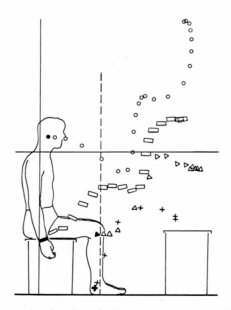

Fig. 1. Schematic picture showing the reflection marks on a projection base sheet.

Between the seventh and the eighth time the subjects had an ergometer test (ÅSTRAND 1961) lasting six minutes.

The measurements covering the movements were carried out on a projection base sheet on which they had been copied by means of a microfilm reading device. The characteristics of the movement were represented by the following variables: total time, variance of movement velocity, width of movement path, smoothness of movement (all these from the motion of head), timing of foot action, effectiveness of hand motion, and timing of hand motion. The reliability of the measuring devices was good (rel. coefficients between successive trials were about 0.85–0.90).

Results

As result of factor analysis six interpreted factors were extracted by using the method of principal axis and varimax rotation. Three of these factors represented movement pattern, viz. coordination, tension and auxiliary movements. The remaining three, viz. powerfulness, endurance and body constitution, were factors of physical fitness. *On the basis of this study it was not possible to explain the interindividual differences in the scores of the performance of the movement by means of the differences in physical fitness.*

As the result of the variance analysis it was found that the scores taken after physical exertion showed that the velocity of the movement had increased in general, but that it was statistically significant only in the groups with poor and with good endurance. At the same time also the auxiliary movements of the hands had increased in these two groups, whereas in the middle group they tended to decrease. *Furthermore, it was noted that the main effect of muscular exertion, which increased the variation of the movement velocity, was statistically significant.* The change was largest in the group with the poorest endurance.

Discussion

By using stroboscopic photography techniques it was possible to register a simple movement performance so well that it also became possible to develop measuring devices using physical scales. The greatest difficulty was transforming the data obtained by photorecording into a form which could be used for statistical treatment. The development of electrical devices for registration and analysis will probably in due course create new possibilities in this line for the treatment of the data in an easier and more automatic way. Before that, or at the latest at that time, we need, however, a theory covering the whole range of the motor systems based on all the available physiological, neurological, and psychological findings about the human organism.

On the basis of this study it is not possible to explain the techniques, i.e. the pattern of a movement by means of the individual differences in physical fitness. They are two separate phenomena.

Though it was not possible to find logical changes based on the effect of muscular exertion on groups of various endurance levels, the results confirmed the assumptions of DEESE (GLASER 1962, 199–222) and some other scholars that muscular exertion increases the velocity of motor performance but simultaneously decreases the level of coordination.

In studying the influences of activation and stress we can hardly avoid a redefinition of these rather ambiguous concepts, before it becomes possible to make progress also at a theoretical level in this field.

References

ÅSTRAND, P.-O.: Arbetsprov med ergometercykeln (AB Cykelfabrik Monark, Varberg 1961).

DEESE, J.: Skilled performance and conditions of stress; in GLASER, R. (Ed.) Training, research and education, pp. 199–222 (Wiley, New York 1957).

DUFFY, E.: The psychological significance of the concept of "arousal" or "activation". Psychol. Rev. *64:* 265–275 (1957).

DUFFY, E.: Activation and behavior (Wiley, New York 1962).

JONES, F.P. and O'CONNELL, D.N.: Color-coding of stroboscopic multiple-image photographs. Science *127:* 1119 (1958).

WILKINSON, R.T.: Sleep deprivation; in EDHOLM, O.G. and BACHARACH, A.L. (Ed.). The physiology of human survival, pp. 399–430 (Academic Press, London 1965).

Author's address: J. KIRJONEN, M. Ed., Pitkäkatu 29 A 11 *Jyväskylä* (Finland).

Biomechanics I, 1st Int. Seminar Zurich 1967
pp. 209–212 (Karger, Basel/New York 1968)

Institute of Hygiene, Prague

Biomechanics of Training of Simple Rhythmic Efforts

L. KOMÁREK

In spite of the fact that improvements in industrial production together with automation bring about a number of problems concerning the activity of man as an operator, simple manual work remains the essential prerequisite of mastering technology at a higher level. Many a failure and exhaustion of personnel controlling intricate production systems are actually due to imperfect training for elementary operations. And that is why we attach great importance to the investigation of the biomechanics of simple manual operations.

As one of the fundamental principles of working skill in rhythmic operations is the application of the laws of reciprocal innervation during alternating rhythmic activation of the antagonistic muscles, it seems to be advantageous to study the development of working skill using the example of sawing. As far as training is concerned, this operation is relatively demanding, that is why all first year trainees in the metal-working branches are taught this operation, and one has to oppose the force of friction to get full synchronization (WAGNER [5]).

The physiological principle of training consists of time and movement concentration, while concentration of muscular action is closely related to the concentration of nervous processes which take place with conditioned strengthening of the right variations of movements on the basis of a higher lability (KOSILOV [3], JAKOVLEV [2]). Training makes for elimination of wrong, unnecessary movements, useless for the given task. Skill is then ability to perform a given movement or working operation as purposefully, accurately and rationally as possible.

Skill has several measurable characteristics. The first one is the rhythm in rhythmic operations, which is a representative characteristic (ČÁP [1]). In sawing the training is directly related to stabilization of

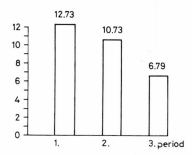

Dispersion of amounts in intervals of 30 seconds in 3 periods

the rhythm (KOSILOV [3]). Next comes frequency. Stabilization of a certain level of frequency is likewise a criterion of the degree of skill. Otherwise frequency is an individual quality rather than a group criterion. Also the amount of work done indicates the level of training. And finally, there are actual biomechanics, the action muscular potentials. In the case of sawing the characteristic of skill is the concentration of potentials in the antagonistic muscles (PERSON [4]).

Our measurements were made in the course of a school session on 19 fitter's apprentices and in the case of EMG studies on 14 fitter's apprentices. All measurements were repeated twelve times in the course of the year, the EMG was measured twice and the results are summarized and evaluated by a comparison of three periods of the school year (1st period: September-October, 2nd period: November-January, 3rd period: February-May) during which sawing was taught. Each measurement lasted 10 minutes. The amount of movement was measured by means of a mechanograph with a potentiometric record of bendings of the elbow joint. The amount of material sawn off was weighed on technical scales. EMG studies were made by a Schwarzer direct writing instrument with superficial electrodes from the m. biceps and m. triceps brachii. EMG studies were carried out in a laboratory, while the other measurements were made under natural conditions in a workshop.

First of all, the rhythm of work was evaluated. The totals of bendings were evaluated in 30-second intervals in the individual persons under test in the three periods of the year. The rhythm can be evaluated by means of F-testing of dispersion variance. It has been found that almost all persons under test show a significantly higher dispersion variance in the first period than in the last period. In most of them dispersion variance fell from the first through the second to the third period of the year, the work thus becoming rhythmic with training.

The situation was similar with the amount of material sawn off, which increased in the course of training.

Interesting results were produced by evaluation of frequency. The persons under test were divided into two groups, one of them being led by foreman S and the other one by foreman H. The group led by foreman S had a higher frequency which remained practically unchanged throughout the year. The group of foreman H had a significantly lower frequency which significantly increased in the course of the year. Because foreman H was much stricter than foreman S, we expected that he recommended the apprentices to work slowly, which is in conformity with the traditional idea of good work. However, as frequency is rather an individual characteristic, the apprentices of foreman H increased frequency in the course of the year. The apprentices of foreman S were free from the outset to select whatever pace they pleased.

EMG potentials from the antagonistic muscles were evaluated merely in the sense of a time concentration of muscular activation during the training. Two measurements were made, one on October 14th, a week after the beginning of training, the other one on December 20th. It appears from the duration of activation of the antagonistic muscles that first of all useless action of the m. triceps

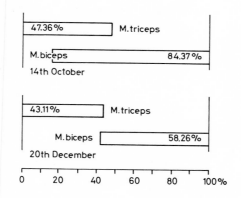

Activation of muscle antagonists in the course of training

is inhibited, and only then that of the m. biceps. As a matter of fact, in the working phase the corrective mechanism of the m. biceps must work more accurately, the training thus lasting longer. The corrective mechanism does not have to work so accurately in the reverse, return phase and thus the m. triceps needs not correct the movement so accurately and, therefore, it is trained earlier.

In conclusion we can state that the rhythm, the amount of work done and the duration of activation of the antagonistic muscles during a working operation are representative criteria for skill in sawing taken as a rhythmic operation.

References

1. ČÁP, J.: Psychologie pracovního vycviku (SPN, Prague 1964).
2. JAKOVLEV, N.A.; KOROBKOV, A.V. a JANANIS, S.V.: Fyziologické a biochemické základy sportovního tréninku (STN, Prague 1962).
3. KOSILOV, S.A.: Otscherki fiziologii truda (Medicina, Moskva 1965).
4. PERSON, R.S.: Mischci antagonisty tscheloveka (Nauka, Moskva 1965).
5. WAGNER, R.: Über die Zusammenarbeit der Antagonisten bei Willkürbewegung. Z. Biol. *83:* (1925).

Authors' address: L. KOMÁREK, Institute of Hygiene, *Prague* (CSSR).

VI. Principles of Human Motion:
Partial Functions and Specific Problems

Biomechanics I, 1st Int. Seminar Zurich 1967
pp. 213–219 (Karger, Basel/New York 1968)

Centre Psychiatrique Sainte-Anne U$_{39}$ I.N.S.E.R.M., Paris et Centre Sportif de l'Armée,
Fontainebleau

Statokinesimetric Recording of the Body Balance
in Sport Medicine

J.B. BARON, J. MOLINIE and A. VRILLAC

Body at rest is never perfectly immobile. It swings continuously. The oscillations are characterized by an individual amplitude and frequency. Normally they are not felt being outside the field of the conscience. Statokinesimeter apparatus, constructed by 'Electronique Appliquée' since 1962 from works published in 1951, allows the record of this motion, gives a measure of the displacements of the body gravity center and localizes them in regard of the center of the body basis.

Since MAREY's works on the record of body motion, these last ten years many searchers have worked in the same field: in URSS GURFIN-KEL, in Czechoslovakia LITVINENKOVA, VANEKOVA, OBRDA, in DDR PROHL, REHBERG, in West Germany LEHMAN, in Sweden VIIDIK, CAR-LOO, in Denmark ANDERSEN, in USA ISMAIL, in Japan SUGANO, in England PAYNE, BLADER, in Switzerland CORTI, in France SOULA, LAURU, MOYNIER, JARRIGUE, RABISCHONG, SOULAIRAC, ISCH, COLL-ARD, BOUSSENS, BURGEAT, DANON, PARQUET, NAYRAC.

The purpose of this paper is to correlate in sports medicine on pistol marksmen the body balance motion recorded on statokinesimeter and results of shots on the target.

Apparatus and Method

Schematically a statokinesimeter is constituted by a four points square detector plate transforming variations of pressure in electric informations by means of electromagnetic plungers. These informations are amplified by direct or alternative amplifiers. They are recorded on:

1. 2 beams cathode ray oscilloscope,
2. 4 counters,
3. ink paper recorder (Fig. 1).

Fig. 1. Statokinesimeter.

On the oscilloscope a picture of the figure of the body balance is recorded, giving X Y displacements of the vertical projection of the gravity center in regard of the center of the body basis.

On counters a dynamic of motion utilized by body balance in four directions Anterior, Posterior, Right, Left, is recorded in regard of the threshold of amplitude of this motion.

On an ink recorder the chronotopology of these motions can be obtained.

An electronic device automatically pounders the weight of each subject (Fig. 2).

Subjects are required to stand in the middle of the plateform, relaxed or acting.

Effects of vigilance level by aiming or shooting can be approached, in addition the influence of oculomotor reflex tone, using prismatic

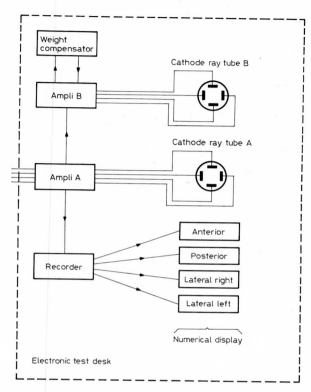

Fig. 2. Schema of the apparatus.

lenses method, on body balance motion and result of the score have been examined.

Applications

The method has been applied to four excellent marksmen. The first time, results of GURFINKEL by stabillographic method showing that body balance is different when marksmen aim or shoot, have been corroborated. In first case body balance motions are slow and of great amplitude, in second case body balance motions are fast and of small amplitude.

When body balance is improved by prismatic lenses aiming or shooting records are the same: body balance motions are fast and of small amplitude (Fig. 3).

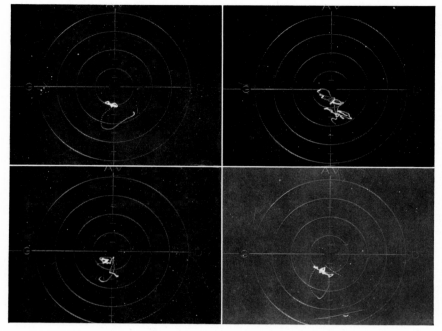

Fig. 3. Statokinesimetric record of posture of marksman aiming (up) and shooting (down) when normally balanced (right) or ameliorated by prismatic lenses (left).

Repetition of shooting 6 times 5 shots of four marksmen, with normal or ameliorated balance, shows a correlation between amplitude and frequency of displacements of the body and the results of the shooting on the target. The greater the amplitude of the body balance motion, the fewer the results of the shooting on the target and vice versa (Fig. 4–5).

All these results have been obtained from electronical multichannel analysis (Fig. 6).

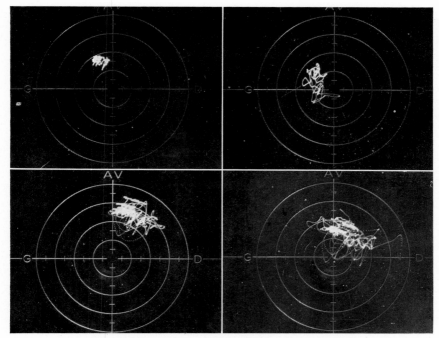

Fig. 4. Statokinesimetric record of posture of marksman at rest (up) or shooting 6 times 5 shots (down) normally balanced (right) or ameliorated by prismatic lenses (left).

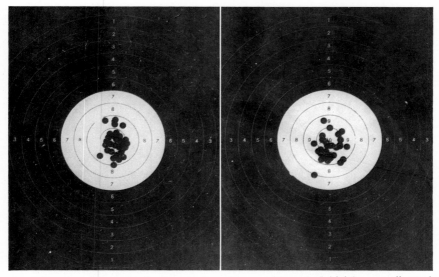

Fig. 5. Results of shots on the target of marksman with normal (right) or ameliorated balance by prismatic lenses (left).

Fig. 6. Multicanal electronic analyser.

Discussion

It is interesting to note that in sports medicine, the results of the statokinesimeter can be used to account for the form of the sportsman and even be useful for controling it, by means of the picture of the body balance motion.

References

BARON, J.B.: Prismatic lenses for vertigo and some experimental background of the role of the extrinsic ocular muscles in desequilibrium. Trans. amer. Acad. Opthal. Otolaryng. *56:* 916–26 (1952).
BARON, J.B.: Verres prismatiques dans la thérapeutique du vertige. Rev. Oto-Neuro-Ophtal. *24:* 142–46 (1952).
BARON, J.B. et SOUDET, P.: Scoliose d'origine oculaire. Rev. Oto-Neuro-Opthal. *24:* 181–83 (1952).

BARON, J.B; BOBOT, J. et BESSINETON, J.C.: Statokinésimètre. Presse Méd. *64: 36:* 863 (1956).

BARON, J.: Présentation d'un appareil pour mettre en évidence les déplacements du centre de gravité du corps dans le polygone de sustentation. Applications pratiques. Arch. Mal. prof. *16:* 8–14 (1964).

BARON, J.: Paralysies oculomotrices post-traumatiques, origine de certains troubles frustes de l'équilibration, séquelles tardives des traumatismes crâniens. Rap. VIIIe Congr. Int. Neurol. Vienne, Excerpta med. *I:* 143–47 (1965).

BURGER, I; NEUSCHL. S. and LITVINENKOVA, V.: Les processus stochastiques dans les systèmes biologiques et l'évaluation des qualités dynamiques des systèmes. Prob. Kybernetiky. 166–75 (1965).

GURFINKEL, V.S.: Stojanije celovekia v norme i patologii. 8-ij vsesojuznij sjezd fiziology, biochimikòv i farmakologov. Tezisy dokl. ...: 198–200 (1955).

JARRIGUE, P.: Présentation d'un appareil de mesure automatique des déplacements au cours du test de Romberg. Arch. Mal. Prof. T. *29:* 43–50 (1968).

LAPEYRIE, P.; RABISCHONG, J.; AVRIL, J.; POUS, G. and PERRUCHON, E.: L'électropodographie, son intérêt en orthopédie. Montpellier-Chirurg. T. *XIII:* 3 (1967).

LITVINENKOVA, V.: Niektore metody hygieniceho hodnotenia obuvi deti predskolshehoveku. Čs. Hyg. *5:* 302–308 (1960).

MOYNIER, R.: Etude de la fatigue et des fatigabilités anormales. Soc. Méd. mil. franç. Bull. *50:* 239–247 (1956).

NAYRAC, P; MILBLED, G. et PARQUET, P.: Le statokinésimètre. Etude clinique neurologique. Lille méd. *II:* 476–480 (1966).

NEUSCHL, S. and LITVINENKOVA, V.: Prispevok k metodike stabilographie. Čs. Hyg. *10:* 581–593 (1963).

SOULAIRAC, A.; BARON, J.; COIRAULT, MOYNIER, R. and GUIOT, G.: Troubles de l'équilibration statique d'origine oculomotrice mis en évidence par l'appareillage piézo-électrique. Soc. Méd. mil. franç. Bull. *50:* 248–252 (1956).

SOULAIRAC, A.: L'examen de la régulation posturale au statokinésimètre, son application à l'étude des niveaux de vigilance chez le sujet normal avant et après traitement par le PC 63–14. Cah. Coll. Méd. *7:* 669–672 (1966).

SUGANO, H.: Recording of body movement (statokinescope) and its clinical application. Digest of the 7th Int. Conf. on med. and biol. Engin. Stockholm. August. 1967.

THIEBAUT, F.; ISCH, F.; COLLARD, M. et CONRAUX, C.: La statokinésimétrie (Technique et résultats). Rev. Neurol. clin. *114:* 123–134 (1966).

Adresse de l'auteur: Dr J.B. BARON, Maître de Recherches au C.N.R.S., U$_{39}$ I.N.S.E.R.M., Centre Psychiatrique Sainte-Anne, 1, rue Cabanis, *Paris 14e* (France).

Biomechanics I, 1st Int. Seminar Zurich 1967
pp. 220–224 (Karger, Basel/New York 1968)

Department of Human Anatomy, University of Gothenburg and the Department
of Mechanical Engineering, Chalmers Institute of Technology, Gothenburg

The Motion Pattern of the Ankle Joint in Standing

A. Viidik and M. Mägi

Introduction

The standing posture is not a passive motionless act. It involves a
continuous change of angles at levels from the ankle to the atlanto-
occipital joint, resulting in an equilibrium. This consists of a summation of active muscular forces counteracting gravitational and external
forces acting upon different parts of the human body and is visible as
oscillating movements that are largest in Romberg's position or with
closed eyes [8] and largest in children and elderly people [1a, 10] while
the young adult is most stable [2]. These movements have been recorded from the iliac crest [11] with two frequencies superimposed
0.3 and 8 cps, as well as from the tibial tuberosity [9] the higher
frequency being 15 cps. Such frequencies have also been found in
measurements of the center of gravity [12] being 0.12–0.39 and 0.36–
1.13 cps. The low frequencies have generally been interpreted as adjustments of the posture and the high frequencies have been attributed
to fluctuations in muscle tension [11], to muscular twitch-time [13] and
to many minute motions in the body to achieve balance [9].

Since all external forces that act upon the human body in a normal standing posture pass through the ankle joint, we chose therefore
to investigate the motion pattern of that joint and its correlation to the
alterations of the position of the whole body's center of gravity.

Previous investigators have measured the motion of various parts
of the body with different techniques, i.e. photography of a lamp placed
on the head of the subject [1a, 4], mechanical devices fastened to the
head recording the total sway [8] or the pattern of sway [7], or to the
shoulders [10]. Photographic techniques with multicoloured strobos-

copic light has been used for analysis of motion in different joints [3] and so have accelerometers [9] and kymographs with lever systems [11]. The position of the center of gravity has usually been measured by using the *static* equilibrium conditions [1, 2, 5, 6, 11] and a more multidimensional analysis [12] has also been made.

Materials and Methods

Two 20-year-old healthy students were investigated, each for 30 min in Romberg's position, first with open eyes, then blindfolded and screened from outside noises and at last with open eyes again.

The apparatus used consisted of a horizontal board-shaped lever, supported at one end by an edge and at the other by a force transducer (Bofors KRK-1,20 kp). The persons investigated stood on the lever with markers placed on the tibial tuberosity of each leg and the movements in the horizontal direction (sagittal plane) were recorded with displacement transducers (Bofors, differential transformers, RLL-1, ± 25 mm). Signals from all three transducers were continuously registered with an ink jet recorder (Siemens Oscillomink).

Mechanical analysis

The test equipment, described above, is shown schematically in Figure 1, where also an x-y-coordinate system is introduced. The arrangement enables a two-dimensional analysis of the system.

The coordinates of the center of gravity (C.G.) of the human body are x, y, with the steady-state or mean value position indicated by the subscript o, i.e. x_o, y_o. Here it must be pointed out that the center of gravity is not a fixed point (as by a rigid body), but mathematically defined in the usual way, and thus subjected to change, when any joint of the body is moved.

The force transducer is electrically calibrated in such a way that the influence of the lever weight is eliminated.

If the center of gravity of the human body is moved, the body must be subjected to external forces. A dynamical problem of motion may be analysed by means of statical methods, if the so-called d'Alembert forces are used, here introduced as $m\ddot{x}$ and $m\ddot{y}$ (the influence of rotation in the x-y-plane is omitted here, thus $J\ddot{\varphi} = O$).

Moment equilibrium (around the edge) gives then:

$$Fl + m\ddot{x}y = m(g + \ddot{y})x, \qquad \text{or}$$

$$F = \frac{mgx_o}{l} + \frac{mg\Delta x}{l} + \frac{m\ddot{y}x}{l} - \frac{m\ddot{x}y}{l} \qquad (1)$$

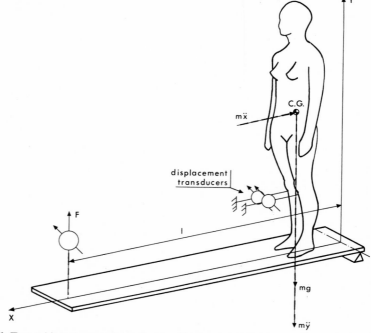

Fig. 1. Test subject shown schematically with the coordinate system for the mathematical analysis indicated.

It is seen from Eq. 1 that it is impossible to evaluate explicitly the displacement of the center of gravity in the forward direction, Δx.

With some special assumptions a solution may be obtained. These assumptions are, for a harmonic motion only in the x direction:

$$x = x_o + \Delta x = x_o + (\Delta x)_{max} \sin\omega t$$

$$y = y_o = \text{const.} \tag{2}$$

The displacement of the center of gravity is then:

$$\Delta x = \frac{Fl - mgx_o}{m(g + \omega^2 y_o)} \tag{3}$$

If the inertial influence were negligible when determining the displacement of the center of gravity, then the following is required:

$$\omega^2 y_o << g$$

If, however, e.g. a 10% error is accepted, in this case the harmonic frequency may be up to 0.5 cps.

Results

The ankle joints were found to move synchronously mutually and with the centre of gravity. The movements seemed to be augmented when the test subject was blindfolded. The motion of the ankle joint displayed low frequency oscillations about 1.5 cps with an amplitude of about 0.02 rad. A recording is shown in Figure 2.

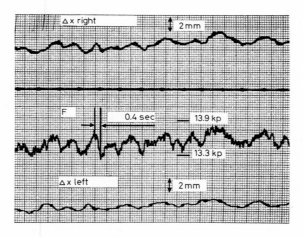

Fig. 2. A recording showing from the top: the movements of the right leg, a blank trace, the alterations of the force and the movements of the left leg.

The force recordings displayed the same low frequency oscillations but also high frequency disturbances superposed. These were notably influenced by environmental events.

Conclusions

1. This commonly used static method to measure the motion of the body's centre of gravity was analysed and, due to the inertial phenomena, failed to give quantitative results with reasonable accuracy. It was shown above that an oscillation of 0.5 cps gives an error of

more than 10%. Here peak to peak time on the load curve was at times 0.4 s, which gives the inertial phenomena a very dominating effect.

2. These experiments failed to confirm the high frequency motion at the ankle joint described by others. The same type of high frequency phenomena was, however, found in our load recordings. Therefore, we believe that this phenomenon has rather a mechanical than a biological cause, such as e.g. resonance somewhere in the system.

References

1. ÅKERBLOM, B.: Standing and sitting posture (Nordiska Bokhandeln, Stockholm 1948).
1.a BOMAN, K. and JALAVISTO, E.: Standing steadiness in old and young persons. Ann. Med. exp. Fenn. *31:* 447–455 (1953).
2. HELLEBRANDT, F.A. and BRAUN, G.L.: The influence of sex and age on the postural sway of man. Amer. J. phys. Anthropol. *24:* 347–360 (1939).
3. JONES, F.P.; HANSON, J.A.; MILLER, J.F. and BOSSOM, J.: Quantitative analysis of abnormal movement: the sit-to-stand pattern. Amer. J. phys. Med. *42:* 208–218 (1963).
4. JONSSON, B. and SYNNERSTAD, B.: Electromyographic studies of muscle function in standing. Acta morph. neerl. scand. *6:* 361–370 (1966).
5. KELSO, L.E.A. and HELLEBRANDT, F.A.: Devices for the study of two plane shifts in the center of gravity of a swaying body. Science *86:* 451–452 (1937).
6. KELTON, I.W. and WRIGHT, R.D.: The mechanism of easy standing by man. Austr. J. exp. Biol. med. Sci. *27:* 505–515 (1949).
7. MIKULINSKII, A.M.; SAMOILOV, V.I. and GRITSEVSKII, M.A.: K metodike izučenia ustoičiosti prjamostojanija čeloveka. Gig. tr. prof. zabol. *7:* 51–53 (1964).
8. MILES, W.R.: Static equilibrium. Methods med. Res., vol. 3, pp. 157–165 (Year Book, Chicago 1950).
9. NILSSON, O.: High frequency postural movements in man. Acta morph. neerl. scand. *6:* 9–16 (1964).
10. SHELDON, J.H.: The effect of age on the control of sway. Geront. clin., Basel *5:* 129–138 (1963).
11. SMITH, J.W.: The forces operating at the human ankle joint during standing. J. Anat., Lond. *91:* 545–564 (1957).
12. THOMAS, D.P. and WHITNEY, R.J.: Postural movements during normal standing in man. J. Anat., Lond. *93:* 524–539 (1959).
13. WHITNEY, R.J.: Mechanics of normal muscular activity. Nature, Lond. *181:* 942–944 (1958).

Author's address: A. VIIDIK, M.D., Department of Human Anatomy, University of Gothenburg. M. MÄGI, D. Eng., Department of Mechanical Engineering, Chalmers Institute of Technology, *Gothenburg* (Sweden).

Biomechanics I, 1st Int. Seminar Zurich 1967
pp. 225–227 (Karger, Basel/New York 1968)

Abteilung Biomechanik der Fakultät für Leibeserziehung und Sport der
Karls-Universität, Prag

Die geometrische Disponibilität und die Kräfte, die im Kniegelenk bei statischer Extension wirksam werden

V. Karas, S. Otáhal und P. Sušanka

Die in eine Ebene verlegte geometrische und kinematische Analyse von 20 von medialer Seite aufgenommenen Röntgenaufnahmen des unbelasteten Kniegelenkes von vier Versuchspersonen zeigte, daß in den Flexionen $\alpha = 60°$ bis $160°$ die Tibia gegenüber dem Femur praktisch nur eine Gleitbewegung ausführt. Die Bewegung der Tibia, in der Ebene von vorne nach hinten beobachtet, kann man dann als Rotation um den Pol P_i (momentaner Rotationsmittelpunkte) abschätzen (Steindler). Diese Rotationsmittelpunkte füllen eine gewisse Evolute aus, die als Durchschnitt der Evoluten der lateralen und medialen Kondylen des Femurs gegeben ist.

Bei Anwendung der geometrischen Parameter, die die notwendigen Elemente der Formgestaltung des Knies in rechts-links Projektion ausdrücken (Abb. 1), werden die grundsätzlichen Kraftverhältnisse im Kniegelenk bei statischer und quasistatischer Extension analytisch gelöst. Die Größe der Extensionsmuskelkraft, die zum Gleichgewicht im Kniegelenk notwendig ist, ist die Funktion der Größe des Belastungsmomentes und der senkrechten Entfernung des ligamentum patellae vom P_i der Tibia, $F \cdot h + G \cdot r \cdot \cos \alpha = 0$. Das Maximum der Muskelkraft offenbart sich in der Flexion $\alpha = 140°$ bis $150°$, das Minimum in der Flexion $\alpha = 70°$ bis $80°$. Die Senkung der Muskelkraft vom maximalen Wert zum minimalen beträgt ca. 60% bis 70% des Wertes der maximalen Kraft.

Die Messung der integrierten elektrischen Aktivität des m. rectus femoris durch drei Paare bipolarer Ableitungen zeigte, daß die elektrische Spannung U (μV) an den Ableitungen bei verschiedenen Winkeln der Flexion linear mit der Größe der Belastungskraft steigt (Bigland et al., 1953) (Abb. 2).

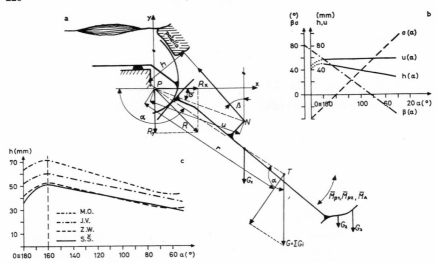

Abb. 1. a) Schematische Darstellung der statischen Verhältnisse im Kniegelenk und deren geometrische Parameter. b) Abhängigkeit der geometrischen Parameter u, h, β, σ vom Flexionswinkel α. c) Funktionsverlauf des Hebelarmes h der resultierenden Muskelkraft F für verschiedene Flexionswinkel α.

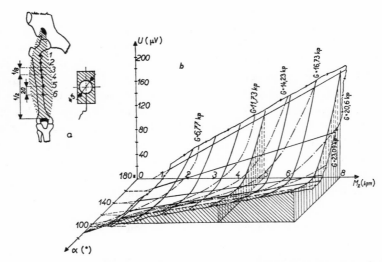

Abb. 2. a) Ausmaß der angewandten Elektroden und ihre Plazierung am m. rectus femoris. b) Abhängigkeit der elektrischen Aktivität U des m. rectus femoris vom Belastungsmoment M_z (Widerstand gegen jede Kniestreckung) und vom Winkel α.

Mit Hilfe des Zahlenwertes h, welcher mit der Transferierungszahl γ identisch ist und deren Wert von den geometrischen Eigenschaften des Knies abhängig ist, kann man die geometrische Disponibilität für die gegebene bestimmte Flexion bestimmen. Auf Grund des Transferierungsverhältnisses

$$\Gamma = \frac{1}{\alpha_2 - \alpha_1} \int\limits_{\alpha_1}^{\alpha_2} \gamma\,(\alpha)\,d\,\alpha$$

ist es möglich, die Disponibilität des Knies nach Bedürfnis zusammenfassend für den gesamten Bewegungsbereich, oder für dessen bestimmte Intervalle, zu testen.

Den entscheidenden Einfluß auf die Größe des Transferierungsverhältnisses hat nicht die Robustheit der artikulierenden Knochen, sondern die weitläufigen geometrischen Zusammenhänge des Kniegelenkes.

Literatur

BIGLAND, B.; LIPPOLD, O.C.J. and WRENCH, A.: The electrical activity in isotonic contractions of human calf muscle. J. Physiol., Lond., *120:* 40–41 (1953).
STEINDLER, A.: Kinesiology of the human body. Thomas, Springfield, Ill. (19..).
Adresse des Autor's: V. KARAS, S. OTÁHAL, P. SUŠANKA, FTVS UK, Ujezd 450, *Praha* I (CSSR).

Biomechanics I, 1st Int. Seminar Zurich 1967
pp. 228–237 (Karger, Basel/New York 1968)

Department of Orthopaedic Surgery, School of Medicine, Tokushima University,
Tokushima

Statico-dynamic Analysis of Movement of the Knee

N. Shinno

The knee joint is situated in the middle of the lower extremity and it
is characterized by a high degree of stability and a wide range of movement while bearing body weight. It is made up of two joints, and these
articular surfaces are not in any conformity with each other. The
stability of the knee joint during its movement is maintained chiefly by
dynamic action of the muscles around the joint. The quadriceps muscle
with the patella is a powerful dynamic stabilizer, and the menisci and
ligaments, collateral and cruciate, play a role as static stabilizers.

Femoro-patellar Joint

The modus of movement of the knee joint was radiocinematographi-
cally analysed. Each point on the patella moves respectively on a
circular track. The nearer the point is to the patellar apex, the longer
is its excursion, and the greater is the radius of its locus (Fig. 1). This
movement of the knee joint is a rolling from full extension to 80 degrees
of flexion, sliding between 80 and 60 degrees. And finally, the full
flexion is accomplished by a rolling movement again (Fig. 2).

For that reason, the patella moves in combined rotation and revo-
lution.

The patella can be compared to something added to one side of the
trochlea. By adding the patella, the extending moment of this side
increases. That is, the existence of the patella increases the extending
moment in the initial movement of the knee by holding the patellar
tendon away from the axis (Fig. 3).

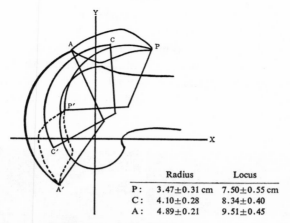

	Radius	Locus
P:	3.47±0.31 cm	7.50±0.55 cm
C:	4.10±0.28	8.34±0.40
A:	4.89±0.21	9.51±0.45

Fig. 1. The movement of each point on the patella.

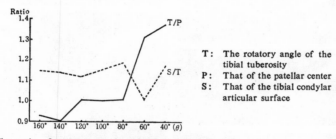

T: The rotatory angle of the tibial tuberosity
P: That of the patellar center
S: That of the tibial condylar articular surface

Fig. 2. The ratio of rotatory angles of the patella and tibia.

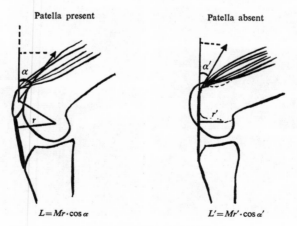

Patella present   Patella absent

$L = Mr \cdot \cos \alpha$ $L' = Mr' \cdot \cos \alpha'$

Fig. 3. The extending moment in the patella present or absent.

Slit Ray Cinematography (Fig. 4)

By slit ray cinematography, the form of the articular surfaces of the femoral condyles was analysed. Frontally, the breadth and curvature were the same in the lateral and medial condyles. But, the angle of inclination of the lateral was larger than the medial. The lateral condyle is smaller than the medial.

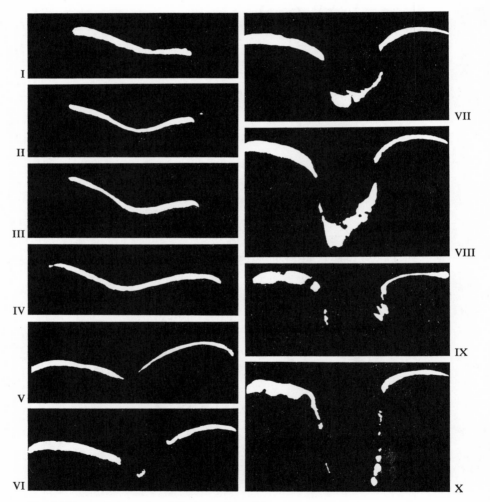

Fig. 4. Slit-ray photographs of the femoral condyles.

Screwing-home

A two-wheeled vehicle of unequal size doesn't go forward in a straight line. The rotation followed by flexion and extension of the knee causes torsion of the cruciate ligaments. Therefore, at the final of the extension of the knee, 'screwing home' takes place as shown in Figure 4. Just like screwing the locking key of a window. This mechanism is a stabilizing function of the knee fully extended.

At the straight position of the knee, the patella cannot be fixed by the femoro-patellar articular surfaces. On a slight flexion of the knee, it is caught by the femoral condyles. In more than 90 degrees of flexion,

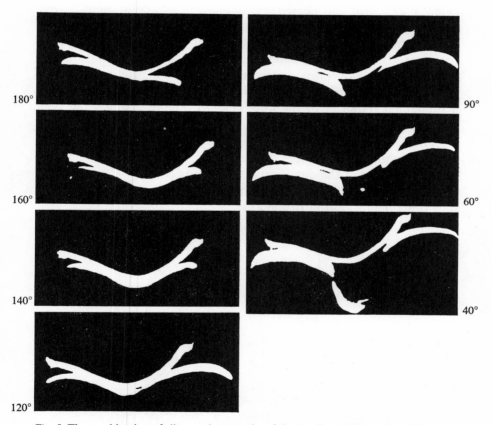

Fig. 5. The combination of slit-ray photographs of the patella and femoral condyles.

the central portion of the patella gets into the intercondylar groove of the femur (Fig. 5).

Statico-dynamic Relation Standing on one Leg

The statico-dynamic relation of the knee in a half-sitting posture, standing on one leg is considered in Figure 6 which shows the oppressing power against the patella by body weight, and the oppressing power against the patella by the quadriceps muscle power. In proportion as the knee is flexed, the oppressing power against the patella by body weight becomes greater. The oppressing power against the patella by the quadriceps muscle power also increases. To about 60 degrees of flexion, these two oppressing powers keep an equilibrium (Fig. 7). But near full flexion the oppressing power by body weight exceeds that of the muscle power. In this part, support of the knee is performed by the integrating power produced by soft tissues around the knee. The acting direction of the oppressing power against the patella during movement concentrates upon the neighbourhood of the intercondylar groove of the femur, so that it can play effectively as a functional stabilizer of the knee (Fig. 8). Figure 9 shows the same thing in profile.

The functions of the patella can be summarized as follows;
1. a protector of the knee,
2. a transmitter of the quadriceps muscle power,
3. an amplifier of the extending moment,
4. a functional stabilizer of the knee.

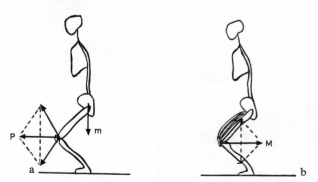

Fig. 6. a) Oppressing power against the patella by body weight. b) Oppressing power against the patella by the quadriceps muscle power.

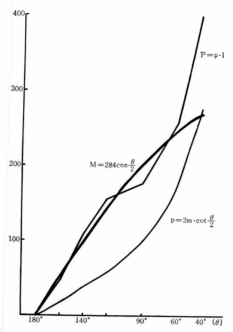

Fig. 7. The oppressing power against the patella by the body weight and muscle power standing on one leg.

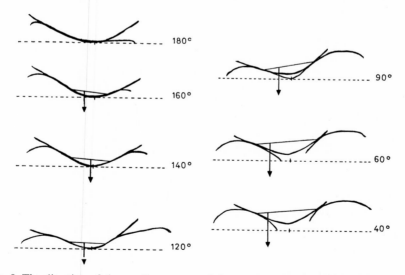

Fig. 8. The direction of the resultant power of the oppressing power against the patella.

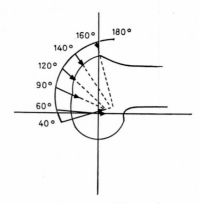

Fig. 9. The action direction of the oppressing power against the patella in profile.

Analysis of the Quadriceps Muscle Power

By applying electromyography to measure the muscle power, the action potential of the quadriceps muscle was picked up by surface electrodes. The muscle power of the rectus femoris, vastus lateralis and medialis in the pulling movement of the patella was measured. The proportion of each muscle power in pulling the patella is diagrammatically shown by the fan-shaped graph (Fig. 10). Both vastus muscles play a more important role than the rectus muscle.

Fig. 10. The proportion of each muscle power in pulling the patella.

Femoro-tibial Joint

The menisci are interposed between these articular surfaces. The power acting between the femoral and tibial condyles are divided into two powers, one is the oppressing power on the tibial surfaces and the other is the gliding power on them. Over 90 degrees, the oppressing power acts in the opposite direction (Fig. 11). In proportion to flexion of the

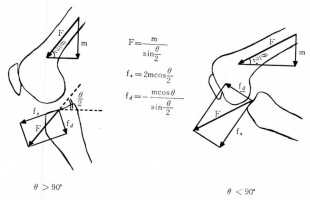

Fig. 11. The relation between the oppressing power of the menisci and flexion angle of the knee.

knee, the gliding power on the tibial surfaces becomes smaller, and over 90 degrees, this power becomes negative. This means that both articular surfaces are forced apart (Fig. 12). It is a function of the quadriceps muscle power acting through the patella that prevents the shearing force on these articular surfaces. The stability of the knee in the semi-flexed position depends mostly upon the muscle power of the quadriceps acting through the patella.

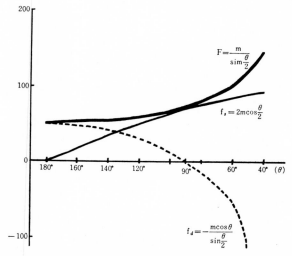

Fig. 12. The relation between the oppressing power of the menisci and flexion angle of the knee.

On ascending and descending stairs, the highest degree of function of the knee joint is required. Going up and down common stairs, the knee joint must be flexed to about 90 degrees theoretically. On descending stairs, the knee joint becomes more unstable than on ascending. This fact can be summarized in the following three points;

1. unlocking of the screwing-home mechanism of the knee,
2. relaxed tension of the quadriceps muscle,
3. increased accelerated gravity.

Acknowledgements

The author desires to express his gratefulness to Prof. K. YAMADA for his guidance and for reviewing the manuscript.

References

1. BRANTIGAN, C. and VOSHELL, F.: The mechanics of the ligaments and menisci of the knee joint. J. Bone Jt. Surg. *23:* 44 (1941).
2. BROOKE, R.: The treatment of fractured patella by excision, a study of morphology and function. Brit. J. Surg. *24:* 733 (1937).
3. DEPALMA, A.F. and FLYNN, J.J.: Joint changes following experimental partial and total patellectomy. J. Bone Jt. Surg. *40-A:* 395 (1958).
4. FICK, R.: Handbuch der Anatomie und Mechanik der Gelenke (Fischer, Jena 1911).
5. FLOYD, W.F. and SILVER, P.H.S.: Electromyographic study of standing in man. J. Physiol., Lond. *111:* 5 (1950).
6. *Grant:* Method of Anatomy (Williams & Wilkins, Baltimore 1952).
7. HAXTON, H.: The function of the patella and the effects of its excision. Surg. Gynec. Obstet. *80:* 389 (1945).
8. HELFET, A.J.: Mechanism of derangements of the medial semilunar cartilage and their management. J. Bone Jt. Surg. *41-B:* 319 (1959).
9. KITAMURO, Y. and SHINNO, N.: Functional significance of patella in the movement of the knee (in Japanese). J. jap. orthop. surg. soc. *23:* 1047 (1959).
10. LEWIN, P.: The Knee and Related Structures (Lea & Febiger, Philadelphia 1952).
11. LIBET, B. and FEINSTEIN, B.: Analysis of changes in EMG with changing muscle length. Amer. J. Physiol. *167:* 805 (1951).
12. MARKEE, J.E.: Two-joint muscles of the thigh. J. Bone Jt. Surg. *37-A:* 125 (1955).
13. O'DONOGUE, D.H. and HAYS, M.B.: The patella basic considerations. J. Oklahoma St. med. Ass. *45:* 248 (1952).
14. SHINNO, N.: Statico-dynamic analysis of movement of the knee. Report I: modus of movement of the knee. Tokushima J. exp. Med. *8:* 101 (1961). – Report II: functional significance of the patella in the movement of the knee. Tokushima J. exp. Med. *8:* 112 (1961). – Report III: functional significance of the flexors and extensors of the knee. Tokushima J. exp. Med. *8:* 124 (1961). – Report IV: functional significance of the menisci in the movement of the knee. Tokushima J. exp. Med. *8:* 189 (1961).

15. WATSON-JONES, R.: Fractures and Joint Injuries (Williams and Wilkins, Baltimore 1955).
16. WATSON-JONES, R.: Excision of patella (Correspondence). Brit. med. J. *12:* 195 (1945).
17. WHEATLEY, M.D. and JAHNKE, W.D.: Electromyographic study of the superficial thigh and hip muscles in normal individuals.
18. WIBERG, G.: Roentgenographic and anatomic studies on the femoro-patellar joint. Acta Orthop. scand. *12:* 319 (1941).

Author's address: N. SHINNO, M.D., Department of Orthopedic Surgery, School of Medicine, Tokushima University, *Tokushima* (Japan).

Biomechanics I, 1st Int. Seminar Zurich 1967
pp. 238–240 (Karger, Basel/New York 1968)

Institute of Physical Education, Ghent State University, Ghent

The Measurement of the Pelvic Movements
and its Applications

R. Claeys and E.K. Gomes

Measuring the pelvic inclination relative to the longitudinal axis of the trunk is important in diagnosis and therapy of the postural defects of the spine.

The clinical orthopaedic methods, measuring the degree of retroversion and ante-version of the pelvis [3, 4], are of no value when trying to register these movements during total deplacements of the body.

Nevertheless, the interpretation of the antero-posterior pelvic movements is interesting, when registered simultaneously with an EMG record of the different muscle groups attached to the pelvis. Indeed, the activity of these muscles (the abdominals, the dorsals, the flexors and extensors of the leg etc.) is very important for the mobilisation of the whole body, because of their action on the pelvic movements.

In our laboratory, the mobilisation of the pelvis, during movements of the whole body is registered by means of a small apparatus, fixed with three blades on the posterior part of the sacrum. One of the blades is mobile, for individual adaptation.

For the analysis of slow movements or postures, a plumb-bob makes direct reading possible on a calibrated scale. For normal movements the scale is replaced by a stick, so that, after having filmed the movement, the angle between the apparatus and the longitudinal axis of the body can be measured from a screen picture. The direction and the intensity of the pelvic movements can be derived from the evolution of this angle. The new apparatus has been tested radiologically in two extreme positions of the pelvis, simultaneously with the direct measurement on 14 subjects, males and females.

There was no greater difference than $\frac{1}{2}$ a degree between the direct and the roentgenological measurement. Figure 1 confirms this correlation and shows the good repartition of the values, so that more measurements were unnecessary.

Also 98 maximal antero-posterior movements of the pelvis were measured on 32 subjects, simultaneously with the new apparatus and

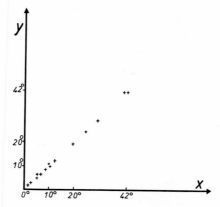

Fig. 1. Measurement of the pelvic mobilisation, correlation between the results of the direct (x) and the roentgenological (y) methods.

with the clinical pelvic inclinometer of Wiles, for determination of the validity of both.

After each measurement the apparatus were replaced.

Results

	$\overline{\text{x}}$	T
Wiles' pelvic inclinometer	20.3	2.6
new one	18.3	2.3

$$r = \frac{\frac{1}{n} E U - \overline{U}.\overline{V}}{\tau U \cdot \tau V} = 0.88$$

The level of significance is 83–92 %. The regression line of the classical apparatus in relation with the new one is $Y = 0.78 + 6.1$.

The t of difference between $\overline{X}$ and $\overline{Y}$ is not significant (Student-Fischer test). However, we observe that the regression line cuts a part of the y-axe above 0 (zero). The sign test shows that the values taken with the classical apparatus are higher than those taken with the new one.

There is a systematic difference of 6 degrees.

No investigation was done to know the cause of this systematical difference, which can be due to methodical reasons. The new apparatus has proved its utility in a EMG study on the dentists' position at

Fig. 2

work. As well in the standing as in the sitting position at work, the forward leaning of the trunk causes a notable bending in the different segments of the spine, without or with only a slight, insignificant anteversion of the pelvis; this finding explains the inactivity of the abdominals in the normal standing and sitting position at work [1]. The apparatus has also been used in the analysis of the kipping movement of the waist in gymnastics (to be published). This movement is realised by a dorsal muscle chain, involving the long dorsals and the extensors of the hip joint. The records of the movements of the pelvis show clearly, in all cases, a large anteversion during the active part of the exercise, due to the predominant action of the long dorsal muscles. The new apparatus has been used in other studies [2] and let predict several applications in the futur.

References

1. CLAEYS, R.: La position de travail du praticien en art dentaire: orthogrammes et étude électromyographique. Rev. belge Méd. Dent.: *6:* 619–624 (1966).
2. CLAEYS, R.; DELBEKE, M.A. et GOMES, E.K.: Etude électromyographique concernant l'utilité de l'appareil Bali dans les maladies professionnelles du praticien en art dentaire. Rev. belge Méd. Dent.: *6:* 625–631 (1966).
3. COLSON, J.H.C.: Postural and relaxation training (William Heinemann, London 1956).
4. WILES, P. and SWEETNAL, R.: Essentials of Orthopaedics, 4th edition. (Churchill, London 1965).

Author's address: R. CLAEYS M.D., and E.K. GOMES, Institute of Physical Education, Ghent State University, *Ghent* (Belgium).

Biomechanics I, 1st Int. Seminar Zurich 1967
pp. 241–244 (Karger, Basel/New York 1968)

Department of Human Anatomy, Medical Faculty, Gothenburg

The Morphological Basis for Studying the Function of the Spine

BO E. INGELMARK

In this short address I shall not go into particulars for it seems to me to be a matter of urgency to present to this group of people interested in biomechanics some basic aspects relevant to our current and future research.

Biomechanics is a discipline in its own right and a fairly young one. A sign of this is that the world total of institutions for and professors of biomechanics is extremely small and as a consequence the training future doctors get in this subject is modest indeed. Nevertheless, biomechanical problems have been dealt with in medical research since time immemorial. Often, too, mechanical factors have been sought when the aetiology of biological phenomena has been considered. Formerly this frequently led to exaggeration of the mechanical aspects because adequate biomechanical knowledge was lacking.

As an object for research, biomechanics is and always will be a subject on the borderline between mechanics and biology. Successful biomechanical work demands a comprehensive knowledge not only of biology, including human biology, but also of mechanics. Ladies and gentlemen, I do not feel I have to apologize, even in this exclusive congregation, when I state my conviction that there exists only very few persons whose training and knowledge adequately cover both these domains. And that situation will undoubtedly persist. For our body knowledge is incessantly growing at an accelerating rate at the same time the intellectual resources of mankind remain on the whole stationary.

Biomechanical research implies that one must strive to make a synthesis of valuable biological and mechanical facts. This requires intimate collaboration between biologists and mechanical scientists. Thus biomechanics is not merely a borderline but also a collaborative discipline.

Those of us who are biologists must in this connection chiefly contribute the following facts about the tissue or organ that is to be studied biomechanically:

1. The gross, microscopic and submicroscopic structure. This means that we must specify the natures, amounts and topography of the components of these invariably polyphase structural materials.

2. We must establish the relationship between structure and function of the object under study. If one fails to take into consideration this relationship and its dependence on nutritional condition, hormonal state, age, and so forth, one will risk analyzing incompatible biological series. Conversely, it is possible by systematically varying the functional state and then analyzing the results mechanically to obtain a wealth of biologically valuable information about the limits within which a living being's mechanical state is susceptible to modification.

3. Functional adaptation is the sum total of new formation and wear. New formation has been studied extensively. Wear, fatigue of the materials and the removal of worn out materials are phenomena which we must clear up from the biomechanical points of view as well.

4. Biological relationships are also intimately associated with genetic factors. These can be analyzed in experimental animals but they are very difficult to get at in human beings. We are of course anything but genetically homogeneous. For what would happen to research if everybody thought alike? Yet genetic uniformity would obviously be an advantage from biomechanical points of view.

Genetically induced changes of form are especially important here. Some are congenital and are then called malformations. Others need not be present at birth but can appear much later in life. In such cases it is often extremely hard to decide whether they are genetic or mechanical. In the human being this question can only be answered by studying large random series.

If biologists supply data meeting the requirements I have just outlined, we would have information suitable for collaboration with our mechanical colleagues. They have to be responsible for the apparatus used for studying the vital material supplied by the biologists. They must also analyze the results mathematically. Then comes intimate collaboration in drawing the correct conclusions.

What I have just said may seem rather obvious. But how often does one not see and carry out studies where sufficient information is lacking about the morphological background, the state of functional adaptation, wear and genetic factors and about how intravital mechanical and biological conditions are maintained?

At the Department of Human Anatomy, Gothenburg, we have for a good many years attempted to conduct our work along these lines. We set out by analyzing the structure and functional adaptability of ligaments, tendons and articular cartilages. Then we went on to study the spine from morphological and biomechanical points of view. All this made it necessary to acquire basic knowledge regarding the components and their development.

Our research team, whose permanent members are *Doctors Jonsson, Lewin, Reichmann, Viidik* and myself, has carried out anatomical, anthropometric, radiographic and histological investigations on, chiefly, the lumbar spine. *Ingelmark and Lewin* have on a large series studied the sites of degenerations, probably due to hyperfunction, and the ages when they appear. The joints of the articular processes have been studied with regard to their structure, topography and radiographic anatomy. These investigations have been parallelled by anthropometric and radiographic examinations on living subjects. In so doing one must make sure that the adopted methods are reliable. Not least, radiographic observations on living subjects have on further scrutiny turned out to be overdiagnosis of degenerative states.

But the mechanical aspects remain inaccessible for study unless one first examines the relevant muscles from both functional and morphological points of view. Hence *Jonsson* is doing an electromyographic investigation. The intention is, with the aid of needle electrodes, to seek to study in detail the several dorsal muscles while the subject performs various movements. *Viidik* has comprehensively analyzed the mechanical properties of ligamentous tissue and its attachment to bone. Everywhere in the locomotive organs the ligaments play a major mechanical part. Therefore, it is essential to acquire considerable fundamental knowledge about them before one can hope to analyze the larger functional units.

It is our considered opinion that we shall not be able to form a reliable picture of what is normal and abnormal with regard to the structure and function of the spine unless we learn more about its postnatal development. To a large extent this remains unknown. Hence *Lewin* and *Reichmann* have assembled a large random series of autopsy specimens from children. For the past year or so this series has been studied with respect to its gross and microscopic morphology and radiology. We hope that this will enable us to form a satisfactory impression of the relationship between mechanical properties and the normal curvatures of the spine, spondylosis, spondylolisthesis, coronar clefts, etc.

The human spine is exceedingly complex. A single institution and one research team can only aspire to deal with a few of its problems. Consequently, it is essential that many research units with biomechanical expertise devote their energies to this cornerstone of our organs of locomotion. But if their findings are to have optimal usefulness to other teams doing similar work, it is essential that the materials and methods are adequate and fully described so that the results obtained become comparable. I sincerely hope that this symposium will provide valuable assistance to this end.

Author's address: Prof. BO E. INGELMARK, Director of the Department of Human Anatomy, Medical Faculty, *Gothenburg* (Sweden).

Biomechanics I, 1st Int. Seminar Zurich 1967
pp. 245–250 (Karger, Basel/New York 1968)

Department of Anatomy, Institute of Sports Medicine, Leipzig

The Three-dimensional Structure of Skeletal-free Muscles as a Basic Principle of Movements
(Considering Genetic, Functional and Structural Relations)

K. Tittel and S. Pieper

Introduction

Powerful aimed movements put a great strain on the efficiency of the active kinetic apparatus so that the very close relations between structure and function of the skeletal muscle are of special importance. In the following we report on our own macro- and microscopic investigations of 'skeletal-free muscle bodies'. They have been systematically dissected into several space dimensions and afterwards again synthetized to obtain a possibly plastic picture of their structure. This principle has already been the basis for several functional-anatomical works, for example, in the investigations of the functional structure of the connective tissue (Benninghoff 1931, Dabelow 1962, Feneis 1935, Heringa 1931, Nagel 1938, Rehn 1931), the bone (Benninghoff 1931, 1931, 1931, Gebhardt 1903, 1906, 1910, 1910, Knese 1956, 1956, 1958, Kummer 1959, 1959, Pauwels 1949/50, 1949/50, 1950, 1951, 1951, 1955, 1958, 1959, 1960), the tendon-ligamentous apparatus (Ploetz 1937, 1938, Rollhäuser 1952, 1953, 1954), the skeletal muscles (Rohen 1954, Schultze 1912, Schwarzacher 1960, 1960, 1960), the heart musculature (Benninghoff 1929, 1933, Feneis 1935), the blood and lymphatic vessels (Baum and Thienel 1904, Benninghoff 1928, 1930, Büttner 1962, Fischer 1951, 1959, Fritsche 1952, Gänshirt 1951, Goerttler 1951, 1953, Häussler 1933, v. Hayek 1935, Horst-mann 1945, 1951, v. Kügelgen 1951, Puff 1960, Schultze-Jena 1939), the uvula (Graf 1949/50), the oesophagus (Nagel 1938), the intestine coat (Goerttler 1931, 1932, 1951), the spleen capsule (Hofmann 1951), the renal fat (Niessing 1935), the ureter (Beck 1955), the mamma and mammilla (Dabelow 1941, 1957, Nagel 1942), the uterus (Goertt-ler 1929, 1931), the plica lata uteri (Petry 1942), the vagina (Schreiber and Born 1943), the ductus deferens (Goerttler 1934), and the tunica dartos (Nagel 1939). From these mostly hollow muscle organs, which are characterized by a screw-like structure of the muscular and connective tissue fascicles as well as by 'transpositional layers' from loose connective tissue, the massive, free movable skeletal muscle bodies differ very essentially.

To them belong, among others, the tongue of the mammalia (A. Dabelow 1951, R. Dabelow 1951, Dontenwill 1949, Lubosch 1931, Nussbaum and Markowski 1896, 1897, v. Schumacher 1927, Tittel 1962, 1963, 1964, Tokarski 1904), the arm of the cuttle-fish with the suckers (Tittel 1962, 1965), and the snail foot (Schmidt 1965). We refer to two of these examples and will prove in what nearly ideal form the suitably con-structed muscle body offers optimal conditions for the movements and for the energy with which the movements can be made.

Material and Methodology

For analyzing the spacial and also functional relations of individual tissue formations, the investigated tongues of the mammalia and arms of the cuttle-fish with the suckers (of the species eledone cirrhosa) were prepared in three dimensions by 50–300 μ thick frozen serial sections. The staining was done with alauncarmin, azan, resorcinfuchsin and orcein; unstained serial sections were investigated in polarized light. All photographs were made on highly orthochromatic autolithe plates (Fa. Wolfen) with the 'Panphot' (Fa. Leitz, Wetzlar).

Findings of the Macro- and Microscopic Investigations

The great active deformability of the intrinsic musculature of the *tongue mammalia* to which the authors refer in the following, derives from the plastic, three-dimensional structure of longitudinal, transversal and vertical muscle bundles and the connective tissue elements belonging to them as a 'functional system' as used by BENNINGHOFF. The *longitudinal* fibres which go parallel to the surface over only a short distance, deriving aborally from the tongue aponeurosis and in continuation orally again connecting with the aponeurosis, form a 'muscle coat' around the central tongue body, padding the epithelium and connective tissue cover and connecting all parts of the surface and base of the tongue by short or medium-long tracts which equally shorten the tongue without wrinkling it. The strong *transversal* muscle bundles, rich in sarcoplasm, form an artistic-like system of ramifications and decussations. Here always one transverse bundle—after splitting up—of one side of the tongue body combines with similarly constructed parts of the transversal muscle fibres located in the same layer of the other side. Thus, finally, an accordeon-like structure arises, composed of several quadratic and rhombic grids. The gaps in this network are filled by vertical or longitudinal muscle bundles. These linkages of the transverse intrinsic musculature of the tongue do not only offer ideal presuppositions for the taking-up of growing organs in the evolution period (which, e.g., is true of the ramifications of the lingual glands in the foetal period, PROBST 1951), but they facilitate also the extension and congestion of the tongue and prevent, moreover, too strong a spreading of the transversal muscle bundles.

The cylindrically formed muscle parts of the *vertical* tongue musculature are characterized by the fact that they are split-up in a pencil-like way closely under the tongue aponeurosis. These very thin ramifications combine with neighbouring column bundles, thus forming a 'reticulated vaulting' or an 'ogival grid' which is formed in three dimensions and goes close to the epithelium (Fig. 1). Part of the vertical muscle fibres even infiltrates the network of the tongue aponeurosis to build up in the subepithelium connective tissue a very fine, again three-dimensional precollagenic fibril net, part of which changes into the connective tissue fibres of the lingual papillas. The deeper function of this structure of the vertical lingual musculature lies in the fact that in the contraction of the fibres the power of this contraction is immediately transferred to a comparatively great surface so that the formation of punctiform retractions or smallest dimples is prevented. The tongue of the mammalia, therefore, with its functional intrinsic musculature represents in an ideal form the basic principle of a finely articulated skeletal-free muscle body, an architecture from which it derives its active deformability and considerable strength. Nevertheless, we must clarify and this should refer to KANT's state-

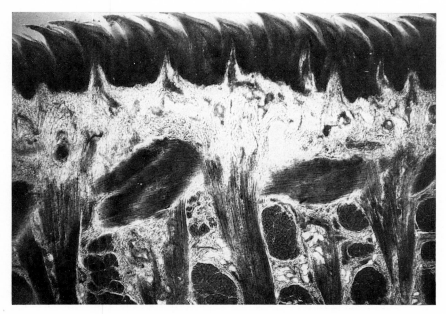

Fig. 1. Cross-section of the tongue back of a mammalian: three-dimensional arrangement of the longitudinal transversal and vertical muscle bundles; the last ones split up in pencil-like fashion and penetrate to the subepithelial connective tissue—interspersing at many places the aponeurosis linguae. Frozen section, 100 μ, Haemalaun-Eosin, 22 : 1.

ment in his 'Kritik der Urteilskraft' (Critique of the Aesthetic Faculties), which says that only some parts of our body (such as, e.g., the connective and bony tissues) can be understood exclusively on the basis of the laws of mechanics—how far the stimuli arising during strain of the mammalia tongue are at the same time differentiating factors. Our own biogenetic investigations (which were also studied by ROUX and MURRAY) of embryonic (52 mm distance vertex—coccyx) and foetal (118 mm distance vertex—coccyx) tongues clearly reveal that already in these early periods of evolution the musculature of the mammalia tongue shows a three-dimensional structure. Even such details as the pencil-like splitting-up of the vertical muscle elements can be clearly seen in the foetus. Also considering that, beginning with the 2nd month, the embryo is swallowing (CLARA 1938), we can see in these facts, reported about the mammalia tongue, a changing of the 'genetic growth structure' to the 'functional structure' following mostly the laws of mechanics as was also observed by DABELOW, CARVALHO and STOFFT (1966) for the reconstruction of the interior structure of vertebral bodies and their ligamentous apparatus of new born up to adult persons.

The following question is of special interest: how far can we see this functional system of the intrinsic musculature of the mammalia tongues in organs of other species which are characterized by a special wide scope of movements? Therefore we selected from the highest developed class of molluscs–the *cephalopodes* or *'cuttle-fishes'*—the eledone cirrhosa common in the Mediterranean Sea and East Atlantic, to investigate the structure of the extraordinary movable and musculous head arms which serve for the taking-up of food and the creeping movements, and to investigate the structure of the suckers which are used like grasping fingers. After a first survey about the structure of the different muscle layers of the head arm (strong intrinsic and extrinsic longitudinal musculature and intrinsic and extrinsic circular musculature) the question arises as to how these elements of the active kinetic apparatus are kept together to guarantee the permanent form and stability of the head arm, because there are no supporting substances in the sense of a 'connective tissue skeleton'. Instead of them there are radial muscle bundles (comparable with the vertical fibres in the tongue) which go through all longitudinal and circular muscle parts of the arm. Here they do not only establish a very close contact with the musculature surrounding the nervous axis-medullary tract (by splitting-up palm branch-like in the direction of the arm's centre; in the gaps of each palm branch there are muscle fibres in other directions thus creating a broad, stabile muscle network), but moreover, the radial muscle bundles are split-up in the intrinsic circular arm musculature into fibre tractus which at the end of their ramifications partly combine with neighbouring muscle bundles, thus creating big scissor grids. The reconverged bundles of the radial musculature —after having passed the extrinsic longitudinal musculature—are split up in pencil or screen-like fashion. There the final fibres, going into the connective tissue of the subepithelium, interlace in the form of three-dimensional musculous reticular vaults with tracts of the extrinsic circular musculature of the head arm.

The structure of the globular thick suckers and of their muscular connections with the corresponding head arm is also interesting. We can see in the eledone cirrhosa muscle tracts on the surface, deriving from the arm fascia and ending in the sucker body as well as longer transversal muscle tracts connecting the suckers. In addition to this exterior musculature which can move the suckers in medial and lateral as well as in proximal and distal direction, there is an intrinsic musculature of the sucker consisting of circular, radial and screw-like muscle fibres crossing at an obtuse angle. The ruff-like adhesive surface is composed of radial and circular muscle parts. By the mutual work of the extrinsic and intrinsic musculature the sucking chamber can be opened or closed. One can explain the astonishing movements and strong and flexible work of the cuttle-fish arms and their suckers especially with the structural and functional connection of the extrinsic and intrinsic musculature of the suckers. Here we must consider that the extrinsic musculature does not exclusively derive from the sucker aponeurosis but—comparable to the pencil-like splitting-up of the vertical tongue musculature—that a part of their fibres goes through the network of the aponeurosis grid between the radial and circular fibres of the sucker (Fig. 2).

Thus we got acquainted in the cephalopode arm with its suckers with another skeletal-free muscle body where we found again an astonishing similarity to the basic principle of the three-dimensional constructed skeletal musculature with its ogival, quadratic to rhombic scissor grid as well as with the pencil or palm branch-like splitting-up of several muscle parts, as we had already found in the mammalie tongue. Only the close interlacing of the three-dimensional muscle

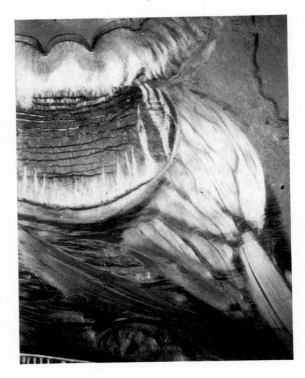

Fig. 2. Longitudinal section of the sucker, and the epi- and hypofasciale muscular system of a cuttle-fish arm (in polarized light): demonstrated are the very strong longitudinal and oblique parts of the extrinsic muscles of the sucker and their close contact with the intrinsic muscles. Undyed frozen section, 200 μ, 15 : 1.

systems to a uniform muscle body guarantees the best possible stability (without using stronger supporting substances) and an optimal flexibility, which are necessary for the implementation of the demands put to the active kinetic apparatus.

References

Full details of the literature mentioned can be obtained from the authors on request.

Authors' address: Prof. Dr. K. TITTEL and Dr. S. PIEPER, Department of Anatomy, Institute of Sports Medicine, *701 Leipzig* (DDR), Jahn-Allee 59.

Biomechanics I, 1st Int. Seminar Zurich 1967
pp. 251–254 (Karger, Basel/New York 1968)

Laboratoire de l'Effort, University of Brussels

Experimental Contribution to the Biomechanical Study of the Femoral Bone

A. Leduc

Introduction

Most former studies concerning the resistance of the femoral bone, particularly those by Fick (1911), Halleman (1935), Kuntscher (1935), Marique (1945), Massa (1957), Hirsch (1960) and Pauwels (1965) used a technique which applied to the investigation of the resistance of materials. We shall report on an original method of investigation.

We shall examine the behaviour of the femoral bone, holding up loads varying between 0 and 250 kg. We shall then see the influence of the muscular action on the different loads and the distortions we have defined.

A. The First Part of the Work is Based on Photoelasticity

Definition and Techniques

Photoelasticity deals with the effects of stress on the light which goes through the transparent elements. It is also possible to deduce the strains from the optical effects.

When varnish has been put on the bone, it is subjected to stresses which are transmitted to the varnish, which becomes birefringent. The degree of this birefringence immediately gives the value of the principal strain difference, in each of the spots on the bone.

Results

The strains first appear at the upper curve of the neck, at the junction between neck and head. It is at this level that the fracture must begin (Fig. 1).

The inspection of the isoclinic lines shows that the strains are spread in the shape of a horse tail from the head to the neck, and that they

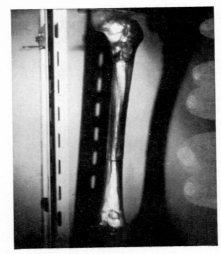

Fig. 1. The aspect of the isochromatic fringes.

go in a parallel direction with the diaphysis. The comparative examination of the autopsy specimen and that of the artificial femoral bone in araldite show great differences in the propagation of the strains. These experiments caused us to write on the methods which test models of bones, made in homogeneous materials.

B. The Second Part Tests of Behaviour of the Femoral Bone by Means of Stress Gauges

On the basis of information provided by photoelastic study we have put 13 crowns of gauges along the length of the femoral bone (108

Fig. 2. The shaded part is compressed, the other one put in traction.

Fig. 3. Influence of the 'gracilis'. The shifting of the neutral lines shows a distortion of the neutral surface. Everything takes place as if the gracilis stressed the relative movement of both femoral extremities in relation to each other.

Fig. 4. Influence of the tensor fascia lata. The direction of the shifting of the neutral lines is this time the same for both halves of the bone. So the antagonism of the muscular intervention is to be found in the distribution of the distortions of the proximal half of the femoral bone. We have also examined the influence of the simultaneous actions of the gracilis and the tensor (Fig. 5).

Fig. 5. Simultaneous influence of both tensors. The inversion which took place under the influence of the gracilis working alone has been lessened by the action of the tensor fascia lata.

Charge poids de 0 à 250 kg

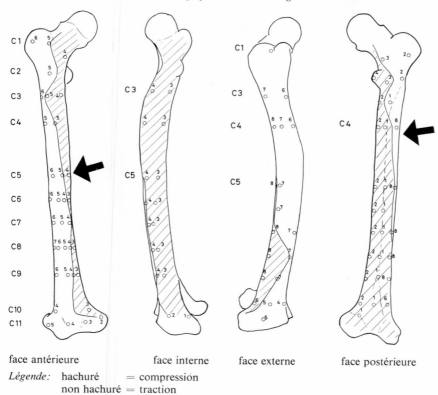

face antérieure   face interne   face externe   face postérieure

Légende: hachuré   = compression
             non hachuré = traction

Fig. 2

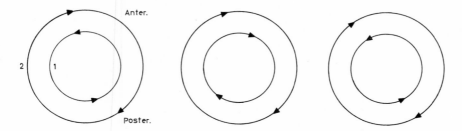

1 Projection of the proximal half of the femoral bone
2 Projection of the distal half of the femoral bone

Fig. 3. Tensor TI   *Fig. 4.* Tensor T2   *Fig. 5.* Tensor TI-T2

gauges). The gauges which have been placed according to the stress direction give the values of the distortion at any moment.

The imposed loads varied between 0 and 250 kg. Figure 2 shows the directions of the neutral lines which join the places without distortion.

C. The Part Estimates the Importance of the Action of Some Muscles

We have chosen to study the action of the gracilis (TI) and the tensor facia lata (T2), two antagonistic muscles without attachment to the femoral bone (Figs. 3 and 4).

Author's address: ALBERT LEDUC, M.D., Laboratoire de l'Effort, University of Brussels, *Brussels* (Belgium).

Biomechanics I, 1st Int. Seminar Zurich 1967
pp. 255–257 (Karger, Basel/New York 1968)

Laboratory of Pathophysiology of the Nervous System and Brain Research Unit
(Professor J.E. Desmedt) University of Brussels, Brussels

Effect of Temperature on Muscle Potentiation in Man

K. Hainaut

Studies on contraction kinetics in man are still rather scarce and recent work has emphasized the interest of staircase potentiation and depression as a dynamic test in muscular diseases (Desmedt, Borenstein, Hainaut and Emeryk, 1966). Control studies on normal man are thus needed to define the parameters of this test which is carried out as follows. Supramaximal electric pulses of 50μsec duration are delivered to the ulnar nerve at the wrist while the electric composed potential of the adductor pollicis muscle (Fig. 1, EMG), the isometric myogram (MG) and its first derivative (1st deriv.) displayed on cathode ray oscilloscopes are recorded simultaneously on a 35 mm film. Details of the technique can be found elsewhere (Desmedt, 1958). When a series of 360 shocks is delivered to the nerve at the rate of 2 per second, the mechanical response first decreases progressively for the first 10–20 shocks and thereafter increases up to 120–160% of the initial response (Fig. 1, D). The latter potentiation is accompanied by a reduction in contraction time and by a marked increase of the first differential (Fig. 1, C) but there is no significant change in the electrical response.

Discussion of possible mechanisms involved in the mechanical phenomenon can be found in our first publication (Desmedt and Hainaut, 1967).

The above sequence of events is characteristic of all normal muscles when their temperature measured by a thermistor needle inserted in the muscle is 37–38 °C. When the hand is locally cooled by application of ice bags, marked changes are seen in the responses to a single shock. The distal latency and duration of the electric response increase (Fig. 2, A). The twitch tension and its first differential decrease while contraction time increases.

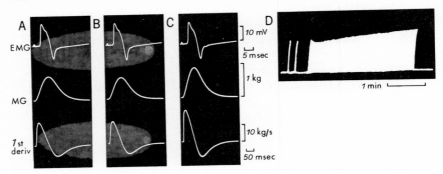

Fig. 1. Normal subject, intramuscular temperature 36.5 °C. A–C, cathode-ray oscillograms of muscle responses elicited by 1st (A), 15th (B) and 360th (C) indirect shock of a series at 2/sec. (D) polygraph record at a slow speed of the isometric myogram during the series.

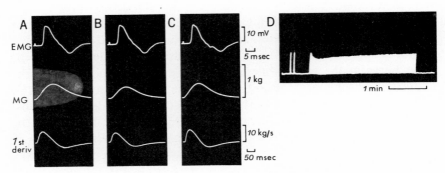

Fig. 2. Same subject and same experiment, but with the hand cooled so as to achieve a local intramuscular temperature of 28 °C.

When a series of shocks at 2 per second is delivered to the nerve in the cooled hand, the succession of mechanical responses shows rather marked staircase depression with little subsequent potentiation (Fig. 2, D). At the end of the series the twitch tension has not recovered to its initial value (Fig. 2, C) while contraction time is markedly reduced and the first differential shows little or no increase. These changes, which are considered to involve the mechanical process, are reversible when the hand is warmed and brought back to normal temperature.

These results emphasize the muscle temperature as an initial parameter of twitch kinetics and potentiation. This parameter was carefully considered in studies on patients with muscular diseases in whom other anomalies of muscle contraction potentiation can occur in spite of normal muscle temperature (Desmedt, Borenstein, Hainaut and Emeryk, 1966).

References

Desmedt, J.E.: Méthodes d'étude de la fonction neuromusculaire chez l'homme. Myogramme isométrique, électromyogramme d'excitation et topographie de l'innervation terminale. Acta neurol. belg. *58:* 997–1017 (1958).

Desmedt, J.E.; Borenstein, S.; Hainaut, K. et Mme Emeryk, B.: Etude de l'activité contractile dans les maladies musculaires: modifications de la secousse isométrique au cours de la stimulation électrique du nerf moteur à cadence basse. Rev. neurol. *115:* 997–1002 (1966).

Desmedt, J.E. et Hainaut, K.: Modifications des propriétés contractiles du muscle strié au cours de la stimulation électrique répétée de son nerf moteur chez l'homme normal. C. R. Acad. Sci. *264,* 2: 363–366 (1967).

Author's address: K. Hainaut M.D., Laboratory of Pathophysiology of the Nervous System and Brain Research Unit, University of Brussels, 115, boulevard de Waterloo, *Brussels 1* (Belgium).

VII. Applied Biomechanics in Work

Biomechanics I, 1st Int. Seminar Zurich 1967
pp. 258–263 (Karger, Basel/New York 1968)

Aus dem Max-Planck-Institut für Arbeitsphysiologie, Dortmund

Kinetische Probleme beim Führen von Kraftfahrzeugen

VON R.R. COERMANN

Der Mensch, der ein Fahrzeug führt, ist ein Teil eines komplexen Regelsystems, in dem der Mensch zwar das scheinbar flexibelste aber auch entscheidendste Regelglied darstellt. Bei kurzen Fahrstrecken, die mit mäßiger Geschwindigkeit und ohne unerwartete Ereignisse durchfahren werden, kann der Mensch in der Regel die Anforderungen, die an ihn gestellt werden, auch dann noch erfüllen, wenn das Fahrzeug seinen physiologischen und psychologischen Fähigkeiten nur schlecht angepaßt ist. Bei längeren Fahrstrecken, insbesondere dann, wenn diese mit hohen Durchschnittsgeschwindigkeiten gefahren werden, kommt es häufig zur Überlastung bestimmter Körperfunktionen, so daß frühzeitig Ermüdung auftritt oder sogar körperliche Schädigungen entstehen. Das führt in häufigen Fällen in höchsten Gefahrenmomenten zu Fehlreaktionen des Menschen und damit nicht selten zu Unfällen.

In Abbildung 1 ist der psycho-physische Regelkreis beim Führen von Fahrzeugen schematisch dargestellt. Wir müssen in einem solchen Regelkreis unterscheiden zwischen den aus der Außenwelt ‚exogen‘ aufgenommenen Informationen und der größtenteils unbewußten Verarbeitung dieser Informationen. Die Verarbeitung geschieht in erster Linie durch Vergleich mit Erfahrungsgut, das größtenteils aus unseren alltäglichen Erfahrungen stammt und nur zum kleineren Teil aus der Fahrschulung und der Fahrpraxis. Als Resultat dieses Vergleiches entsteht die Entschlußfassung, die zur motorischen Reaktion führt. Über die Wirkungswahrnehmung und den Vergleich des Ist- mit dem Soll-Zustand kommt die ‚endogene‘ Information wieder zum Fahrer zurück. Werden dagegen vom Fahrer Reaktionen verlangt, die mit dem tief eingeprägten Erfahrungsgut nicht übereinstimmen, so verschiebt sich ein großer Teil des Regelkreises in das Bewußtsein, wodurch nicht

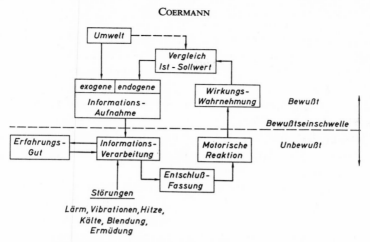

Abb. 1. Psycho-physischer Regelkreis beim Führen von Fahrzeugen

nur die Reaktionszeit, sondern besonders auch die Reaktionsunsicherheit ansteigt. Wichtig ist auch, daß die vom Menschen geforderten psychomotorischen Reaktionen innerhalb seines alltäglich gewohnten Bewegungsraumes bleiben und in ihrer Richtung sinnfällig sind. Von großer Bedeutung ist dabei, daß zur Zeit der Wahrnehmung und Entschlußfassung keine äußeren, störenden Einflüsse auf den Menschen einwirken und die benötigten Muskelgruppen nicht ermüdet sind.

Als wichtigste Forderung für den Arbeitsplatz ‚Fahrerraum' müssen wir fordern, daß er den anthropometrischen Dimensionen des menschlichen Körpers angepaßt ist. Die den heutigen menschlichen Körpermaßen angepaßten optimalen Abmessungen von Fahrerräumen wurden in letzter Zeit von meinem Mitarbeiter Dr. KROEMER und mir mehrfach veröffentlicht. Ich möchte daher zu diesem Punkt nur auf das Problem der Akzeleration aufmerksam machen. Zwischen 20jährigen und 60jährigen Menschen besteht heute ein mittlerer Größenunterschied von ca. 5 cm. Wir rechnen augenblicklich mit einem durchschnittlichen Größenzuwachs von ungefähr 1 cm pro Dekade. Da alle Körpermaße, wie Armlänge und Beinlänge von der Körpergröße abhängig sind, muß bei der Konstruktion von Fahrzeugen dieser Größenzuwachs in Rechnung gestellt werden.

Die Anordnung von Betätigungsteilen im Fahrerraum muß dem Greifraum des Menschen angepaßt sein. Alle häufig gebrauchten Betätigungsteile sollten in dem Bereich zwischen kleinem Greifraum und physiologisch maximalem Greifraum liegen. Diese Forderung ist ganz besonders wichtig für Betätigungsteile, die bei kritischen Verkehrssituationen benötigt werden. Nur die selten benötigten Betätigungsteile sollen im geometrisch maximalen Greifraum liegen.

Selbstverständlich sollte keine Bewegung gefordert werden, bei der Gelenkbewegungen erforderlich sind, die den normalen Drehbereich der Gelenke überschreiten. Bewegungen außerhalb dieser Drehbereiche erfordern stets eine Mitbewegung größerer Körperteile und damit eine Erhöhung der Bewegungszeit.

Wir wissen, daß die Bewegungen unserer Körperglieder nicht mit homogener Geschwindigkeit erfolgen, sondern daß sie infolge der Wechselwirkung von Agonisten und Antagonisten ruckweise ablaufen. G. LEHMANN fand bereits vor 40 Jahren, daß die Bewegungen eines Fingergliedes in Stufen, deren Frequenz proportional der Wurzel aus der Bewegungsgeschwindigkeit ist, erfolgen. Dies ist mit einer der Gründe, weshalb auch bei relativ kleinen bewegten Körpermassen die Treffsicherheit und -genauigkeit unserer Bewegungen mit der Bewegungsgeschwindigkeit wesentlich abnehmen. SCHMIDTKE hat in unserem Institut die Bewegungsgenauigkeit von Armbewegungen eingehend untersucht. Im mittleren Entfernungsbereich zwischen 20 und 50 cm ist die Spitzengeschwindigkeit etwa proportional der Wurzel aus der Entfernung. Nimmt man die Beschleunigungskurven dieser Bewegungen auf, so sieht man, daß die höchsten Beschleunigungen innerhalb der ersten Zehntelsekunde des Bewegungsablaufes auftreten und im mittleren Abstandsbereich um 3 m/sec² betragen. Auch die daraufhin folgende Verzögerung der Bewegungen ist für die Kurven im mittleren Abstandsbereich ungefähr gleich und liegt in der Größenordnung von 1,5 m/sec². Erst bei größeren Entfernungen steigen Beschleunigung und Verzögerung wesentlich an. Daraus ergibt sich, daß bei größeren Entfernungen die Bewegungsgenauigkeit wesentlich abnimmt. Entsprechend ist auch die Wegzeit vom Zieldurchmesser abhängig. Bei derselben Zielentfernung von 50 cm benötigt man bei einem kleinen Zieldurchmesser von 2 mm 1,2 sec, um das Ziel zu erreichen, während bei einem Ziel von 10 mm Durchmesser nur 0,8 sec benötigt werden. Aus diesen Versuchen von SCHMIDTKE folgt, daß in Kraftfahrzeugen die Abmessungen der Betätigungsteile um so größer werden müssen, je größer die Entfernungen des Betätigungsteils von der Körperachse des Fahrers sind. Es ist also unsinnig, Schalter an den Armaturenbrettern in Form von kleinen Knöpfen auszuführen, vielmehr muß die Forderung gestellt werden, daß nur großflächige Betätigungsteile mit optisch und taktil eindeutig unterscheidbaren Formen und Oberflächen verwendet werden.

Für die optimale Lage von Hebeln und Pedalen, besonders dann, wenn größere Betätigungskräfte erforderlich sind, liegen bereits umfangreiche Untersuchungen vor. Für einen handbetätigten Hebel können die maximalen Kräfte im Bereich zwischen 70 und 100% des maximalen Greifraumes aufgebracht werden. Die optimale Zugrichtung liegt um 150° abwärts. Diese Daten legen die optimale Lage von Bremshebeln oder anderen Betätigungsteilen, bei denen größere Kräfte aufgewendet werden müssen, eindeutig fest. Auch für die Lage der Pedale liegen ähnliche Untersuchungen vor. Um die optimale Tretrichtung in beiden Ebenen zu erreichen, muß das Pedal relativ zum Sitz umso höher liegen, je größer die geforderte Kraft ist.

Für das Umsetzen des Fußes vom Fahr- zum Bremspedal wird ziemlich viel Zeit verbraucht, und zwar in der Größenordnung 0,2–0,3 sec, weil hierbei der Fuß abgehoben, seitlich bewegt und wieder aufgesetzt werden muß. Ein Zeitgewinn ließe sich dann erzielen, wenn das ,Umsetzen' zum ,Übergleiten' vereinfacht würde. Voraussetzung hierfür ist, daß das Fahrpedal auch bei Vollgas körpernäher und höher als das Bremspedal liegt. Eine Vergrößerung der Fläche des Bremspedals würde nicht nur das Ziel vergrößern und damit die Treffsicherheit erhöhen, sondern, besonders bei fehlendem Kupplungspedal, auch wahlweises Bremsen mit dem rechten und linken Fuß ermöglichen, und damit einen weiteren Zeitgewinn bewirken.

Seit Jahrzehnten werden immer wieder Vorschläge für ein kombiniertes Fahr-Brems-Pedal gemacht, um ein schnelles Betätigen der Bremse zu ermöglichen. Das Problem bei der Konstruktion eines solchen Gas-Brems-Pedals liegt darin, daß Gas- und Bremspedal nicht gleichzeitig betätigt werden können. Durch Verwendung der heute hochentwickelten Hydraulik könnte man jedoch ein solches Gas-Brems-Pedal wahrscheinlich konstruieren, wie es als Beispiel die Abbildung 2 zeigt. Der höhere technische Aufwand ist durch die wesentlich erhöhte Fahrsicherheit durchaus gerechtfertigt. Eine Umschulung auf dieses Gas-Brems-Pedal wird wahrscheinlich in kürzester Zeit möglich sein, da das Gasgeben genau so wie bisher erfolgt und die Bremsung durch ein Stemmen gegen die Bewegung mit dem Absatz durchgeführt wird, was einer tief eingeprägten Bewegungsart aller mit Beinen ausgerüsteten Lebewesen entspricht.

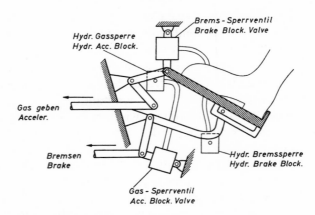

Abb. 2. Gas-Brems-Pedal mit hydraulischen Sperren

Von unseren konventionellen Steuerrädern wissen wir, daß sie beim Unfall zum tödlichen Spieß für den Fahrer werden können und auch dann, wenn sie nicht in den Fahrerraum eindringen, erhebliche Verletzungen des Brustkorbes erzeugen können. Der große Betätigungsweg unserer Steuerräder an Kraftfahrzeugen schützt uns zwar oft davor, das Fahrzeug bei hohen Geschwindigkeiten zu übersteuern, verlangt jedoch andererseits bei mittleren Geschwindigkeiten unnötig lange Zeiten, um rasche Steuerbewegungen bei Ausweichmanövern durchzuführen. Mit der Entwicklung der Servosteuerung sollte man daher überlegen, ob nicht andere Steuersysteme wesentlich unfallsicherer sind. Aus eigener praktischer Erfahrung wissen wir, daß bei den heutigen Lenkrädern uns nach längerer Fahrzeit leicht die Hände ‚einschlafen', weil sie meist über Herzhöhe liegen. Wir sollten daher ein neues Lenkungssystem finden, bei dem wir eine bequemere Haltung unserer Arme innehalten können, mit dem wir bei niedrigen Geschwindigkeiten schnellere Steuerausschläge durchführen können und bei dem durch eine Dämpfung, die abhängig von der Fahrgeschwindigkeit ist, trotzdem eine Übersteuerung des Fahrzeuges nicht möglich ist. Prinzipiell ist hierfür nicht nur eine Hand- sondern auch eine Fußsteuerung möglich. Abbildung 3 zeigt einige solcher Möglichkeiten für die Ausführung von Steuersystemen, wobei der größte Teil der Systeme natürlich nur mit Servosteuerung ausführbar ist. Zuerst muß jedoch untersucht werden, mit welchem dieser Systeme man vom psycho-physiologischen Standpunkt aus die schnellsten und zuverlässigsten Steuerbewegungen ausführen kann.

Eine solche Untersuchung ist in unserem Institut augenblicklich im Gange, und wir hoffen, daß wir in Bälde die ersten Resultate dieser Untersuchungen veröffentlichen können.

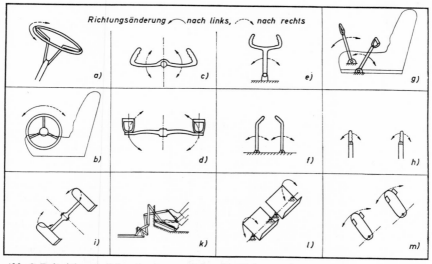

Abb. 3. Beispiele möglicher Lenkungssysteme für Fahrzeuge

Adresse des Autors: Dr. Ing. R.R. COERMANN, Max-Planck-Institut für Arbeitsphysiologie, *46 Dortmund,* Rheinlanddamm 201, Deutschland.

Biomechanics I, 1st Int. Seminar Zurich 1967
pp. 264–270 (Karger, Basel/New York 1968)

Max-Planck-Institut für Arbeitsphysiologie, Dortmund

Untersuchungen zur Ergonomie des Klavierspiels[1]

CH. WAGNER

Einleitung

Über die Abhängigkeit der musikalischen Leistung von physikalischen, physiologischen oder psychologischen Faktoren läßt sich nur dann etwas Genaueres sagen, wenn *beide* Seiten, Leistung und Leistungsbedingungen, quantitativ beobachtet werden.

Musikalische Leistung *messen* zu wollen, erscheint problematisch, weil das dem Wesen der Kunst widerspricht. Beschränkt man sich jedoch darauf, den Grad des *,technischen' Könnens* festzustellen, der ohnehin den ästhetischen Wert einer musikalischen Wiedergabe weitgehend bestimmt, so ergibt sich der Maßstab für eine quantitative Beurteilung von alleine: Als ,technisch fertig' wird man denjenigen bezeichnen, der in der Lage ist, *Höhe, Dauer und Stärkegrad der zu spielenden Töne* nur nach *musikalischen* Gesichtspunkten zu bemessen, ohne darin durch mehr oder weniger zufällige Umstände physikalischer, physiologischer oder psychologischer Art entscheidend, d.h. hörbar behindert zu werden. In ,technischen Übungen' versucht der Lernende, hinsichtlich Tonhöhe, Tondauer und Tonstärke bestimmten Sollwerten, die im Notentext festgelegt sind, immer wieder möglichst nahe zu kommen. Das Maß an Übereinstimmung zwischen Aufgabe und Ausführung entspricht dem Grad spieltechnischen Könnens, der sich durch die Messung der drei Variablen exakt bestimmen läßt.

Eine der grundlegenden Schwierigkeiten der *Klaviertechnik* liegt in der rhythmisch genauen Wiedergabe von Tonfolgen, die aus gleichen Notenwerten bestehen. Abbildung 1

Abb. 1. Dreifinger-Übung für Klavier. Zeitintervalle der aufeinanderfolgenden Töne, entsprechend der Vorschrift des Notentextes.

[1] Die Untersuchungen wurden von der Fritz-Thyssen-Stiftung gefördert.

zeigt an einem Beispiel einfachster Art, was der Notentext bezüglich der Tondauer an sich vom Ausführenden verlangt; der Sollwert der Sechzehntelnote beträgt in diesem Fall rund 104 msec, wie sich aus der Bezeichnung MM ♩ = 144, d.h. 144 Viertelschläge pro Minute, ergibt. Einige der Beobachtungen, die sich mit der Registrierung der rhythmischen Struktur beim Spiel derartiger Aufgaben ergeben haben, sollen im folgenden mitgeteilt werden.

Methodik

Es ist in der Natur des Instruments begründet, daß die rhythmische Struktur beim Klavierspiel nicht durch die Dauer der einzelnen Töne entsteht, sondern durch die Zeitintervalle, die jeweils zwischen dem Beginn eines Tones und dem Beginn des nächsten Tones liegen. Deshalb ist der Bechstein-Flügel, den wir zur Zeit bei unseren Versuchen verwenden, so hergerichtet, daß jedesmal in dem Zeitpunkt ein elektrischer Impuls entsteht, in dem einer der 88 Hammerköpfe die zugehörige Saite anschlägt. Zeichnet man die Folge der Impulse auf, dann entsprechen die Zeitintervalle zwischen den Impulsen dem Rhythmus der gespielten Töne.

Während des Versuchs werden die Impulsfolgen auf Magnetband gespeichert; die Messung der Zeitintervalle, das Fixieren der Werte auf Lochstreifen und eventuell als Klartext erfolgt nach dem Versuch. Der Meßfehler des Verfahrens beträgt ± 1 msec.

Um später den musikalisch nicht vorstellbaren Meßergebnissen das entsprechende akustische Ereignis gegenüberstellen zu können, ist es zweckmäßig, während des Spielens auch eine akustische Aufzeichnung auf Tonband vorzunehmen. Das Spieltempo wurde in den hier gezeigten Beispielen jeweils unmittelbar vor Beginn einer Übung mit Hilfe eines Metronoms vorgegeben, auch im Fall der Wiederholungen.

Untersuchungen

Man wird zunächst danach fragen, welchen Grad an rhythmischer Präzision ein Klavierspieler, der sein Instrument *beherrscht,* in einer so einfachen Testaufgabe wie der in Abbildung 1 gezeigten erreicht. Ein Beispiel dafür gibt Abbildung 2a. Man erkennt, daß trotz der Verwendung verschiedener Fingersätze, wie 1.2.3.2. und 3.4.5.4., die Breite der Schwankungen ungefähr gleich bleibt, daß aber innerhalb dieses Bereichs charakteristische Unterschiede auftreten. Auffallend sind hier vor allem die Veränderungen im *Verlauf* einer Übung. Der relativ hohe Grad der Gleichmäßigkeit, der sich bei Verwendung des Fingersatzes 2.3.4.3. in der ersten Hälfte der Übung einstellt, scheint sich, auch auf dem Fertigkeitsniveau eines Konzertpianisten, nur schwer aufrechterhalten zu lassen. Darauf deutet die Zunahme der Schwankungsbreite in der zweiten Hälfte der Übung, und vor allem die *Wiederholung* der Übung (Abb. 2b), die nach einer Pause von ca. 5 sec ausgeführt wurde.

Das Spiel mit dem Fingersatz 1.2.3.2. zeigt dagegen eher die umgekehrte Tendenz (Abb. 2a); die in den ersten beiden Takten auftretenden stärkeren Schwankungen engen sich ein in den beiden folgenden Takten. Dieser Vorgang wiederholt sich beim zweiten Mal (Abb. 2b), jedoch mit geringerem Erfolg.

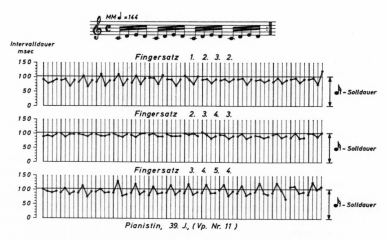

Abb. 2a. Zeitintervalle der aufeinanderfolgenden Töne beim Spiel einer Dreifinger-Übung am Klavier, rechte Hand, erster Durchgang.

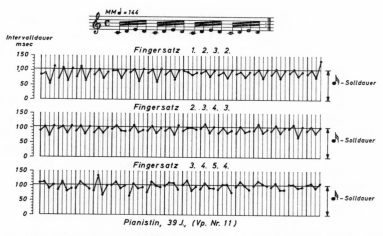

Abb. 2b. Zeitintervalle der aufeinanderfolgenden Töne beim Spiel einer Dreifinger-Übung am Klavier, rechte Hand, zweiter Durchgang. Die Pause zwischen 1. und 2. Durchgang betrug ca. 5 sec.

Nicht zu übersehen ist, wie häufig die den Tonschritten entsprechenden Zeitintervalle *gleichsinnig* verkürzt oder verlängert werden, mitunter um nahezu denselben Betrag. Während sich in den beiden ersten Fällen – Fingersätze 1.2.3.2. und 2.3.4.3. – ein bestimmtes Abweichungsmuster für alle vier Zeitintervalle durchzusetzen scheint, zeigt die Wiederholung der Übung mit dem Fingersatz 3.4.5.4. ein unregelmäßigeres Bild (vgl. Abb. 2a und 2b). Beide Male stimmen nur insofern überein, als das zweite Intervall in der Regel das relativ längste der Gruppe ist.

Verhältnismäßig große Abweichungen von der Solldauer der Notenwerte weisen die Klavierschüler auf, welche in Abb. 3 unserer Konzertpianistin gegenübergestellt sind.

Während in dem rhythmisch noch sehr ungeordneten Spiel der Vp. Nr. 12 (Abb. 3 unten) bereits die Tendenz zur Bildung von Fehlerstereotypien auffällt – man betrachte das zweite Intervall jeder Gruppe – scheint diese Entwicklung im Fall der Vp. Nr. 15 (Abb. 3, Mitte) weitgehend abgeschlossen. Die regelmäßige Verzerrung des vorgeschriebenen Rhythmus zu einem annähernd triolig punktierten (Verhältnis 2:1, statt 1:1) ist hier offensichtlich fixiert. Die Vp., mit ihrer Leistung recht unzufrieden, war außerstande, den ,wie von sel-

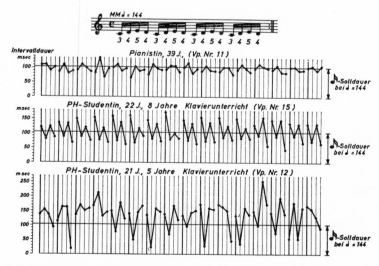

Abb. 3. Zeitintervalle der aufeinanderfolgenden Töne beim Spiel einer Dreifinger-Übung am Klavier, rechte Hand; zweiter Durchgang.

ber' ablaufenden Spielvorgang irgendwie zu beeinflussen im Sinne größerer Gleichmäßigkeit der Zeitintervalle. Einen entsprechenden Kommentar gaben häufig gerade ‚fortgeschrittene' Laien über ihre Leistung. Abbildung 4 vermittelt einen Eindruck davon, mit welcher Präzision bestimmte Intervallzeiten wiederkehren können, wenn eine Übung mehrere Male unmittelbar hintereinander gespielt wird. Die Pause zwischen den Wiederholungen betrug ca. 5 sec.

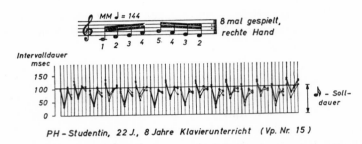

PH - Studentin, 22 J., 8 Jahre Klavierunterricht (Vp. Nr. 15)

Abb. 4. Zeitintervalle der aufeinanderfolgenden Töne beim Spiel einer Fünffinger-Übung am Klavier, rechte Hand; erster, zweiter und dritter Durchgang.

Die Abweichungsmuster können individuell verschieden sein und sich ändern, wenn zwischen den Wiederholungen eine Zeitspanne von Wochen oder Monaten liegt, scheinen aber bei fortgeschrittenen Laien wesentlich stärker fixiert als bei Schülern mit kürzerer Ausbildungsdauer. Wie sich häufiges Wiederholen einer Übung gerade bei fortgeschrittenen Klavierspielern auswirkt, zeigt Abbildung 5. Die viertaktige Aufgabe bestand aus 12 der dargestellten Spielfiguren und wurde viermal ausgeführt, jeweils mit einer Hand allein. Zwischen den Wiederholungen lag eine Pause von ca. 5 sec. Das Ergebnis im Verlauf des 'Übens' ist nicht ein Ausgleich der rhythmischen Fehler im Sinne des Notentextes, im Gegenteil, die Abweichungsbeträge bestimmter Intervalle (rechte Hand: 2., 3. und 6., linke Hand: 2. und 6. Intervall) nehmen von Mal zu Mal zu; und je größer der Abweichungsbetrag, desto größer scheint die Präzision, mit der er sich wiederholt.

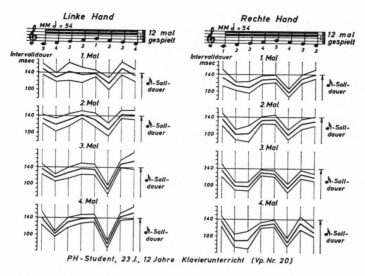

Abb. 5. Zeitintervalle der aufeinanderfolgenden Töne bei einhändigem Spiel einer Fünf-finger-Übung am Klavier; vier Durchgänge (Mittelwert und Streuung). Die Pause zwischen den einzelnen Durchgängen betrug ca. 5 sec.

Diskussion

Bei der Betrachtung der hier dargestellten Spielleistungen ergibt sich eine Reihe grundsätzlicher Fragen: Welche Eigentümlichkeiten des rhythmischen Verlaufs sind möglicherweise beabsichtigt, welche entstehen unwillkürlich; wodurch kommen die nicht beabsichtigten Zeitintervallunterschiede zustande; welche der auftretenden Unregelmäßigkeiten werden dem Ausführenden bewußt, welche werden vom Zuhörer wahrgenommen.

Keine dieser Fragen läßt sich zum gegenwärtigen Zeitpunkt endgültig beantworten. Bemerkenswert in diesem Zusammenhang ist jedoch folgendes: Den in Abbildung 2a und b sichtbaren Unterschieden stand *kein entsprechender Höreindruck* gegenüber. Die Feststellung einer annähernd gleichen Variationsbreite bei Verwendung des ersten und dritten Fingersatzes – letzterer gilt als schwierig – war für die Versuchsperson ebenso überraschend wie der Nachweis der deutlich höheren Präzision beim Spiel mit dem zweiten Fingersatz. Auch von den charakteristischen Veränderungen im *Verlauf* der Übungen (Abb. 2a und b) hatte die Versuchsperson nichts bemerkt. Obwohl hier also offensichtlich eine bewußte Kontrolle und Steuerung einzelner Intervallzeiten nicht stattgefunden hat – man vergegenwärtige sich auch die Anschlagfrequenz von 9,6/sec – scheinen, allein auf Grund der Intension, rhythmisch genau zu spielen, Einflüsse wirksam zu werden, die dennoch zu einer Angleichung der Zeitintervalle führen. In der Unterschiedlichkeit des Erfolges dürfte die Verschiedenartigkeit der Hindernisse zum Ausdruck kommen, die sich dieser Angleichungstendenz entgegenstellen und die entweder erst nach einer gewissen Einspielzeit überwunden werden (Abb. 2a und b, oben), oder umgekehrt zu Beginn noch kaum eine Rolle spielen, sich aber allmählich verstärken (Abb. 2a und b, Mitte) oder auch plötzlich auftreten (Abb. 2a, unten). Die Analyse dieser begrenzenden Faktoren dürfte für das Verständnis der Lernvorgänge am Musikinstrument sehr aufschlußreich werden. Das bis jetzt vorliegende Material widersetzt sich jedoch in seiner Vielgestaltigkeit allen einfacheren Erklärungsversuchen.

Auch die Frage, welche Bedeutung in diesem Zusammenhang der Ausprägung der Zeitintervallmuster zukommt, läßt sich noch nicht entscheiden. Jedenfalls weist die Erscheinung daraufhin, daß die zugrunde liegenden Bewegungsvorgänge weitgehend automatisiert wurden. Der typische Unterschied im Übungsniveau zwischen dem mehr nud dem weniger fortgeschrittenen Laien (Abb. 3, Mitte und unten) zeigt sich hier im Prinzip als derselbe, den man beim vergleichenden Spiel der beiden Hände beobachten kann (Abb. 5) oder beim Vergleich ‚angenehmer‘ und ‚unangenehmer‘ Fingersätze (Abb. 2b, oben und unten).

So notwendig die Entstehung von Bewegungsautomatismen für das Instrumentalspiel ist, so gefährlich erweist sich diese Fähigkeit, weil sie bei mangelhafter Kontrolle des klanglichen Ergebnisses auch zur Fixierung von spieltechnisch *unbrauchbaren* Fertigkeiten führen kann. Diese Entwicklung setzt offenbar schon in einem frühen Stadium der Ausbildung ein. Abbildung 4 und 5 zeigen, daß die Ausführung musikalischer Aufgaben in solchen Fällen schließlich weitgehend vom Zwang bestimmter Bewegungsgewohnheiten diktiert wird und kaum noch von *musikalischen* Gesetzen.

Adresse des Autors: Dr. CH. WAGNER, Max-Planck-Institut für Arbeitsphysiologie, D-46 *Dortmund*, Rheinlanddamm 201 (Deutschland).

Biomechanics I, 1st Int. Seminar Zurich 1967
pp. 271–272 (Karger, Basel/New York 1968)

Institut für Hygiene und Arbeitsphysiologie der Eidgenössischen Technischen Hochschule, Zürich

Multimomentaufnahmen und Ermüdungserscheinungen beim Verkaufspersonal eines Warenhauses

E. GRANDJEAN und H. KRETZSCHMAR

Die Multimomentaufnahmen erfolgten an 24 Arbeitstagen bei 24 Verkäuferinnen eines Warenhauses. Die 5280 Beobachtungen ergaben u.a. folgende Resultate:

Gehen	58 Minuten
Stehen ohne abzustützen	3 h 55 Minuten
Stehen mit Abstützen	1 h 30 Minuten
Gebeugte Haltungen	62 Minuten

Die statische Muskeltätigkeit umfaßte, je nach Kundenfrequenz,

für Rumpf und Bein	4 h 30 Minuten bis 5 h 12 Minuten
für Rumpf und Arm	1 h 42 Minuten bis 1 h 54 Minuten

Mit einem bipolaren Fragebogen wurde das subjektive Ermüdungsempfinden von 33 Verkäuferinnen an insgesamt 9 Tagen jeweilen siebenmal pro Tag erhoben. Die statistische Auswertung ergab am Ende des Arbeitstages eine signifikante Verschiebung der Selbsteinstufungen im Sinne vermehrter Ermüdungsempfindungen für folgende vier Gegensatzpaare:

geschwächt	—	stark
gespannt	—	gelöst
müde	—	frisch
erschöpft	—	gekräftigt

Eine gleichzeitige Erhebung bei 200 Angestellten des Verkaufspersonals ergab u.a. folgende Resultate:

	22 bis 36 Jahre	37 bis 51 Jahre	52 bis 70 Jahre
Rückenschmerzen	15%	15%	23%
Beinbeschwerden	20%	17%	13%
Fußbeschwerden	11%	14%	16%

Adresse der Autoren: E. GRANDJEAN und H. KRETZSCHMAR, Institut für Hygiene und Arbeitsphysiologie der Eidgenössischen Technischen Hochschule, CH-8006 *Zürich* (Schweiz).

Biomechanics I, 1st Int. Seminar Zurich 1967
pp. 273–277 (Karger, Basel/New York 1968)

Abteilung X für Naturwissenschaften der Eidgenössischen
Technischen Hochschule, Zürich

Eine Testbatterie zur Erfassung von Grundeigenschaften der menschlichen Motorik

J. Wartenweiler

Einleitung

Sowohl im Sport als auch in der Arbeit werden optimale Bewegungsformen und Höchstleistungen angestrebt. Man möchte auch wissen, ob ein Mensch manuell begabt ist für einen bestimmten Beruf, oder ob sich der Aufwand für ein sportliches Spezialtraining lohnt.

Aber nicht nur ideale Bewegungsformen und Höchstleistungen sind von Interesse. Jeder Mensch hat seine eigene Bewegungscharakteristik, die es zu erkennen und zu beachten gilt.

Wir fragen daher:
Gibt es Grundeigenschaften der Motorik, nach denen die Bewegungen, oder die Menschen, welche sie ausführen, bewertet werden können? Positive Eigenschaften wären z.B. Präzision, Regelmäßigkeit, Feinfühligkeit in der Bewegungsanpassung, negative Eigenschaften: langsame Reaktion, Steifheit, Kraftlosigkeit.

Wenn sich solche Komponenten der motorischen Eigenart *wissenschaftlich* bestimmen lassen, so wird es möglich sein, eine wesentliche Seite der menschlichen Persönlichkeit besser zu beleuchten, und zu einem tieferen Verständnis der menschlichen Natur überhaupt vorzudringen.

Nun existieren z.B. auf dem Gebiet der Arbeitspsychologie schon sehr gute Bewegungstests. Sie betreffen jedoch meistens *komplexe Eigenschaften* der Bewegungskoordination, vor allem in der Handgeschicklichkeit.

Wir haben uns hier die Aufgabe gestellt, *elementare Grundeigenschaften* der menschlichen Motorik zu bestimmen. Die betreffenden Tests wurden in Zusammenarbeit mit Herrn A. Wettstein entwickelt.

Methode

Als Vergleichsklassen dienen zwei Männer- und zwei Frauengruppen zu je 30 Personen bei einem durchschnittlichen Alter zwischen 20 und 30 Jahren. Je eine Gruppe setzt sich aus Sportstudenten, die andere aus Studenten verschiedener Richtungen, Laboranten und Bureaupersonal zusammen. Bezüglich Größe und Gewicht entsprechen sich die beiden Frauengruppen genau. Bei den Männern ist die Gruppe der sportlichen Auswahl im Mittel um 3 cm größer und 4 kg schwerer als die Vergleichsgruppe. Zur statistischen Sicherung der Vergleichswerte wurde der t-Test verwendet.

1. Druckkraft: Ein elektronischer Druck-Meßring von 15 cm Durchmesser ist auf der Brusthöhe vor dem Körper mit beiden Armen zu komprimieren.

2. Bewegungsgeschwindigkeit: Auf einem leichten Gestell, welches über die Schultern der Versuchsperson gehängt wird, ist mit Drehpunkt über der rechten Achsel ein Hebel angebracht, der dem Arm entlang zur rechten Hand führt. Mittels eines Potentiometers im Drehpunkt wird die Winkelgeschwindigkeit des Armschwingens einwärts bestimmt (der linke Arm schwingt in Gegenbewegung). Daraus läßt sich die Bewegungsgeschwindigkeit auf Höhe der Fingerspitzen berechnen.

3. Reaktionszeit: Die Versuchsperson hat auf ein akustisches Signal hin mit der rechten Hand eine Reaktionsbewegung auszuführen. Gemessen wird die Zeit vom Signal bis zum Beginn des Ausschlages eines elektronischen Accelerometers, welcher in der Hand gehalten wird.

4. Bewegungsfrequenz: Mittels eines in der rechten Hand gehaltenen Accelerometers wird die Frequenz einer Auf- und Abwärtsbewegung des Unterarmes bei einem Ausschlag von 5 cm gemessen.

5. Zeitliche Wiederholungsgenauigkeit: Die Versuchsperson hat einen Hebel von 70 cm Länge in freier Art hin und her zu bewegen. Die Ausschläge des Hebels werden mittels eines Potentiometers elektronisch registriert. Berechnet wird die mittlere Abweichung der 40. bis 50. Hin- und Herbewegung von der Ursprungsfrequenz.

6. Räumliche Wiederholungsgenauigkeit: Bei der unter 5) beschriebenen Versuchsanordnung wird der Ausschlag des Hebels auf 25 cm begrenzt. Die Versuchsperson hat die Augen verdeckt. In 10 Hin- und Herbewegungen wird die Distanz abgetastet, dann ist die Bewegung 20mal ohne Beschränkung auszuführen. Berechnet wird die mittlere Links- und Rechtsabweichung von der ursprünglichen Mittellage.

7. Bewegungsadaption: a) Vorgegeben ist eine regelmäßige, maschinell ausgeführte Hin- und Herbewegung über eine Distanz von 40 cm. Die

Versuchsperson muß der Bewegung möglichst widerstandslos folgen,
indem sie einen an der Maschine angebrachten «Kraftfühler» zwischen Zeigefinger und Daumen hält. Gemessen wird die durchschnittliche Widerstandskraft über eine Zeit von 10 sec.
b) Der oben beschriebene Versuch wird mit einem zweiten Programm
ausgeführt, bei welchem Amplitude und Frequenz der vorgegebenen
Bewegung vielfältig variieren.

8. *Koordination der Totalbewegung:* Die Versuchsperson hat die Aufgabe, einen kugelförmigen Wurfkörper von 25 cm Durchmesser und
einem Gewicht von 1,2 kg, der an einer senkrecht stehenden Stange
geführt wird, in rhythmisch geschlossenem Bewegungsablauf abzufangen und wieder hochzutreiben. An der Hüfte und am Handgelenk der
Versuchsperson werden Accelerometer angebracht, welche die vertikale

Tabellarische Zusammenstellung der Messwerte
($\bar{x}$ = Mittelwert, s = quadratische Abweichung)

Gruppen	Körpergröße $\bar{x}$ cm s	Gewicht $\bar{x}$ kg s	Druckkraft $\bar{x}$ kg s	Geschwindigkeit $\bar{x}$ m/s s	Reaktion $\bar{x}$ s s
Sportl. Auswahl Männer	177,8 5,90	72,1 6,47	62,8 8,39	14,05 1,63	0,112 0,017
Allg. Durchschnitt Männer	174,5 6,33	68,1 6,94	52,8 6,66	12,58 1,76	0,110 0,033
Sportl. Auswahl Frauen	165,3 5,91	56,1 6,19	31,4 4,77	11,83 1,28	0,108 0,019
Allg. Durchschnitt Frauen	165,5 5,13	56,2 6,04	28,7 5,54	10,23 1,52	0,111 0,020

Gruppen	Frequenz $\bar{x}$ Hz s	Zeitl. Wiederholung $\bar{x}$ % s	Räuml. Wiederholung $\bar{x}$ % s	Adaption $\bar{x}$ g* s	Koordination $\bar{x}$ % s
Sportl. Auswahl Männer	7,03 0,84	3,98 2,64	8,09 6,75	38,10 8,84	74,59 17,21
Allg. Durchschnitt Männer	6,87 0,71	4,24 3,27	8,37 6,70	40,09 12,56	57,50 12,66
Sportl. Auswahl Frauen	6,76 0,65	3,44 2,86	7,98 6,29	28,53 9,40	68,85 15,90
Allg. Durchschnitt Frauen	6,34 0,76	3,62 3,17	14,07 11,22	30,05 7,78	58,41 21,79

Beschleunigung aufzeichnen. Die Auf- und Abwärtsbewegung von Hüfte und Handgelenk, sowie der Bodendruck werden gleichfalls registriert. Die Kriterien für eine positive Totalbewegung sind:

1. Deutliches Ausholen (negative Beschleunigung) vor dem Auffangen
2. Weiches Auffangen des Wurfkörpers
3. Deutliche Phasendifferenz: Hüfte vor Arm
4. Regelmäßige Beschleunigungskurven
Die Idealform wird mit 100% bewertet. Fehler ergeben Abzüge. (Abb. 1 und 2).

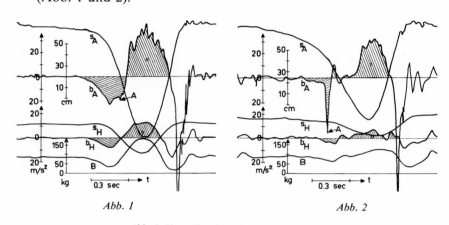

Abb. 1   *Abb. 2*

Abb. 1. Koordination der Totalbewegung

S_A = Weg Arm (Handgelenk) S_H = Weg Hüfte
b_A = Beschleunigung Arm b_H = Beschleunigung Hüfte
B = Bodendruck

Gute Form

1. Deutliche (negative) Ausholbeschleunigung vor Auffangen bei A
2. Kleine Beschleunigungsspitze (A) entspricht «weichem» Auffangen
3. Richtige Phasendifferenz in der positiven Beschleunigung: Hüfte vor Arm
4. Regelmäßige Beschleunigungskurven

Abb. 2. Koordination der Totalbewegung

S_A = Weg Arm (Handgelenk) S_H = Weg Hüfte
b_A = Beschleunigung Arm b_H = Beschleunigung Hüfte
B = Bodendruck

Fehlerhafte Form

1. Keine deutliche (negative) Ausholbeschleunigung vor Auffangen bei A.
2. Große Beschleunigungsspitze (A) entspricht hartem Auffangen
3. Keine Phasendifferenz in der positiven Beschleunigung von Hüfte und Arm
4. Verzögerte, unregelmäßige Beschleunigungskurven

Diskussion der Messwerte

Erste Voraussetzung für die *Bewegungsgeschwindigkeit* ist die *Kraft.* Da wirkt es erstaunlich, daß die Frauen, welche in unserer Messung – ohne Unterschied ob ‚sportliche Auswahl' oder ‚allgemeiner Durchschnitt' – nur gerade die Hälfte der männlichen Kraft erreichen, in der Bewegungsgeschwindigkeit nahe an die männlichen Leistungen herankommen.

Überraschend sind auch die ermittelten Werte der *Reaktionszeit.* Die erwarteten Unterschiede blieben vollständig aus. Die Reaktionszeit ist also bei allen Vergleichsgruppen praktisch dieselbe. Auch die sportliche Auswahl der Versuchspersonen reagiert nicht schneller als der allgemeine Durchschnitt.

Eine entsprechende Feststellung gilt für die *Bewegungsfrequenz,* die man als nervöse Schaltgeschwindigkeit bezeichnen könnte. Auch hier zeigen sich keine signifikanten Unterschiede zwischen Frauen und Männern, bzw. sportlicher Auswahl und allgemeinem Durchschnitt.

Beim Vergleich von *zeitlicher* und *räumlicher Bewegungsgenauigkeit* zeigt sich, daß das zeitliche Maß viel genauer eingehalten werden kann als das räumliche Maß. Ein Unterschied zwischen Frauen und Männern ist – wie zu erwarten war – nicht festzustellen, doch hätte es nahegelegen, daß die beiden Gruppen der sportlichen Auswahl in der Bewegungsgenauigkeit positiv hervorgestochen hätten. Das ist nicht der Fall.

In der *Bewegungsadaption* erweisen sich die Frauen gegenüber den Männern als anpassungsfähiger. Ihre Widerstandsreaktion ist geringer. Daß es sich dabei um einen echten Unterschied in der Bewegungsanpassung handelt, und nicht nur um eine Folge der geringeren trägen Masse der weiblichen Hände und Arme, geht u.a. daraus hervor, daß die Männer der sportlichen Auswahl trotz ihrer größeren Körpermasse den geringeren Bewegungswiderstand aufweisen als die Männer des allgemeinen Durchschnitts.

In der *Bewegungskoordination* erreichen die sportlich orientierten Gruppen signifikant bessere Werte als die Gruppen des allgemeinen Durchschnitts. Geschlechtsspezifische Unterschiede lassen sich nicht erhärten.

Der Koordinationstest zeigt, daß sich eine einfache Auffang-Stoßbewegung gut dazu eignet, Unterschiede in der Bewegungsqualität sichtbar zu machen. Wir werden daher in Zukunft unser Augenmerk besonders auf diesen und eine Reihe ähnlicher Bewegungstests richten. Im übrigen wird es uns beschäftigen, die Tests, die keine statistischen Unterschiede ergeben haben, in bezug auf die Möglichkeit individueller Bewegungscharakteristik zu untersuchen.

Literatur

WARTENWEILER, J.: Grundeigenschaften der menschlichen Motorik. Verh. Schweiz. Naturforschende Gesellschaft *147:* 153–156 (1967).

WARTENWEILER, J.: Zur Technik der Bewegungsstudie, Verh. Schweiz. Naturforschende Gesellschaft *144:* 146–147 (1964).

WARTENWEILER, J. und WETTSTEIN, A.: Die Entwicklung der Koordination beim Stoßen und Werfen 7–22jähriger Knaben und Mädchen. Bull. Schweiz. Ges. für Anthropologie und Ethnologie *42:* 40–43 (1965/66).

WARTENWEILER, J. und WETTSTEIN, A.: Biomechanische Grundprinzipien für schwunghafte Bewegungen. Die Körpererziehung, Heft 7/8, Bern 1965.

WARTENWEILER, J. und WETTSTEIN, A.: Charakteristik schwunghafter Bewegungen nach biomechanischen Gesichtspunkten. XVI. Weltkongreß für Sportmedizin, Hannover 1966, p. 783–789.

Adresse des Autors: Prof. Dr. J. WARTENWEILER, Abteilung X für Naturwissenschaften der Eidgenössischen Technischen Hochschule, *CH-8006 Zürich* (Schweiz).

VIII. Applied Biomechanics in Sports

Biomechanics I, 1st Int. Seminar Zurich 1967
pp. 278–281 (Karger, Basel/New York 1968)

Mechanical Engineering Department, University of Birmingham

The Analysis of Movements and Forces in the Sprint Start

F.B. BLADER

The work currently being carried out at Birmingham on the sprint start is one of several exercises aimed at providing a fuller understanding of athletic events. From these studies it is hoped to achieve possibilities of improved performance and more information on body loading under extreme physical conditions.

The equipment designed for the sprint start consists of individual force and couple instrumented starting blocks and some ancillary timing equipment. The blocks are designed to measure normal and tangential forces in the vertical plane along the direction of running and a couple about an axis perpendicular to it. The apparatus is shown in Figure 1. The instrumentation uses half proving rings with strain gauges attached to form suitable a.c. bridge circuits, feeding the unbalanced signal to an ultra-violet recorder.

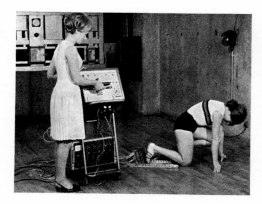

Fig. 1

A diagram showing the bridge circuits is given in Figure 2. Thus six traces, three for each foot are achieved. The mechanical design of the equipment, carried out by the author, has provided a very high frequency linear suspension giving an accurate representation of the forces produced on the starting block. There have been and still are some improvements to be made. The calibration of normal force shows that machining accuracy on the rings produce on one block a 3% variation in normal force dependent on its position of application. While this has not invalidated the results, it is felt that improvement is desirable. All other calibrations show linearity and absence of any hysteretic effects.

The results are recorded and produce traces such as those shown in Figure 3. The analysis of the data produced is being carried out using a digital computer. The records are digitised using a semi-automatic procedure and fed as data on tape into a programme arranged to give results at any instant in time for resultant forces, angles and positions for each foot separately and the combination of both feet. As an example of the computed output, the total maximum force exerted by

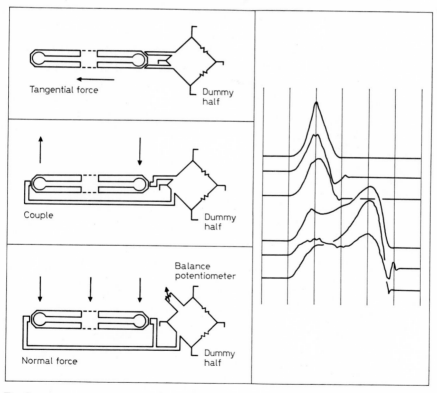

Fig. 2

Fig. 3

each foot and their vector sum is shown in Figure 4 for the record shown
in Figure 3. The total horizontal and vertical components of impulse
are also computed. The method is a general one and will be used in
future studies of other events.

In order to construct and validate criteria for the improvement of
the sprint start, it has been necessary to determine a suitable timing
method for comparison. Little evidence is available giving a satisfactory
scientific basis for a critical timing position to record only start
controlled effects. Experiments have therefore been carried out using
6 photoelectric devices along the track to make direct comparison
between the time-position history for runs from the normal blocks
and those made from an upright starting position by the same athlete.
Consistent performances have been achieved by mixing the types of
start which show that during the runs there exist identical velocity and
acceleration histories for several feet beyond a location 20 feet from the
block start even when the block spacings are altered. Figure 5 shows the
time-displacement curve for 12¼ inch spaced blocks and a standing
start. Both were consistent best performances and the standing start
results are moved to show when the slope, i.e. velocity, becomes identical. In this case this critical point was at 22 feet. The result for the
17¼ inch spacing showed a critical position of slightly less than 20 feet.
It has therefore been concluded that the most appropriate position
for timings to be taken to take account of the start alone is during

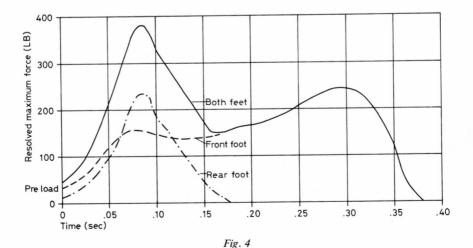

Fig. 4

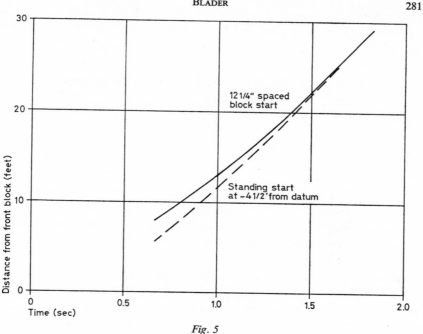

Fig. 5

the airborne part of the movement at or near to 20 feet down the track. The height of the timing device was ascertained from a study of film records taken for the purpose to coincide with the neck shoulder junction at mid-stride. The results so far achieved suggest that the most noticeable effect of a poor start on the records is the late and unconsistent application of force by the front foot. The results also show clearly the high proportion of impulse which is provided by the rear foot and the manner in which the ankles of both feet rotate under the initial loading.

Finally the record of each run is synchronised with a film record by means of a clock which gives pulses at predetermined points on to the force record. A segmental approach to finding the inertia and centre of gravity position is being investigated using a similar digital approach to that used for analysis of the force trace, although some doubts still exist as to its accuracy. If successful, it is hoped to correlate the force records with the resulting movements. The largest problem would seem to be the variation of total inertia and its inclusion in the analysis.

Author's address: F.B. BLADER, Mechanical Engineering Department, University of Birmingham, *Birmingham* (Great Britain).

Biomechanics I, 1st Int. Seminar Zurich 1967
pp. 282–290 (Karger, Basel/New York 1968)

School of Education, University of Tokyo, Tokyo

Biomechanics of Sprint Running with Respect to the Speed Curve

M. Ikai

As the fundamental pattern of human locomotion, walking and running must be most important for practical as well as for theoretical considerations. The present author has been interested in recording the change of speed and acceleration during running of human subjects.

The purpose of this study was to test the usefulness of the Cadmium cell as a photosensitive material to check the moment of passing a certain point along the running track. Secondly, the author wanted to know the improvement of running performance with advance in age not only from the running record but from the pattern of variation of the speed curve of 50 or 100 meters' running. Thirdly, the author wanted to find some relation between running performance and the maximum strength of the lower extremities of the subject. Fourthly, he wanted to know the usefulness of the speed-distance curve in achieving a better running performance in trained athletes.

Speed Curve in Sprint Running

Since the end of last century the speed of running had been studied by MAREY and other physiologists. According to the description by MAREY in 1894, he used a simple mechanical system with poles and horizontal bars along the running track. In 1927 HILL had introduced a method of recording using the electromagnetic principle. In his experiment, the subject carried a thin magnet tied around the waist. Each time he passed one of the coils, the magnet induced electric current in the circuit. A series of coils was accurately placed with certain intervals from the start to the end of 60 yards. Based on the results obtained by this experiment, he made a theoretical consideration on the relationship of speed, acceleration and propelling force. In 1951 HENRY and TRAFTON revived a classical method followed by an accurate theoretical discussion. They analysed the main factors governing the speed during the first stretch and the last stretch of 50 yards running.

The present author used a photosensitive Cadmium cell connected in a series with an oscillograph. The pairs of the source of light (projecting part) and Cadmium cell (receiving) were placed at distances of 1, 2, 3, 5, 10, 15, 20, 25, 30, 40, 50, 60, 70, 80, 90 and 100 meters from the start. From the record obtained by this measurement, a distance-time relation curve was drawn for each subject. By differentiating this curve, speed and acceleration were related to time as shown in Figure 1.

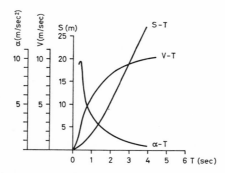

Fig. 1. Distance, velocity, and acceleration curve related to time.

To reveal the improvement of running performance with advance in age in Japanese boys and girls, the average speed in each section of running distance was related to the running distance. As the subjects for this study, male and female students of elementary, junior and senior high schools from 6 to 18 years of age and College students from 19 to 25 years of age were employed. The number of male subjects was 407 and female 324. The number of the subjects of same age was 25 and 30 in both sexes at elementary and high school respectively. The subjects of 6 and 7 years of age ran 50 meters, and the others 100 meters.

As the running speed varies as a function of time, the speed-distance curve was related to age and sex as shown in Figure 2 and 3. It is easy to find out from these curves that the speed on average

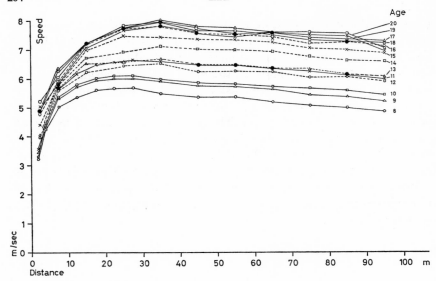

Fig. 2. Velocity curve of Sprint Running Boy.

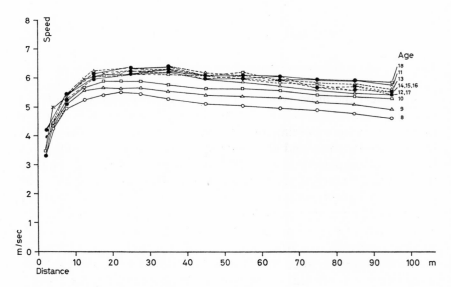

Fig. 3. Velocity curve of Sprint Running Girl.

increases progressively up to 16 years of age in male subjects, and up to 11 years of age in female subjects. From individual records of this measurement, some significant parameters were calculated, such as acceleration just after the start, propelling force, maximum speed, and decreased rate of speed in the last stretch as shown in Table I and II.

Table I. Acceleration, propelling force calculated from speed curve.

Age	Male Acceleration m/sec^2	Propelling force kg	Female Acceleration m/sec^2	Propelling force kg
6	3.00	5.60	2.90	5.40
7	3.30	7.60	3.18	6.00
8	3.58	9.60	3.38	7.40
9	3.80	10.80	3.42	9.20
10	3.84	11.40	3.64	10.40
11	4.00	12.00	3.72	11.20
12	4.04	12.80	3.72	11.40
13	4.15	14.60	3.72	11.80
14	4.40	17.20	3.72	13.00
15	4.80	22.00	3.76	15.00
16	5.36	27.60	3.94	16.80
17	5.70	31.00	4.20	19.00
18	5.92	32.20	4.42	21.80
19	6.00	33.60	—	—
20	6.10	34.40	—	—
Trained	9.60	72.24	6.20	28.47
Untrained	5.90	33.53	—	—

Table II. Maximum speed and rate of decrease of speed.

Age	Male max. speed m/sec	decrease %	Female max. speed m/sec	decrease %
6	4.82	2.0	4.67	4.0
7	5.26	2.0	5.11	4.0
8	5.63	1.8	5.36	4.0
9	6.02	1.8	5.68	4.0
10	6.23	1.9	5.81	4.0
11	6.35	2.7	6.19	4.5
12	6.57	6.0	6.28	5.8
13	6.67	8.0	6.36	8.5
14	7.13	9.2	6.18	12.5
15	7.50	9.4	6.30	13.5
16	7.84	10.2	6.32	13.8
17	7.98	10.4	6.24	13.8
18	7.96	10.6	—	—
19	7.80	11.0	—	—
20	7.95	11.0	—	—

Note: Decrease of speed at 50 meters from the start in children from 6 to 11 years of age, and at 100 meters from 12 to 20 years of age. Maximum speed was also measured during 50 meters in the former, and during 100 meters in the latter.

On the other hand, the maximum strength of the knee extensor of each subject was measured by tensiometer to compare the propelling force calculated from the mass of the body and the acceleration of running. As shown in Figure 4, there was found an intimate relation between the propelling force and the maximum strength of the extensor. If the results obtained in trained sprinters were plotted in the same graph as ordinary subjects, the relation became a little different. It was worthy to note that the propelling force calculated from the speed curve was significantly higher in trained sprinters than in untrained subjects of the same muscle strength. This fact may suggest that the isometric muscle strength could be transformed to the dynamic propelling force more efficiently in trained subjects than in the others. The main reason for this difference in both groups may be the difference of the speed of muscle contraction and the grade of neuromuscular coordination.

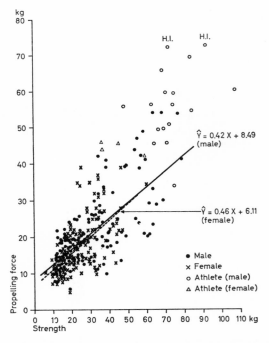

Fig. 4. Relation between maximum strength of the knee extensor and propelling force calculated from the speed curve. (Male): r = 0.733, 0.1% significant. (Female): r = 0.618, 0.1% significant.

Significant Features of Trained Athletes

The same measurement was conducted in trained sprinters of three different grades as shown in Figure 5. Even in the speed curve observed in one of the best runners in Japan, there was still found a steep slope at the beginning of running up to 30 meters, and an uneven plateau of speed after 70 meters to 100. However, it would be expected he could improve his best record by 0.2 second, if he could get a sharp start and keep up the maximum speed in the final stretch as was shown by the dotted line in curve A in Figure 5. It was supposed that the gain would be 0.1 second at the beginning and 0.1 second in the final stretch. Actually, after extensive practise of the starting dash together with specific muscle training of the lower extremities, the record improved from 10.3 seconds to 10.1 seconds in the 100 meters sprint event.

The improvement of the first stretch must be caused by the increasing muscular strength, and of increased muscle power. As the muscular power consisted of force and speed, the strength of the muscle and the speed of muscular contraction of the legs were measured by special devices together with the measurement of mechanical power of the same

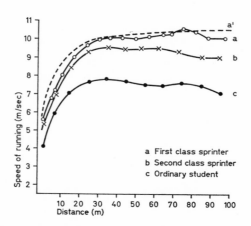

Fig. 5. Speed curve of 100 meter running in trained athletes.

muscles. The mechanical power was measured by a modified inertia ergometer originally devised by Professor HILL (IKAI and KANEKO, 1966). The speed of muscular contraction was measured by a straingauge-Vertical Jump-Reaction Time equipment devised by the present author (IKAI and ASAMI, 1962). The improvement of strength, speed and power was observed in one of the best sprinters in Japan, Mr. Hideo Iijima, as shown in Table III accompanied by the improvement of running performance.

Table III. Improvement of strength, speed and power in sprinter H.I.

Factor	1962 Dec.	1963 Dec.
Muscle strength of knee extensor	98 kg	→ 108 kg
Speed of muscular contraction*	122 msec.	→ 96 msec.
Mechanical power of knee extensor by inertia ergometer. Equivalent mass: 685.0 kg	0.19 HP →	0.32 HP

* A parameter of strain gauge-vertical jump-reaction time (IKAI and ASAMI).

For Improvement of Running Performance

As the next step in the study, strength, speed and power of the extensor muscle of the lower extremities were compared among sprinters with special respect to the best 100 meters running record as shown in Table IV Among male sprinters, H. Iijima, whose best record was 10.1 seconds for 100 meters, showed the highest values of strength, speed and power. Among female sprinters, I. Yoda, whose best record for the 80 meters hurdle was 10.4 seconds, showed the highest values as well.

Table IV. Strength, speed, and power in trained sprinters.

Name	Best record sec	Strength kg	Speed msec	Power HP	
Iijima	10.1	108	96	0.32	Male
Ishikawa	10.5	70	100	0.14	
Hayase	10.5	71	110	0.20	
Yasuda*	10.6	88	94	0.19	
Yoda*	11.6	75	104	0.14	Female
Sukegawa	12.1	70	116	0.14	
Yamazaki	12.2	80	145	0.10	

* Hurdler

It may be concluded from these results that the seasonal measurements of fundamental factors of work capacity such as muscle strength, speed of muscular contraction and mechanical power by muscular contraction, together with the recording of the speed curve of running could present some useful information to improve the performance of running events.

For improvement of ability to keep the speed constant over 70 meters in 100 meters running, the speed-endurance or power-endurance involving the anaerobic muscle activity should be increased sufficiently (IKAI, 1967). From these considerations, the maximum oxygen debt was measured in trained runners after a 300 meters' sprint with effort on a track. The result showed that the maximum oxygen debt was highest in the two top Japanese sprinters, around 15 and 16 liters, while in the average sprinters it was around 10 liters. It was found, as shown in Table 5 that the maximum oxygen debt per kilogram of body weight was higher in sprinter R. Yoshioka than in another sprinter H. Iijima, while the maximum oxygen debt itself was a little lower in the former than the latter. In the meantime, it must be noted here that the measurement of the maximum oxygen debt and the body weight was conducted in Mr. R. Yoshioka in 1934 by members of Japanese Society of Sports Medicine. At that time Mr. Yoshioka's best time was 10.3 seconds for the 100 meters event. Thirty years after sprinter Yoshioka broke the Japanese record, his student sprinter Iijima broke his teacher's record with a time of 10.1 seconds for this distance. It is fortunate that it is possible to compare their anaerobic capacity with their best performance.

Table V. The maximum oxygen debt observed in two top sprinters.

Name	Best record for 100 meters	Running distance for measurement of max. O_2 debt	Running time	Maximum O_2 debt	Maximum O_2 debt per kg	Weight
R. Yoshioka (1934)	10.3 sec	400 m	50.0 sec	15.489 l	254 ml/kg	61.0 kg
H. Iijima (1965)	10.1 sec	300 m	34.3 sec	16.775 l	232 ml/kg	72.0 kg

It would be expected that, if sprinter H.I. could improve the anaerobic capacity per body weight towards that of teacher sprinter R.Y., student sprinter H.I. would improve his own record. As to the improvement of the final stage in 100 meters' running, neuromuscular relaxation must be emphasized as well as the increase of energy production.

References

1. Furusawa, K.; Hill, A.V. and Parkinson, J.L.: The dynamics of 'sprint running'. Proc. roy. Soc. B. *102:* 29–42 (1928).
2. Henry, F.M. and Trafton, I.R.: The velocity curves of sprint running with some observations on the muscle viscosity factor. Res. Quart. *22:* 409–422 (1951).
3. Hill, A.V.: Living machinery; pp. 230–232. (Harcourt Brace, New York 1927).
4. Ikai, M. and Asami, T.: Straingauge—vertical jump reaction time measurement equipment and its application. Olympia (in Japanese) *7:* 154–165 (1961).
5. Ikai, M. et Kaneko, M.: Etude de la puissance musculaire à l'aide d'une roue à inertie. Théorie et Pratique Culture physique *3*; 5–11 (1966).
6. Ikai, M.; Shibayama, H. and Ishii, K.: A kinesiological study of sprint running (in Japanese). J. of P.E. Res. (Japanese Society of Physical Education), *7:* 1–12 (1963).

Author's address: M. Ikai, M.D., School of Education. University of Tokyo, Hongo, *Tokyo* (Japan).

Biomechanics I, 1st Int. Seminar Zurich 1967
pp. 291–302 (Karger, Basel/New York 1968)

School of Health, Physical Education, Indiana University Bloomington

Kinesiology of High Jumping

J.M. Cooper

A high jumper is first a runner and then a jumper. He must first overcome the inertia of his body and put it in motion [11, 12, 13]. Then he must compensate for decelerating forces including the action of his feet against the ground by greater acceleration (6 : 149). He runs against internal viscosity, air resistance, gravity, friction and centrifugal forces. He jumps by projecting his center of gravity in the air with a rotational component so that he is able to move upward yet cross over a bar. It must be borne in mind that walks, runs and jumps are modifications of the human stepping reflex pattern. Man as he matures progresses from walking, to running, to jumping. He may make modifications in the hop, leap and jump movements or combine them through practice into many patterns of movement. Yet all of these are made without conscious direction of the details of the action of the joints involved [3].

A recent preliminary attempt by the author to record the forces displayed at take-off by a high jumper showed that the forces appeared to be relatively similar to those recorded in a walking action during the pushing action of the foot against the ground[1].

Three ideas must be kept in mind when studying high jumping:

(1) Forward or linear momentum is converted through the take-off to a vertical component.

(2) Momentum from parts of the body is transferred to the whole.

(3) There is a rotation of the body during the flight phase of the jump [7].

The high jumper attempts to elevate his center of gravity into the air as high as possible vertically. This is accompanied by a rotational

---

[1] Use of force-plate was made available by courtesy of Prof. A.H. Ismail, Purdue University.

component which enables him to go over a bar placed at given height. DYSON [5] assigns a value of 90% to the spring or lift factor in relation to the height attained. The style of jumping is the other main factor involved in the jump. The above value assignment needs further investigation.

The running approach phase results ultimately in vertical lift. The initiation of the rotation needed by the jumper to clear the bar is begun at the take-off.

The optimum proper angle of approach has been debated by the performers and investigators alike for many years. A study of Avant, USA 7' jumper, revealed that he approached the bar from a 60° angle. Brumel (Russia) appeared to use a 35° to 40° angle. It is hypothesized that an angle of 20° is the most optimal. The reasons for proposing this optimum angle are:

(1) The less the bar is at right angles to the jumper's directional line of approach, the less apt it is to be dislodged if struck by a part of his body.

(2) The free leg's thrust upward is less apt to be impeded in its flight if the approach is at a low angle.

(3) In the high angle or frontal approach normally the jumper will need to turn the take-off foot to the right or left of his line of movement in order to plant it, so that the center of gravity will eventually be directly under it momentarily. Thus the line of flight is established. The turn of the foot will be necessary so that the free leg can be comfortably swung upward. However, this movement of the foot from the direct line would interfere with the efficiency of the jump. Brumel's plant of the foot is perpendicular to the bar. On the other hand, the use of an approach angle of less than 20° would mean the jumper would have difficulty crossing the bar between the uprights and would probably land outside the pit.

The take-off foot acts as a fulcrum over which the body rotates. The forces at take-off are forward, vertical and lateral. The vertical and forward forces should be the largest. In a sense the whole body rotates about an axis at a point where the take-off foot contacts the ground. Landing theorically should then be on the back thus signifying the rotation factor.

The height of the jump may be expressed as follows:

$$H = V \sin \Theta - \tfrac{1}{2} g t^2$$
$H =$ height in feet

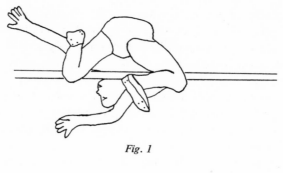

Fig. 1

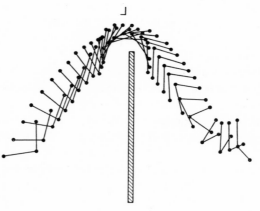

Fig. 1a

V = Velocity at take-off in feet per sec
Θ = angle of take-off from ground in degrees
t   = ½ time in air from take-off to landing
g = 32.2 feet per sec²
S = horizontal distance of jump
T = time of flight in air

Horizontal distance of jump may be expressed S = V cos Θ T.

Increasing (1) Velocity at take-off (2) the angle at take-off and (3) the time in the air should result in greater height being attained. Many estimates of the potentials rise of the center of gravity of the jumper have been made by TARRANT [14], CURETON [4], BUNN [1], DRYSON [5], and others. If a man were to attain a total body velocity of 16–18′ per second thus raising the center of gravity of the body 4½ feet or more plus having a standing center of gravity of 3½ feet this would give him a center of gravity elevation of 8′. Therefore, he could jump anywhere from 7′ 6″ to 8′ or slightly more if he could use a style of clearance of the bar that would have the center of gravity go beneath it.

For purposes of determining the $4\frac{1}{2}′$ lift of the c/gr the following assumptions were made:

(1) The jumper is able to sustain on his take-off leg a weight of at least twice his own actual weight (2g or more).

(2) That he rocks up his toes, extends his take-off leg, flexes his trunk as he takes off.

(3) His arms and swinging leg add 9 or more inches to the c/gr lift (the leg is assumed to be 20% of the total body weight).

(4) He attains a total body velocity of approximately 16–18′ per second.

(5) He is over 6′ tall.

Avant, an American jumper, aside from his standing height did considerably less than those mentioned above. Calculations [1a] on him are as follows:

Time of take-off to landing = 0.95 sec.

Estimated center of mass cleared bar 11″ at a point directly over the bar.

Projection body velocity at take-off 14.4 feet per sec.

Time of last 3 strides = 0.61 sec
Time of final stride = 0.16 sec
Speed of last 3 strides = 36 ft per sec
Speed of last stride = 43.9 ft per sec

Yet it was estimated that he could have jumped 7′ 6″ using his present style and approach but with one exception. He must place his legs (more particularly his take-off leg) in an extended position over the bar. (See Fig. 1, 1a). He cleared the bar at 6′ 8″ jump as follows:

Left or lead leg $12\frac{1}{2}$ in
Left or lead knee $8\frac{1}{4}$ in
Right or take-off foot $16\frac{1}{2}$ in
Estimated center of mass 11 in

Descriptive analysis (Motion pictures of Brumel (Russia) (Fig. 2) with some of Thomas (USA) were used for the analysis contained in the following pages:

Fig. 2

The approach run involves extension and flexion of the arms and legs done in a sound mechanical manner. It is thought that very few high jumpers run as effectively as sprinters. Brumel's (Russia) arms were carried in a rather unusual way during the approach. The fact that he carried them in an abducted position as he swings them back and forth tends to lower his center of gravity and prepare him for first backward and then upward movements of his arms. Perhaps a greater kinesthetic awareness of their position and subsequent use was created. Also, occurring concurrently with the extension and flexion of the legs at take-off is the contraction of the back and trunk muscles and their subsequent release.

The long next to last step followed by a shorter step with a backward lean-trunk extension (displacement of the c/gr to the rear) enables the jumper to firmly but gently place the whole foot, heel first against the ground. This last step is shorter than the previous three. This foot plant occurs at the same time as does flexion of the knee of the take-off foot (CHRISTYALSOV [2]) has stated that 30–45 % of the power developed in the take-off push is related to the strength gotten from the swinging leg).

The sequence of movement of the arms and legs must be timed so that all body impacts (such as one segment for example the arm moving against the body) are utilized with the leg and foot push against the ground. Maximum backward force and transfer of momentum are

Brumel speed of last stride = 7.5 meters per sec. Yessis Review, Vol. 1, Dec. 1966, p. 108.

then utilized in the upward thrust of the body. The pelvis is first dropped as the opposite foot to the take-off one is turned out and the knee is flexed (next to last step). During the last step, the pelvis begins to move forward and upward and then as it passes the vertical slows down in speed. Next, the lead leg swings by the take-off leg. The swing or lead leg is swung from a flexed position at the knee since it was in a previously flexed supporting position. It then is moved rapidly by the contracting muscles to a position of knee extension beyond the horizontal so that the great impact of the swinging leg is made against the body before take-off. The knee is then flexed so that the leg may be carried easier up to the top of the bar.

During the shortened last stride the pelvic is tilted to the rear and the center of gravity has begun to rise. This is the reason that the best high jumpers have a shortened last stride. Yet several good high jumpers because they have not accelerated sufficiently during the run up approach phase (because of running at a slow pace or because of using only a 3 to 5 stride instead of the normal 7 to 9 pattern) must use a quick fast stride to accelerate that does not last enough and the last stride is too short in length to enable them to have the foot on the ground long enough.

It is evident that great strength is needed at positions that last for only fractions of a second (Figure 3). It has been unofficially reported that Brumel spent 80% of his time on strength conditioning and 20% on form in preparation for the 1964 Olympics. This can only be accomplished by having the jumper work against artificial resistance at certain critical angles. Such a device is now being developed at Indiana University with the use of a harness and rubber resistance device.

Fig. 3

Up to now the main emphasis in the training of the high jumper has been on thrust or lift at take-off with the plant foot, very little time is spent on transference of the momentum of the body parts to the whole. This plus improvement of layout should be stressed more in the future in training.

When in the air if a part of the body moves in one direction another part will move in an opposite direction at the same time [9]. If for example, the head moves down the hips move up in relation to the body. However, the parabolic flight of a high jumper is a smooth curve related to the angle of take-off. Thus if the curve is steeper the jumper will go higher.

Flexibility of foot is another consideration often overlooked in training the high jumper. The more flexible the foot the more rocking motion from the heel to toe will take place. It has been found that the longer the malleolus-distal measurement in proportion to the total foot length and the longer the molleolus to metatarsal-phalangeal measurement in proportion to the heel-to-metatarsal-phalangeal measurement the greater the jumping ability. HOWELL [8] refers to this relatively long ankle to toe measurement to be the best adapted for jumping. Perhaps fast runners should make the best jumpers. HILDEBRAND [6, 10, 12] has stated that fast runners are usually high jumpers among the animals since they are equipped structurally for both speed running and jumping.

The rhythm (foot sounds) of the run seems to be consistently similar among the United States' jumpers. Figure 4 shows the rhythm of Erne Shelton USA 6′ 11″ jumper (former world record holder). He stated in conversation with the writer that the higher the bar the more the tendency to run faster and use the quick step sooner. Brumel appears to have a slightly different rhythm. His fast step is his next to last step.

The next to last step taken outward (foot everted-abducted) of Brumel and the arms being abducted and elbows hyperextended to the rear at one point thus raised some interesting questions. It appears that the abducted step would help in the subsequent movement of the center

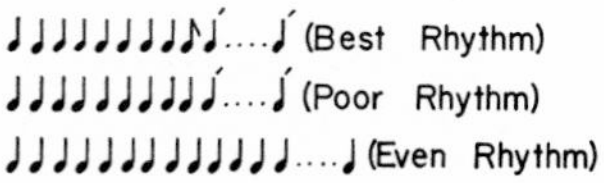

♩♩♩♩♩♩♩♩♩....♩ (Best Rhythm)
♩♩♩♩♩♩♩♩♩♩....♩ (Poor Rhythm)
♩♩♩♩♩♩♩♩♩♩♩♩....♩ (Even Rhythm)

Fig. 4

of gravity toward the left foot. (Several Americans have done this in the past during their last stride. However, this misdirected the path of their flight.) There is also rotation of the shoulders by Brumel so that his body is placed in direct alignment with the bar.

Brumel's arms are moved to the hyperextended and to the rear abducted position as the take-off foot strides the ground. This increases the jumper's forward and upward component. This arm position is so unusual that its potential for increasing thrust and rotation was investigated. It was thought that the backward movement of the arms would enable Brumel to gain greater height. Recently one of my students (JAMES BROWN [16]) did a study in which he compared the so-called Russian and traditional method (arms extended rearward) (arms extended overhead) of executing the front somersault in the floor exercise in gymnastics. The backward movement of the arms of the tumble were similar to those used by Brumel, hence the value of the study. His results (see Fig. 5) are as follows:

Front Somersault Comparison

	Time in Air	Distance traveled	Highest height of part of body	Contact time of feet against floor
Regular or Traditional	1.06	13′ 6″	6′ 1½″	0.23
Russian	1.06	14′ 1″	6′ 3″	0.23
		(same subject in each)		

The difference in favor of the Russian method appears to be in the upward thrust and rotational speed. The tumbler using the Russian style is in more of a sitting position prior to take-off (knees at angles of $142°$ as compared to $150°$). Also there is more flexion at the hips before take-off. The speed of the arms at take-off is more than seven times that of the regular style. Back to the analysis, as soon as Brumel's arms reach the level of the head the arm on the opposite side to the take-off leg continues its upward thrust while the other arm remains stationary. This would be in keeping with the synchronous opposite

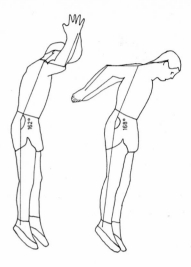

Fig. 5

arm and leg movements involved in most motor activities [9]. At take-off the back at first is kept upright then is flexed. The pelvic is situated somewhat ahead of the shoulders.

It must be remembered that the preparation for the rotation about the bar is made in a large measure at the take-off. The thrust upward is made through the center of gravity but eccentrically. Ideally a 90° angle of take-off would project the jumper upward but would not enable him to rotate over the bar so he must sacrifice a certain amount of optimum angle position to get over the bar. A 78° angle of take-off is the largest angle yet recorded by the writer of any outstanding jumper. The possibility of a higher angle of take-off in the future is not beyond the theoretical realm of accomplishment.

The higher the jumper goes in the air the less rotation he needs to turn about the bar because the higher the center of gravity is raised the more time he has to place his body advantageously about the bar. Yet he has only approximately 0.4 sec. (Avant's time from take-off to landing was 0.95 sec) so the rotation and method of layout are thus somewhat committed at the take-off. The greater the horizontal speed component the more difficult this would be to accomplish. CHISTYALSOV [2] has reported a speed of 7.5 meters (23.7') per sec in the last step.

Avant USA 7′ jumper was recorded at 4.5 meters (14.7 ft per second) for the last stride (jumping 6′ 8″). Attempts at higher speeds would involve a breaking action at the foot plant that present day jumper's muscles aren't conditioned to withstand.

Since the take-off involves rotation about the foot as an axis, the foot plant temporarily checks the linear momentum and enables it to be converted into vertical lift. The arms and swinging leg momenta are transferred as angular momenta from the part to the whole. The jumper is then literally pulled from the ground into the air by his own inertia.

The fully extended free leg begins to flex at the knee when the leg goes just beyond the horizontal (70°). It then flexes and remains in this position until crossing the bar when it almost extends again.

The extension of the elbow and flexion of the shoulder of the arm opposite to the take-off foot enables him to place it over the bar followed by his head and chest. He moves his arm downward in some shoulder flexion and internal rotation. His opposite arm is held in close to and across the chest with the elbow flexed. As the opposite arm goes toward the pit the flexed elbow of the other arm is raised in keeping with the spiral and diagonal principle of movement. The rear leg is flexed and carried behind the body. The rotating action of the body will cause the jumper to land on his back.

Teaching and coaching procedures might involve a sequence of practices that include in progression walking, running, hurdling, and then high jumping. Experiencing the kinethetic feeling of jumping a height of 7′ 6″ to 8′ in the air might be accomplished by the use of a beat board or by jumping off a mound. Perhaps a device could be developed to propel a jumper to a height beyond his present best effort. The hypothesis is that once he attained this height albeit through artificial means he could again accomplish it. His muscles must first be conditioned to this type of experience.

A mental image of the path he must travel in his flight over the bar could be created by having a picture of a top perfomance's path photographed by means of the light tracing technique (see figure 6).

Thus it may be concluded that the requirements heeded for world record high jumping are:

1. Long legs—high center of gravity [12, 8].
2. Enough speed and strength at take-off to give an upward thrust of considerable magnitude.

Fig. 6

3. The jumping foot being placed on the ground long enough for the arms, swinging leg, foot and toe to contribute transference of momentum.

4. A style of crossing the bar more like a tumble so that the center of gravity doesn't actually cross over the top of the bar but goes beneath it.

The last three named are the most important.

References

1.a ABBOTT, L.: A Study of Robert Avant—High Jumper, unpublished report, Indiana University, 1967.
1.b BROWN, J.: Comparative study of two methods of executing the front somersault, unpublished report, Indiana University, 1967.
1.c BUNN, J.W.: Scientific Principles of Coaching, Prentice-Hall, Inc., 000–000 (1955).
2. CHISTYALSOV, U.: Instruction in the take-off technique track and field *6:* 7–8, 1966 (Yessis Translation Review, Fullerton, Calif., 1966). – The run of a high jumper, Track and Field *8:* 7–8, 1966 (Yessis Translation Review, Fullerton, Calif., 1966).
3. COOPER, J.M. and GLASSOW, R.: Kinesiology (Mosby, 1967).
4. CURETON, T.K., Mechanics of the High Jump, Scholastic Coach, April, 1935.
5. DYSON, G.: The Mechanics of Athletics (University of London Press, Cambridge 1966).
6. HILDEBRAND, M.: How animals run, Sci. Amer. *202:* 148–157 (1960).
7. HOPPER, B.J.: The Dynamical Basis of Physical Movement, Strawberry Hill Booklets No. 2, Physical Laboratory, St. Mary's College, Twickenham, 1959.
8. HOWELL, A.B.: Speed in Animals (University of Chicago Press, Chicago 1944).
9. KNOTT, M. and VOSS, E.D.: Proprioceptive Neuromuscular Facilitation (A Hoebes-Harper Book, New York, 1956).

10. KRAKOWER, H.: Skeletal characteristics of the high jumper, Res. Quart. amer. Ass. Hlth. phys. Educ. *6;* 2, 75–84, 1935.
11. LLOYD, B.B.: The energetics of running: An analysis of running. Adv. Sci. *22*; 515–530 (1965).
12. MORTON, D.J.: Human Locomotion and Body Form (Williams & Wilkins, Baltimore, 1952).
13. SLOCUM, D.B. and BOWERMAN, W.: The biomechanics of running. Clin. Orthop. *23:* (1962).
14. TARRANT, G.T.: Mechanics of Human and Animal Activity. The School Science Review, No. 78 (Murray, London 1938).

Author's address: JOHN M. COOPER, Director of Graduate Studies, School of Health, Physical Education, Indiana University, *Bloomington,* Ind. 47401 (USA).

Biomechanics I, 1st Int. Seminar Zurich 1967
pp. 303–310 (Karger, Basel/New York 1968)

Elevation Movement in Man: Theory, Specific Elevation Test, Statistics

F. UCCELLI[1]

Introduction

In this article we shall consider elevation movement in man in its simplest form, which consists in the execution of a break in contact with the ground, either with or without a spring. In undertaking the study of this movement it is necessary to remember that:

a) man is in surroundings characterized both by the presence of a field of force directed towards the ground (the gravitational field), and by a gas of constant density (air).

b) the action of human muscular forces is transferred to an upwards spring which is opposed to the action of the field of gravity.

Movement is determined by applying to the centre of gravity of man the force resulting from the vectorial composition of the muscular thrust of the man with the gravitational force. The presence of air has no appreciable effect on movement given the low speeds reached and the short distances covered by a man during the ascent and the descent phases.

Movement Equations

Let us consider a man of weight-form P_0, and let $F = F(z)$ be the resultant of the muscular forces employed during the first phase of the movement, between the instant when the man is completely crouched on the ground and the moment when he breaks contact with the ground (Fig. 1). In this phase, the centre of gravity B passes from the rate of z_1 to that of z_2, and the equation of movement is therefore:

[1]C.O.N.I.-Scuola Centrale dello Sport, Roma.

$$F(z) - P_0 = -P_0/g \cdot d^2z/dt^2; \tag{1}$$

with: $g = 9,81 \text{ m/s}^2 =$ acceleration of gravity; $d^2z/dt^2 =$ (variable) acceleration along the axis z.

The integration of the differential equation (1) can only be made if the progression of muscular force $F(z)$ is known, which can, however, be found experimentally.

During the second phase which is in course from the moment of breaking contact with the ground (rate z_2 of the centre of gravity) to the instant of maximum distance from the ground (rate z_3), only forces of inertia are in operation so that the movement equation becomes:

$$d^2 z/dt^2 = -g; \tag{2}$$

The third phase of the movement is formed by a return from the rate z_3 to the rate z_2 and during its course the following equation holds good:

$$d^2z/dt^2 = g; \tag{3}$$

Finally, during the fourth phase of the movement, (braking phase) from the rate z_2 to the rate z_1 (or even lower), there is the equation:

$$P_0 - F_1(z) = -P_0/g \cdot d^2z/dt^2; \tag{4}$$

The force $F_1(z)$, which is in a contrary direction to $F(z)$, cannot coincide exactly with the $F(z)$, since the muscles using it operate inversely (those which during the first phase had a stretching action are now used for compression, and vice versa.)

Energy Analysis of the Movement

The transformations of energy connected with the movement are:

a) the muscular work of the first phase is transformed into kinetic energy (which reaches its maximum at the moment when contact with the ground is broken), and this, in proportion as the centre of gravity rises from rate z_1 to z_3 is entirely transformed into potential gravitational energy.

b) at the rate z_3 the potential energy is at its maximum, and with the initiation of the phase of descent its re-conversion into kinetic energy comes about; this energy, at the moment of the impact of the man on the ground again reaches its maximum value, identical to that of the moment of breaking contact with the ground.

c) after the impact, the energy is converted to heat through the work of the muscle which gradually effect a genuine braking action.

Let us indicate with V the speed assumed by the centre of gravity B at the moment of breaking contact with the ground (rate z_2). The energy equilibrium between this instant and that of return to the ground may be expressed as follows:

$$\tfrac{1}{2} \cdot P_0/g \,(V^2 - v^2) = P_0 \,(z - z_2); \tag{5}$$

where v and z are respectively the speed and the rate at an indeterminate instant. Naturally when it is $z = z_1$, then $v = V$.

At rate z_3 then $v = 0$. In these conditions V could be obtained, as follows:

$$V = \sqrt{2\,g\,(z_3 - z_2)} \tag{6}$$

We also propose that the 'time of suspension' be obtained, that is the time that elapses between the instant at which contact is broken and that of impact.

Between the rate z_2 and the rate z_3, since upward movements is naturally decelerated movement, we can write

$$\tfrac{1}{2}\,gt^2 = z_3 - z_2 \tag{7}$$

having represented the time elapsed by t. From (7) we obtain:

$$t = \sqrt{2\,(z_3 - z_2)/g} \tag{8}$$

and for the conservation of the gravitational field, the suspension time will be:

$$t_s = 2\sqrt{2\,(z_3 - z_2)/g} \tag{9}$$

Specific Elevation

In order to describe human possibilities of elevation, it is particularly useful to introduce the *coefficient of specific elevation*[2].

[2] UCCELLI, F.: Elevation, the prime characteristic of the volley-ball player, J. 'SPORT' —INEPS, Brussels, *26:* 74–78 (1964).

This coefficient makes possible the classification and comparison of one with another of individual possibilities, at whatever age and with whatever physical structure.

Let E_{max} (maximum elevation) for an individual be the maximum height (measured from the ground up) reached by the fingertips of a hand (usually the right hand) when executing a short run and a spring upwards from the ground, which is effected by swinging both arms upwards (Fig. 1).

Naturally it is advisable to repeat the experiment several times and to take highest value reached.

Let us also indicate by the total height (at rest) of an individual measured when the contribution of the arm and hand is included and carrying out measurement when the individual is standing on tip-toe (Fig. 1).

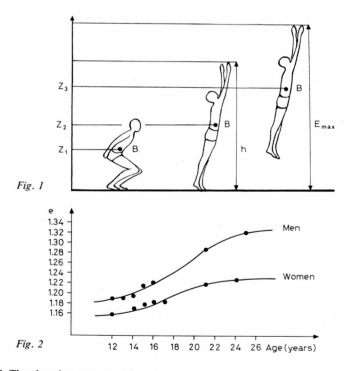

Fig. 1

Fig. 2

Fig. 1. The elevation movement in man.
Fig. 2. The behaviour of the average specific elevation in men and women.

We define as the coefficient of specific elevation (in symbols: e) of an individual the ratio between his maximum elevation and his total height:

$$e = E_{max}/h \qquad (10)$$

The coefficient of specific elevation, if measured in conditions of weight-form, fully expresses the qualities of individual elevation and offers a good basis for estimation of the general motordynamic qualities.

In Tables I and II we show the results of a survey carried out in Belgium of 700 pupils in boys' and girls' schools[3].

In figure 2 we show Tables I and II in diagrammatic form. Measurement of specific elevation carried out in Italy on pupils from boys' teams and volley-ball Juniors, *under training-conditions* produced the results given in Table III.

As can easily be seen the values in Table III are higher than those of Table I, although towards lower age values there is more concordance in the results.

In any case the statistics given above throw light on an essential fact: during the period of physical development (13–20 years) *the specific elevation of an individual,* although subject to oscillations depending on physiological and muscular development and on the condition and training of the individual, *increases on an average with age.*

Table I. Average specific elevation values in relation to age (boys)

Age (years)	Average height (cm)	h average (cm)	E_{max} average (cm)	Average specific elevation
12	151	191	227	1.190
13	155	196	234	1.194
14	159	204	244	1.196
15	168	216	262	1.215
16	170	218	267	1.223
17	174	223	274	1.230
21	175	223	288	1.290
25	179	229	304	1.325

[3] WIELKI, C.: 'Etude de la détente verticale chez les joueurs et joueuses belges de volleyball', J. 'SPORT'—INEPS, Brussels, 7: 29–35 (1961).

Table II. Average specific elevation values in relation to age (girls)

Age (years)	Average height (cm)	h average (cm)	E max average (cm)	Average specific elevation
12	151	190	221	1.160
13	153	193	226	1.168
14	159	201	234	1.170
15	160	203	240	1.180
16	162	204	242	1.185
17	162	204	242	1.185
21	164	208	255	1.225
24	165	210	259	1.232

Table III. Average specific elevation values in relation to age (boys) cont. when in training

Age (years)	13–14	14–15	15–16	16–18	18–20	20–22	22–24
Average Specific Elevation	1.190	1.240	1.260	1.300	1.320	1.335	1.345

This fact immediately suggests that it could usefully be applied to the sports field: the coefficient of specific elevation could be used as a test for pre-selection. It would obviously be advantageous to direct towards those sports requiring frequent vertical elevation movements boys who, independently of their physical-muscular structure, have already at 12–13 years of age a high specific elevation coefficient value (over 1.20, if possible).

The coefficient of specific elevation may also be employed as an absolute method of comparison of the effective possibilities for 'breaking contact' with the ground. Naturally this is only significant for athletes of 22 years of age and more, when the specific elevation can be considered as a constant.

And we can certainly consider as *mediocre possibilities* athletes with specific elevation of 1.24 to 1.28; *good possibilities* those from 1.28 to 1.32 and *excellent possibilities* those from 1.32 to 1.36.

Specific elevation moreover, as is easily seen, influences the speed of breaking contact with the ground V and the time of suspension t_s.

In fact being within the formulas (6) and (9) (Fig. 1):

$$z_3 - z_2 = E_{max} - h = h\,(e - 1) \tag{11}$$

we shall have:

$$V = \sqrt{2gh\,(e - 1)} \tag{12}$$

$$t_s = 2\sqrt{2h\,(e - 1)/g} \tag{13}$$

(12) and (13) clearly show the dependence of V and t_s on the co-efficient of specific elevation.

Influence of Individual Weight on Specific Elevation

As it is logical to suppose, a man can have the maximum values for his specific elevation only if the conditions of weight-form and, naturally, of training are at their best. In the event (which occurs frequently) that his weight exceeds the weight-form, elevation is less. Let us then see what is the dependence of specific elevation on the weight of an individual.

In the development of the calculations we shall suppose that the positive weight variation does not influence the value of the drive supplied by the muscles.

This hypothesis fits in well with reality as long as the variation in excess weight does not exceed 15–20 kg.

Let us indicate with P_0 the weight-form and with e_0 the corresponding specific elevation; with P (greater than P_0) and with both the weight and the corresponding specific elevation in altered conditions.

We shall express the transformation of the muscular work in potential gravitational energy, both in weight-form conditions and in altered conditions:

$$\int_{z_1}^{z_2} [F(z) - P_0]\,dz = P_0 z_2 + P_0\,h\,(e_0 - 1); \tag{14}$$

$$\int_{z_1}^{z_2} [F(z) - P]\,dz = P \cdot z_2 + Ph\,(e - 1); \tag{15}$$

By developing the integrals and subtracting member by member (15) from (14) we have:

$$e = P_0/P \cdot e_0 + (1 - P_0/P)\,[1 - (2z_2 - z_1)/h]; \tag{16}$$

From measurements made directly of the athletes it can be said approximately:

$$1 - (2z_2 - z_1)/h \simeq 0,13;$$

so that (16) becomes:

$$e = P_0/P \cdot e_0 + 0,13\,(1 - P_0/P); \tag{17}$$

The approximation can be considered legitimate, given that the factor $0,13\,(1 - P_0/P)$ does not exceed 1% of the total value of e.

By means of (17), if e_0, P_0, P are known, it is possible to obtain the loss in specific elevation deriving from the increase in weight. It is likewise possible, if e, P, P_0 are known, to obtain the increase in specific elevation that could be reached by a man of weight P if he were able to return to the conditions of weight-form P_0.

Weight-form tables in relation to height and individual types are to be found in medical literature.

Author's address: Ing. FABIO UCCELLI, via Faenza 66, *Firenze* (Italia).

Biomechanics I, 1st Int. Seminar Zurich 1967
pp. 311–314 (Karger, Basel/New York 1968)

Der Hochsprung der Watussi –
im Vergleich zu anderen Hochsprungformen

E. Simon, Tel-Aviv

Der Hochsprung wurde in Europa relativ spät als Wettkampfdisziplin aufgenommen. Leistungsmessung mit Sprungständer, Meßskala und Sprungplatte bzw. -leine setzen schon viel technisches Wissen voraus. Die ersten mir bekannten Abbildungen vom Hochsprung, dem turnerischen *Hock*-sprung, erscheinen bei Gutsmuths im Jahre 1793; er ist dort so selbstverständlich beschrieben, daß er älteren Ursprungs sein dürfte; später 1813, 1845 finden wir den *Hock*-sprung bei Jahn und Eiselen.

Es ist umso überraschender, daß bei einem Stamme in Zentralafrika – bei den *Watussi* – eine Tradition mit einer modernen Technik im Hochsprung bereits bestand, als die ersten Europäer 1854 dieses Territorium aufsuchten. Berichte weisen auf erstaunliche Leistungen von 2,50 m Höhe hin. Der Ethnologe Weule erwähnt, daß nach mündlichen Angaben seines Kollegen Wiedenfeld-Leipzig das Überspringen der eigenen Körperhöhe bei den Watussi zum Ritual der Mannbarkeitserklärung gehörte. Die Watussi gelten als die größten Menschen, im Durchschnitt 1,90 m bis 2,00 m, selbst 2,20 m sind nicht selten.

Technik des Watussi Hochsprunges

Über die Technik des Watussi Hochsprunges gibt die Bilderserie 1 Auskunft. Der Sprung gleicht weitgehend dem «amerikanischen Schersprung».

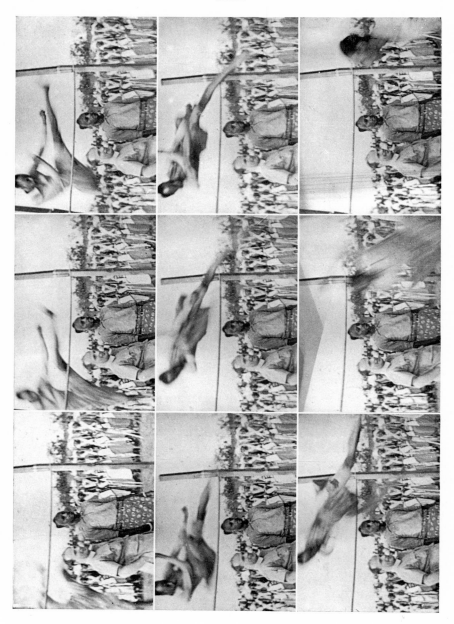

Fig. 1

Vergleich des Watussi-Sprunges mit einer modernen Hochsprungleistung

In Tabelle A sind die Angaben eines vom Autor ausgewerteten Watussi-
sprunges den Leistungen des USA Athleten John Thomas gegenübergestellt. Bei der Berechnung wurde berücksichtigt, daß der Watussi von
einem Termitenhügel absprang, der ca. 30 cm hoch war.

Tabelle A: Vergleich des Hochsprunges eines Watussi mit dem USA-Athleten J. Thomas

	Watussi	Thomas
Körperlänge	200 cm	197 cm
Körpergewicht	90,0 kg	88,0 kg
Höhe der Latte (Leine)	217 cm	223 cm
Minus Thermitenhügel (30 cm)	187 cm	–
KSP im Stehen	107 cm	105,5 cm
vom Thermitenhügel	137 cm	–
KSP in der Höhe des Sprunges	256 cm	240 cm
Tatsächliche Hebung des Körperschwerpunktes	119 cm	134,5 cm

KSP = Körperschwerpunkt

Schlußfolgerung

1. Hochsprung wurde bei den Watussi bereits geübt, bevor er als
   Wettkampf in den modernen Sport eingeführt wurde. Dieser Volks-
   stamm entwickelte selbständig eine Technik, die dem «amerikanischen Schersprung» ähnlich ist.
2. Die Tatsache, daß ein Jüngling zur Mannbarkeitserklärung seine
   eigene Körperhöhe überspringen mußte, spricht für eine weite Brei-
   tenentwicklung des Hochsprunges.
3. Auf Grund der Vergleiche entsprechen die Durchschnittsleistungen
   der Watussi im Hochsprung etwa dem Weltrekord von 1908.
4. Es ist anzunehmen, daß individuelle Leistungen höher waren, jedoch
   gibt es keine exakten Angaben von Sprüngen über 2,50 m.
5. Es wäre zu begrüßen, wenn eine Expertenkommission (Anthropo-
   logen, Physiologen, Sportfachleute etc.) mit entsprechender moder-
   ner Ausrüstung exakte Untersuchungen und Aufnahmen an Ort
   und Stelle vornehmen würde.

Anmerkung

Anschließend an meinen Vortrag machte mich Herr Prof. Dr. E. JOKL darauf aufmerksam, daß er im Jahre 1941 einen Artikel über die Hochsprungtechnik der Watussi veröffentlicht hat:

JOKL, E.: High Jump Technique of the Central African Watussis *in:* Journal of Physical Education and School Hygiene, Vol. XXXIII, Nr. 100, November 1941.

Literatur

EISELEN, E.: Abbildungen von Turnübungen, Berlin (1845).

GUTSMUTHS: Gymnastik für die Jugend, Schnepfenthal (1793 und 1804).

JAHN, F.J. und EISELEN, E.: Die Deutsche Turnkunst, Faksimiledruck der 1. Auflage Berlin (1816), in Quellenbücher der Leibesübungen, Dresden (1927).

WEULE, K.: Ethnologie des Sports *in:* BONGENG, C.A.E., Weltgeschichte des Sports aller Völker und Zeiten, Stuttgart (1926).

Adresse des Autors: E. SIMON, M.D., 40, Ruppin Street, *Tel-Aviv* (Israel).

Biomechanics I, 1st Int. Seminar Zurich 1967
pp. 315–319 (Karger, Basel/New York 1968)

Department of Physical Education for Women of the University of Wisconsin,
Madison, Wisc.

Mechanical Analysis of Kicking

Elizabeth M. Roberts and A. Metcalfe

Kicking is essentially a variation of running [4] (Fig. 1). As in running, rotation of the pelvis precedes joint actions in the swinging limb. Hip flexion follows, accelerating the forward motion of the thigh. Knee extension comes in last adding the final speed to the kicking foot.

The data included here were taken from 16 mm film; overhead, side and front or back views of each performance taken simultaneously. Cameras were set for 64 frames/sec and 1/400 shutter speed, placed 35 to 40 feet from the subject. A clock to establish true frame time was shown in one view. A multidimensional timer[1] [2] to coordinate the three films was included in all 3 views. Belts of aluminium and styrofoam were placed on the subjects to measure pelvic rotation. The adult subjects included professional, city league, and university team performers. Representative case data is used for illustration.

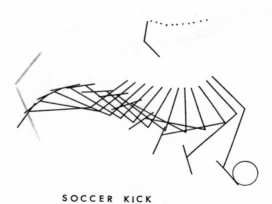

SOCCER KICK

Fig. 1. Segment lines of kicking limb and dot on shoulder at 0.0152 sec intervals.

[1] The timer is under redesign and construction by T.W. Roberts, University of Wisconsin, Madison for purposes of synchronizing films with E.M.G.

The early influence of pelvic rotation on the foot in a kick is best indicated in an overhead view tracing (Fig. 2), in which the kicking foot shortly after it is lifted from the ground can be seen to move laterally (to the right with reference to the head) as well as forward toward the ball. Many soccer players and punters in football approach at an angle to the direction of the kick thereby increasing the useable range of pelvic rotation.

The participation of pelvic rotation in the kick over and above that used in running appears to develop as early as 2 years of age.

Hip flexion which increases foot speed in the sagittal plane follows pelvic rotation. In Figure 1 hip flexion can be identified between the first 4 and the last 2 frames where the thigh lines are not essentially parallel. Though pelvic and hip action would tend to move the foot laterally and downward respectively, knee flexion counteracts the early effect of these actions both on direction and rate of motion of the foot.

SOCCER KICK — OVERHEAD VIEW

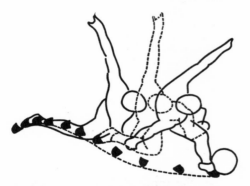

Fig. 2. Path of foot in transverse plane. Intervals 0.0149 sec.

The angular motion of the leg in space in the sagittal plane is a combination of rotation of the thigh and action at the knee joint (Fig. 3). As the non-kicking heel contacts the ground knee flexion is in opposition to thigh rotation forward so that there is little net rotation of the leg. When knee flexion slows the leg begins to rotate due to hip flexion. When knee extension starts and accelerates, the leg gains speed. Meantime the thigh begins to slow and almost stop. Knee extension which does not start until the thigh is past the perpendicular is the

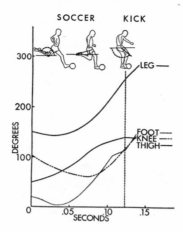

Fig. 3. Knee angle and inclinations of thigh, leg and foot [3] from time of non-kicking heel contact to ball contact.

chief contributor to speed at and through contact. The foot follows the leg rather closely since only slight ankle adjustments occur.

The motions of the leg and thigh in a football punt and place kick follow a pattern very similar to that of a soccer kick. The segments are inclined more forward particularily in the punt since the ball is contacted in the air but the sequence and rate of motion are very similar in all 3 kicks.

The foot speed 15 msec. before contact is of the order of 18 to 24 M/sec: fastest in the punt since the useful ranges of hip flexion and knee extension are greatest. When contact is good the ball speed is 5 to 7 M/sec faster than the foot. The rate of knee extension 15 msec before contact is of the order of 1,500 to 2,000 degrees per sec and it is faster or nearly the same throughout contact (about 15 msec) except in the punt where little range of knee extension remains.

The mechanical and physiological means by which the body achieves these final speeds are not well understood. The thigh slows or stops before contact so that it is contributing little, in a kinematic sense, to foot speed at contact. Yet it seems reasonable to assume that it does make some active contribution to the speed of lower leg rotation.

A similar phenomenon is seen in the overarm throw (Fig. 4). The ball in the hand does not really begin to accelerate in a lateral direc-

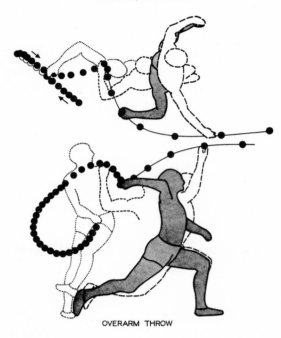

OVERARM THROW

Fig. 4. Overhead (top) and side views with interval between balls of 0.0148 and 0.0117 sec respectively. The shaded figures indicate comparable points in time.

tion (overhead view) until the latter phase of spinal rotation [1] after the shift of weight and pelvic rotation are largely completed. Acceleration in a forward direction does not begin until medial rotation of the humerus starts, about 45 msec. before release.

These facts raise interesting questions regarding the mechanisms of energy transfer from one segment to another. In a mechanical sense the shortening of the radius of rotation by shifting to a more distal axis may tend to initiate rotation around the new axis. This rotation could then be accelerated rapidly by neuromuscular mechanisms which have just undergone active lengthening. The active lengthening which is probably partly due to the inertia of the segment against the motion of the preceeding segment would stretch agonist muscle groups and tend to produce a rate of change response in muscle spindles and joints receptors. These in turn can excite 'reflex' activating and coordinating inputs.

References

1. ATWATER, A.E.: The overarm softball throw; in D.G.W.S. Softball Guide Jan. 1968–70. Amer. Ass. Hlth., phys. Educ., Wash. (in press).
2. BLIEVERNICHT, D.L.: A multidimensional timing device for cinematography. Res. Quart. amer. Ass. Hlth., phys. Educ. *38:* 146–148 (1967).
3. COOPER, J.M. and GLASSOW, R.B.: Kinesiology (C.V. Mosby St. Louis 1963).
4. GLASSOW, R.B. and MORTIMER, E.M.: Analysis of Kicking; in D.G.W.S. Soccer Speedball Guide July 1966–68, pp. 11–16. Amer. Ass. Hlth. phys. Educ., Wash. (1966).

Author's address: ELIZABETH MORTIMER ROBERTS, The University of Wisconsin, Department of Physical Education for Women, *Madison,* Wisc. (USA).

Biomechanics I, 1st Int. Seminar Zurich 1967
pp. 320–323 (Karger, Basel/New York 1968)

Institut für Leibesübungen der Universität Karlsruhe

Motion Recording of Gymnastic Exercises by Means of High-speed Camera Shooting and their Analysis

S. Herrmann

Basic Material

The Institute of Physical Education of the Karlsruhe Technical University, in close cooperation with the Goettingen Institute for Scientific Motion Pictures, has produced films for the documentation of individual gymnastic exercises which combine similar exercises in one block. The single exercise was filmed as a total with 24 and 100 frames per second and as a semi-total with 200 frames per second. The total having 100 frames per second is suitable for analysis. The motion was filmed axially or nearly axially and, at the same time, the exact frame frequency was recorded. The exercises were performed by top-squad members of the German Gymnasts' League.

Analysis

A Lytax analyzer[1] was employed for the analysis. In particular, rotary motions were analyzed using the following procedure:

1. Elaboration of a (Diagram of Motion) Kinegram

Plotting of three determined points of the body: tiptoe, pelvis point as center of the sagittal lines, at the level of the bend of the groin, and shoulder point as perforation point of the shoulder axis at the upper arm. The pelvis and shoulder point plotting requires great accu-

[1] For description of the Lytax analyzer IV/16 see: Research Film, p. 556, Vol. 4, No. 6 (1963).

racy. The (diagram of motion) kinegram (Fig. 1) is obtained by connecting the corresponding points.

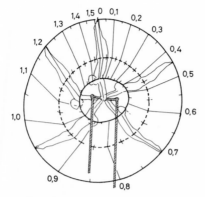

Fig. 1. Kinegram (diagram of motion). The numbers are the times in seconds.

2. Elaboration of a Velocity-time Diagram

Since the available film material's film guiding is excellent it is possible to measure the distance Δs of two continuous points directly. The time difference Δt can be determined with the help of the time scale. The velocity in trajectory v is obtained by dividing Δs by Δt. The velocity-time diagram (v-t) (Fig. 2) results from plotting of v in a reference system.

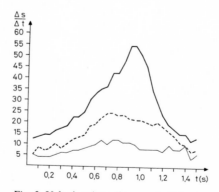

Fig. 2. Velocity-time diagram (v-t) (not smoothed).

In the case of rotary motions around a fixed or nearly fixed axis the angular difference Δφ of leg axis and trunk axis and the angular velocity of legs and trunk are obtained by dividing by Δt. The velocity-time diagram (ω–t) results from plotting in a reference system. (The 'smoothed' diagram shows Fig. 3).

3. 'Smoothing' of the Graphs

Inexactitudes of drawing and measurement make the graphs look like polygonal courses which show, particularly for the angular velocity, many dents. These dents can be 'smoothed' by selection of a larger interval of measurement and by approximation of the polygonal course to a curve (Fig. 3).

4. Calculation of the Hip Angle

The difference of leg and trunk angle for each single position of the body can be derived from the measurement of angle. The result is the hip angle (Fig. 4). This angle shows the degree of bend, i.e. the stretch of the body in the hip area.

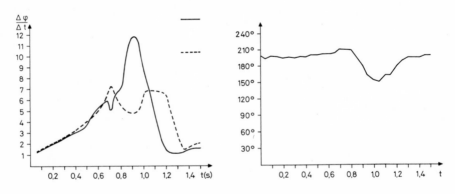

Fig. 3. Velocity-time diagram (ω-t) (smoothed).   *Fig. 4*. Hip angle diagram.

Result

This procedure yields the diagrams 1 through 4 which permit the following statements:

The circling motion (giant circle with fingers held upwards) is a rotary motion in a vertical plane caused by the force of gravity. The loss of energy produced by friction is compensated by reducing the moment of inertia after having passed the vertical line below the horizontal bar. An approach of portions of the body by flexure in the shoulder and hip joint results in the reduction of the moment of inertia and thus in an increase of the speed of rotation. The stretching of the body after having passed the horizontal line causes a deceleration and gain of latent energy which is required in order to compensate the loss of energy and/or to increase the speed of rotation. The velocity-time diagrams and the hip-angle diagram show the point of time for the relative and absolute maxima and minima. By comparing with the motion diagram, the body position for these marked points can be determined.

Authors' address: S. HERRMANN, wissenschaftlicher Assistent am Institut für Leibes-übungen der Universität Karlsruhe (T.H.) (Deutschland).

Biomechanics I, 1st Int. Seminar Zurich 1967
pp. 324–327 (Karger, Basel/New York 1968)

Laboratoire de l'Effort, Université Libre de Bruxelles

Cinematographic and Electromyographic Study of the Front Handspring

M. Hebbelinck and J. Borms

The present paper is concerned with the cinematographic analysis and the general pattern of muscle activity of the upper extremity and with the interplay between specific muscles during the performance of a front handspring on two legs.

The subjects for the investigation were 5 well-trained gymnasts who each performed 4 vaults. In order to have reliable measurements of the center of gravity, according to the method of Braune and Fischer [2], check points were attached to the shoulder, elbow, wrist, hip and foot. By use of a 16 mm camera all vaults were filmed at a camera speed of 64 frames/sec. Six experts in gymnastics evaluated the vaults and on the basis of this judgment two performances were selected, as being excellently and poorly executed from the technical point of view. For both handsprings an analysis was made of the course and the height of the center of gravity of the body, the arms, the swinging and the supporting leg, the head and the hips, as well as an analysis of the speed of different segments. By use of a 4-channel electromyograph action potential registrations were made on the Mm. Trapezius (pars descendens), Triceps brachii (caput longum), Biceps brachii (caput breve), Deltoideus (pars acromialis) and Pectoralis maior (pars clavicularis), according to standardized procedures [3].

Figure 1 shows the comparative EMG sequences on the 5 muscles during the performance of a front handspring. With a precise timing of the action, the drawings show the complete well-performed movement. As we can observe, the muscles begin their action only at the latter part of the run before the take-off (frames 4 to 12). From the beginning the M. Biceps—an antagonistic muscle in this movement—takes part in the action. There is no activity in this muscle when the body rotates

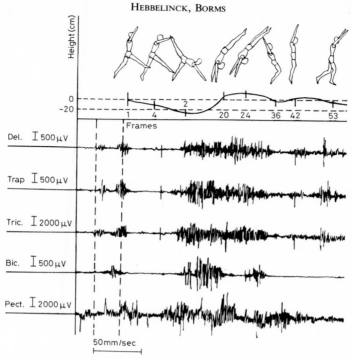

Fig. 1. Comparative electromyographic sequence during the performance of a front hand-spring. The numbering coincides with the numbering of the frames. Abbreviations: DEL: Musculus Deltoideus; TRAP: Musculus Trapezius; TRIC: Musculus Triceps brachii; BIC: Musculus Biceps brachii; PECT: Musculus Pectoralis Maior. The upper curve pre-sents the evolution of the center of gravity of the body.

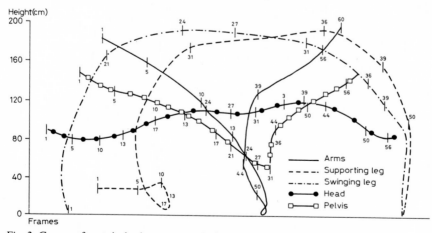

Fig. 2. Curves of certain body segments during a well-performed handspring.

around its transversal axis (frames 20–24). The greatest action potentials are recorded during the push-up phase when the hands hit the floor, followed by a reaction raising the center of gravity and increasing the rotational momentum. During and after the flight phase we observed a fast decrease of muscular activity, which is in agreement with former statements [1].

Figure 2 shows the curves of several body segments during the vault. From the methodical point of view it is interesting to notice the relationship between the course and the height of the swinging and the take-off leg. The evolution of the swinging leg is parabolic. The evolution of the take-off leg corresponds with the general course of the swinging leg, but this leg starts its action earlier. During the take-off phase with the hands, the pelvis functions as an axis around which the legs and trunk rotate; this explains the small variation of the course of the pelvis. The pelvis reaches its highest point during the flight. This height is a major criterium for a well-performed handspring.

References

1. BORRMAN, G.: Untersuchungen über den rhythmischen Charakter bei Übungen. Wiss. Z. D.H.f.K. *3:* 294–295 (1960).
2. BRAUN, W. and FISCHER, O.: Über den Schwerpunkt des menschlichen Körpers. Sächs. Akad. Wiss., Leipzig, Math.-Naturwis. Klasse, Abh. *15:* 559–672 (1889).
3. O'CONNELL, A. and GARDNER, E.B.: The use of electromyography in kinesiological research. Res. Quart. *34:* 167–173 (1963).

Author's address: Prof. Dr. M. HEBBELINCK, Laboratoire de l'Effort, U.L.B., 28, av. P. Heger, *Bruxelles 5* (Belgique).

Biomechanics I, 1st Int. Seminar Zurich 1967
pp. 327–329 (Karger, Basel/New York 1968)

Department of Anatomy, Karolinska Institute, Stockholm

Kinematic Analysis of the Golf Swing

S. Carlsöö

As an example of a combined kinematic and kinetic analysis of a movement I have chosen an analysis of the golf swing performed by the Swedish Champion of 1965 and 1967. About 300 swings with a No. 5 iron have been analysed.

For such an analysis one needs: one: a description of the geometrical form of the movement, two: a chart of the muscle coordination, and three: a record of the magnitude and direction of the forces of support.

In such an analysis it is fundamental that all non-symmetrical body movements are reflected in reaction forces, that is, in forces of support from the ground on which one stands.

The dominating kinematic equation which will be valid is: the torque = the moment of inertia · the angular acceleration. It is consequently the movements of the larger parts of the body and the quicker movements which determine the magnitude of the reaction forces.

The biggest body segment is the trunk, which rotates about an axis which runs approximatively in the body's axis of symmetry through the lower part of the spine. Through a firm grip on the shaft of the club the hands and the club form a mechanical unit, a 'hand-club' segment. This segment rotates round an axis which lies between the left and the right wrist and runs in a radio-ulnar direction. This axis of rotation, however, is, in its turn, moved about the axis of rotation of the trunk. Through the grip of the hands on the club, also the arms and shoulders are coupled to form a mechanical unit, a 'shoulder-arm' segment, which rotates about an axis which on the whole lies within the upper part of the spine. It is the movement of these three

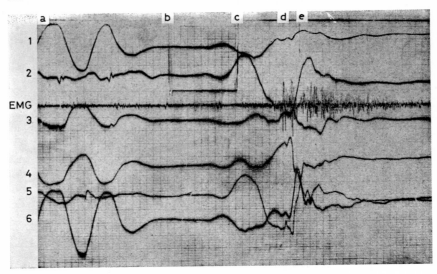

Fig. 1. Kinetic Analysis of the Golf Swing.

Recordings of forces of support and muscle activity. The curves 1, 2 and 3 are the right foot's forces of support (Z, X and Y). When the curve 1 (Z) sinks, the vertical pressure increases, when the curve 2 (X) sinks, there is a horizontal backward-directed force, and when the curve 3 (Y) sinks, there is a medially directed force. The curves 4, 5 and 6 are the left foot's forces of support (Y, X and Z). When the curve 4 (Y) sinks, we have a medially-directed horizontal force, when the curve 5 (X) sinks, there is a forward-directed horizontal force, and when the curve 6 (Z) sinks, the vertical force decreases. The back swing takes place during the period c-d, the down swing during the period d-e, and the impact is in e. EMG is from the oblique abdominal muscles of the right side.

body segments that predominates; and their timing of is decisive for the mechanical result of the swing. We can study this timing by simultaneous recording of the muscle activity and of the magnitude and direction of the force of support, and by filming the sequence of movements.

As measuring instruments for the forces of support, two force plates were used, one for the right foot and one for the left. As force sensitive organs, strain gauges were used (Fig. 1).

Synchronously with these measurements of force, the muscle activity was recorded using the electromyographic technique and the cycle of movements was filmed with a 16 mm camera and with 64 pictures per second. On the camera's rotating shaft was mounted a square metal plate and, adjacent to this on the side of the camera, a microswitch. In this way, every second frame could be marked on the recording paper. As the recorder we used a Honeywell Viscicorder.

It may be added, finally, that when the head of the club was in contact with the aluminium foil which covered the part of the tee where the ball lay, an electric circuit was closed which was likewise marked on the Viscicorder.

This particular player's muscle coordination and timing of the movements of his body segments during the down swing are nearly perfect both from the mechanical and physiological viewpoints. He starts his down swing with a trunk twisting, then follows the soulder segment, then the arm-club segment and finally a very rapid movement in the wrists.

Comparisons between the swing of this champion player and other élite players and swings performed by a couple of average players have been started. Among others we have found that these average players, on the one hand, do not utilize the momentum of the trunk, but work mostly with the arms, and, on the other hand, that the rapid wrist movement at the end of the down swing frequently was missed.

This method gives great possibilities of deciding what is mechanically and what is physiologically essential in the golf swing. Even in an élite player, amateur or professional, one finds individual details in the pattern of movements which are missing in other élite players. Are these details an advantage or a drawback as regards his golfing skill? And are they worth imitating by beginners or the average golfer? These are the questions we hope we can answer with our analyses.

Author's address: S. CARLSÖÖ M.D., Department of Anatomy, Karolinska Institute, *Stockholm* (Sweden).

Biomechanics I, 1st Int. Seminar Zurich 1967
pp. 330–332 (Karger, Basel/New York 1968)

Department of Experimental Pathology and Cancer Research, University of Leeds

Biomechanical Problems in Swimming and Diving

G. Eaves

Although administratively and otherwise swimming and diving are usually linked together, they are, from the biomechanical point of view, very different. This difference may be summarized by saying that in swimming the environment (i.e. water) is of major importance throughout, whereas in diving the environment is usually (and probably justifiably) taken to be so only at the beginning and end of the dive (take-off and entry).

As far as swimming is concerned, the result of this is that very few problems are purely biomechanical, most of them reducing in the end to problems in hydrodynamics. A notable exception is the explanation of the popularity of the six-beat crawl in terms of the conservation of angular momentum. The biomechanical parts of other problems can be solved by the techniques which are being described at this conference. A technique which is worthy of attention but which has not so far been described is the use of nectographs, which produce a trace representative of a swimmer's motion. In the early forms the swimmer was tethered to a machine standing on the bath-side. This produces, however, an artificial action and the results are unreliable. The best instrument so far is the Popham 'Autocritic', which is small enough to be strapped to the swimmer. The main working part is a fan or propellor fixed to an axle which is free to revolve and to slide to and fro in its bearings. When stationary, the system is held in a certain position by a spring. When the system moves through the water, the fan rotates and also moves to and fro. The rotary movement is caused to move a strip of paper under a pen which is made to move across it by the to-and-fro movement. The Lagrangian for the system is separable so, rather surprisingly, the two movements are independent. As described, the system produces a velocity-distance curve. If the paper is driven separately, e.g. by a small electric motor, a velocity-time curve is obtained. The instrument is very sensitive. One can, for instance, very clearly observe the leg-action in crawl superimposed on the movement due to the arm-strokes. There seems to be no reason why a very light model operated by movement through the air should not be made for use in the study of other activities, but this does not appear to have been done so far.

In diving there is scope for a great deal of work which is purely biomechanical. There is, of course, a rapidly developing theoretical mechanics of spring-board function which is beyond the scope of the present meeting, but in the study of the interaction between the body and the board, and in the actions of the body during the flight a great deal has been done and there is still a very considerable amount of purely biomechanical work to be done. I have time to deal with only one problem, which is, however, the central problem in present-day diving theory. I must confess that in putting it before you I hope to pick your brains to find a solution.

We now have a fairly complete general theory of the mechanics of diving [1]. That is to say, we now know in considerable detail the ways in which the various dives may be done. That we cannot say in each case how it has been done is because we have at present no way of determining how much impetus has been taken from the board. In somersaults there is no real problem as we know that all the somersault angular momentum must have come from the board. In twist dives, however, twist may be taken from the board or developed in mid-air and it is the determination of the amount of twist taken from the board which is the real difficulty.

There are two ways of approaching the problem. One is to measure directly the twist taken from the board. The other is to calculate the amount of twist actually shown and that being produced by the action of the body and subtract the second from the first. The difficulty about the first is that some form of force-platform must be used. If it were small enough to go on the end of the board it would upset the diver; if it were large enough to go under the board it would be too insensitive. The difficulty about the second is that of knowing the quantities involved. The only really accurate method would be to kill and dissect each diver. This, unfortunately, is an irreversible process, even to biomechanicists. Measurements on cadavers would give some information but it would be preferable to have the information in respect of the diver himself. A further difficulty is that a synchronised cine-film, taken by three cameras facing along mutually orthogonal axes would be required.

I have had to omit or abbreviate many of the detailed discussions which have been referred to in the text. It is hoped that they will be discussed in full elsewhere, in the near future.

Note. Since the above was written, the Conference has been held and as an outcome of the conversations it now seems to be possible to build a force-platform on to a spring-board in such a way as not to be noticeable by the diver. The way now seems to be open to further experimental studies.

References

1. EAVES, G.: Diring: The mechanics of springboard and firmboard techniques (in press).

Author's address: G. EAVES, Department of Experimental Pathology and Cancer Research. The University of Leeds, *Leeds 2* (Great Britain).

IX. Clinical Aspects

Biomechanics I, 1st Int. Seminar Zurich 1967
pp. 333–338 (Karger, Basel/New York 1968)

Neurologisch-Psychiatrische Abteilung des Städtischen Krankenhauses Neukölln, Berlin

Erkennung und Behandlung
leichter cerebraler Bewegungsstörungen

H. Lange-Cosack

Die Entwicklung der Motorik verläuft nach physiologischen Gesetzen. Dabei gibt es eine gewisse Variationsbreite durch Unterschiede der Begabung, des Entwicklungstempos und auch durch den Einfluß der Übung. Die Veränderungen der Motorik, von denen hier die Rede ist, liegen jenseits der Variationsbreite des Normalen. Sie sind die Folge von Schäden, die das Gehirn im frühen Lebensalter betroffen haben. Die Erkennung schwerer cerebraler Lähmungen bereitet keine Schwierigkeiten. Dagegen werden die leichteren cerebralen Bewegungsstörungen, die sog. ‚minimal palsy‘-Formen, leicht verkannt.

Die Früherkennung und Frühbehandlung cerebraler Bewegungsstörungen gehört heute zu den wichtigsten Aufgaben der Kinderneurologie. Für das Säuglingsalter wurden unter anderem von Peiper, André-Thomas und seiner Schule und von dem Ehepaar Bobath Untersuchungsmethoden ausgearbeitet, die die frühzeitige Erfassung motorischer Störungen ermöglichen. Für das Alter von 4 bis 16 Jahren hat Oseretzki bereits 1923 eine ‚metrische Skale zur Untersuchung der motorischen Begabung‘ entwickelt. Die Oseretzki-Skala wurde verschiedentlich abgeändert und neben anderen motometrischen Methoden zur Unterscheidung hirngesunder von hirngeschädigten Kindern herangezogen (Göllnitz, Hünnekens und Kiphard, Geisler und Förster).

Ich will mich hier ganz auf die *klinische* Beschreibung der Kinder mit leichten cerebralen Bewegungsstörungen beschränken. Zur Abrundung des Gesamtbildes sollen neben den neurologischen Störungen auch die psychischen Auffälligkeiten und die Schwierigkeiten der sozialen Anpassung dieser Kinder skizziert werden.

Es kommen drei verschiedene klinische Typen vor:

1. Reine oder nahezu reine Tetraspastik, Paraspastik oder Hemispastik,

2. Spastisch-athetotische Mischbilder (häufigste Form).

3. Hypotonie mit Überstreckbarkeit der Gelenke und leichten choreo-athetotischen Überschußbewegungen.

Die motorische Störung wird meist nicht erkannt; man hält die Kinder nur für linkisch und ungeschickt. Gelegentlich fallen einem

Turnlehrer die fehlerhaften Bewegungen auf, gelegentlich hat auch ein
Schulpsychologe wegen der starken Bewegungsunruhe oder einer Störung der Schreibmotorik den Verdacht auf eine organische Schädigung.
In der Regel aber werden die Kinder wegen *Verhaltensschwierigkeiten,*
oft in Verbindung mit *Schulversagen,* zur kinderpsychiatrischen Untersuchung geschickt. Dabei ist nur ein Teil der Kinder debil, der größte
Teil durchschnittlich begabt, einige Kinder sind sogar überdurch-
schnittlich begabt. Die psychiatrische Beobachtung und die psychologischen Testverfahren decken bei der Mehrzahl leichte hirnorganische
Symptome, wie Unruhe, Merk- und Konzentrationsschwäche, Verlang-
samung des psychischen Tempos, Neigung zum Perseverieren, Irritier-
barkeit und mangelhafte affektive Steuerung auf. Es kommen auch
heftige seelische Reaktionen auf das körperliche Versagen vor; diese
sind verständlich in einem Alter, in dem die körperliche Leistungsfähigkeit weitgehend das Prestige bestimmt. Häufig werden die motorisch unbeholfenen Kinder von den Mitschülern gehänselt und geschla-
gen. Von den Erwachsenen werden sie für faul und ungezogen gehalten
und dementsprechend oft zurechtgewiesen und bestraft. Einige Kinder
werden verschüchtert, ängstlich und trauen sich nichts zu. So erklärte
zum Beispiel ein Achtjähriger bei der Untersuchung, daß er vor zwei
Dingen Angst habe, vor dem Turnen und vor den Schlägen der Mit-

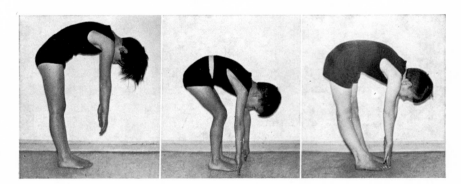

Abb. 1. Übung für 5–8jährige Kinder: Rumpfbeuge nach vorn mit gestreckten Knien.
a) Normale Motorik: Gestreckte, aber nicht rekurvierte Knie, Kopf ist in Mittelstellung,
b) Das spastische Kind knickt in den Knien ein, bleibt mit dem Gewicht hinten und
hebt zum Ausgleich den Kopf an; außerdem stützt es sich mit den Fingern auf den Boden.
c) Bei dem spastisch-athetotischen Kind sind die Knie stark rekurviert, die Zehen in den
Boden gekrallt, die Finger auf die Zehen gestützt; auch hier liegt das Gewicht hinten,
der Kopf wird angehoben.

schüler. Viel häufiger reagieren die Kinder aber mit ungesteuerten Aggressionen oder überspielen ihre Schwierigkeiten mit Clownerien.

Bei der üblichen *neurologischen Untersuchung* findet man Störungen des Muskeltonus, leichte Verminderung der groben Kraft, Reflexdifferenzen, Erschwerung und Einschränkung bestimmter Bewegungen, Koordinationsschwierigkeiten und hyperkinetische Symptome. Die Ergebnisse sind aber oft unbefriedigend, weil die eigentlichen Lähmungen hinter den Störungen der Feinmotorik zurücktreten. Da diese sich erst in der freien Bewegung feststellen lassen, mitunter auch erst bei Ermüdung oder Erregung, haben wir die übliche neurologische Untersuchung durch bestimmte, für den Normalen sehr einfache Haltungsübungen und Bewegungskombinationen ergänzt.[1]

Das *Pneumencephalogramm* kann leichte Veränderungen zeigen, kann aber auch bei sicherer Hirnschädigung unauffällig sein. Das *Elektroencephalogramm* läßt oft ebenfalls nur unspezifische Veränderungen erkennen. *Maßgeblich für die Diagnose* bleiben die *neurologische Untersuchung und die Bewegungsbeobachtung,* die durch psychiatrisch-psychologische Untersuchungen ergänzt werden müssen.

1. Die Kinder, die eine *geringe Spastik* haben oder bei denen die Spastik das Bild bestimmt, wirken bei oberflächlicher Betrachtung motorisch zunächst kaum auffällig. Sie haben oft eine gut entwickelte Muskulatur, sind bewegungsfreudig und versuchen, ihre Schwierigkeiten mit Kraft und Bewegungsüberschuß zu überwinden. Häufig bestehen eine leichte Beugekontraktur in der Hüfte, eine angedeutete Spitzfußstellung und eine Abduktionshemmung, die von manchen Kindern durch Außenrotation der Beine ausgeglichen wird. Mitunter beobachtet man – besonders unter Stress – einzelne Mitbewegungen oder das Auftreten der gesamten Beugesynergie. Während das einbeinige Hüpfen diesen Kindern relativ gut gelingt, können sie beim beidbeinigen Hüpfen nur schwer das Gleichgewicht halten, geraten immer mehr in Beugehaltung, strecken das Gesäß heraus und stolpern schließlich nach vorn. Es entsteht das Bild, das HÜNNEKENS und KIPHARD als «Zick-Zack-Haltung» beschrieben haben.

2. Bei den Kindern mit *spastisch-athetotischen Mischbildern* steht die Bewegungsunruhe ganz im Vordergrund. Oft kommt die Kombination von leichter Spastik in den Beinen mit Hypotonie, Überstreckbarkeit und choreiformen oder athetotischen Bewegungen in den Händen vor.

---

[1] Diese Untersuchungen wurden gemeinsam mit der Krankengymnastin Frl. Eva Bucher durchgeführt.

Abb. 2a. Normale Motorik. *Abb. 2b.* Leichte Spastik. *Abb. 2c.* Athetotisch-spastisches Mischbild.
Abb. 2. Übung für dieselben 8-jährigen Kinder wie Abbildung 1: Aufrichten aus der Rumpfbeuge mit senkrechtem Hochstrecken der Arme. a) Der ganze Körper ist gestreckt, der Kopf bildet die Verlängerung der Wirbelsäule. b) Das spastische Kind kann sich infolge der leichten Hüftkontraktur, die durch die Lendenlordose kompensiert wird, nicht völlig strecken. Die Arme können ebenso wie der Kopf nicht ausreichend zurückgenommen werden. c) Überstreckbarkeit der Gelenke, Hohlkreuz, hochgezogene Schultern mit leicht nach vorn geneigtem Kopf. Neben distalen Hyperkinesen der Zehen, Finger und Gesichtsmuskeln ausfahrende Bewegung der Arme, die nicht parallel gehalten werden können.

Diese Kinder schreiben oder zeichnen mit ausfahrenden Bewegungen; sie versuchen mitunter, die Athetosen durch Schnelligkeit zu überspielen. Die unwillkürlichen Bewegungen werden oft in Pseudospontanbewegungen umgewandelt, so daß die Kinder immer zu kratzen, zu zupfen und zu reiben scheinen. Bei jeder Tätigkeit kommt es zu verstärkten überflüssigen Mitbewegungen. Die Kinder versuchen oftmals diese überschüssigen Bewegungen dadurch zu kaschieren, daß sie sie noch übertreiben, um in der Kindergemeinschaft die Rolle des Clowns zu spielen.
3. Noch ausgesprochener sind diese Störungen bei den Kindern, die gar keine oder nur eine eben angedeutete Spastik haben und bei denen

die Athetosen das Bild bestimmen. Abgesehen von den distalen Hyperkinesen der Finger und der Zehen wirken auch alle anderen Bewegungen ungesteuert, oft auch ausfahrend und bizarr. Bei der Beobachtung
dieser Kinder wird es besonders deutlich, daß die Bewegungsunruhe,
über die Eltern und Lehrer klagen, eine organische Ursache hat und
nicht nur psychisch bedingt ist.

Auf die *Behandlung* kann ich nur kurz eingehen. Ein wichtiger thera-
peutischer Faktor ist bereits die Diagnosestellung mit gleichzeitiger
Aufklärung der Eltern und der Lehrer, die nunmehr in der Lage sind,
das Kind mit seinen Auffälligkeiten richtig einzuordnen und zu führen. Wegen der Reizoffenheit und Störbarkeit ist es wichtig, daß die
Kinder eine ruhige Umgebung haben und daß ein Übermaß an Außen-
reizen abgeschaltet wird. Manchmal muß man sogar intelligente
Kinder aus der Schule herausnehmen und sie längere Zeit einzeln oder
in kleinen Gruppen beschulen. Die Übungsbehandlung muß individuell

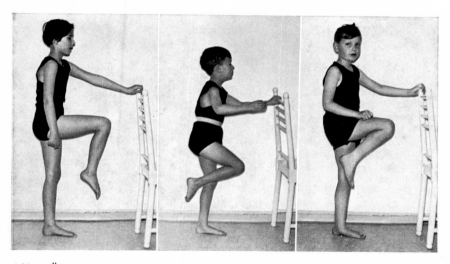

Abb. 3. Übung für dieselben Kinder der Abbildungen 1 und 2: Bei aufgerichtetem Ober-
körper einen Oberschenkel mit rechtwinklig gebeugtem Knie anheben. a) Normale
Motorik: Aufrechte Körperhaltung, müheloses rechtwinkliges Anbeugen des Oberschen-
kels mit herabhängendem Unterschenkel. b) Bei dem spastischen Kind tritt die Beugesynergie an den rechten Extremitäten in Erscheinung. Auch das Standbein ist leicht
angebeugt, die Hüfte kann links nicht gestreckt werden. c) Das spastisch-athetotische
Kind fixiert zur Abwehr überschüssiger Bewegungen den rechten Fuß am linken Knie
und die gefaustete rechte Hand am rechten Oberschenkel. Auch dieses Kind kann das
Standbein nicht völlig strecken.

aufgebaut und abgestuft werden und muß längere Zeit durchgeführt werden. Nach anfänglichem Widerstand merken die Kinder sehr bald, daß ihnen geholfen wird und machen dann meist erstaunlich gut und gern mit.

Die Schaffung einer optimalen Bewegungsbehandlung für diese Gruppe von Patienten mit leichten Störungen bleibt eine gemeinsame Aufgabe der Biomechanik und der Neurologie. Neben dem praktischen Zweck haben alle Behandlungsmethoden das Ziel, die Kinder zu ermutigen, ihnen Sicherheit zu geben und ihnen die Einordnung und die Behauptung in der Gemeinschaft zu ermöglichen.

Literatur

ANDRÉ-THOMAS, A. et SAINT-ANNE DARGASSIES, S.: Etudes neurologiques sur le nouveau-né et le jeune nourrisson (Masson, Paris 1952).

ANDRÉ-THOMAS, A.; CHESNY, Y. and SAINT-ANNE DARGASSIES, S.: The Neurological Examination of the Infant. Little Club Clin. develop. Med., No. 1. London, Spastics Soc. (Heinemann, London 1960).

BOBATH, K.: The Motor Deficit in Patients with Cerebral Palsy (siehe Literatur über frühere Arb. von B.K. BOBATH. und Clin. develop. Med. No. 23 (Heinemann, London 1966).

GEISLER, E. und FÖRSTER, C.: Über Entwicklungsstörungen der Motorik bei cerebral geschädigten Kindern und deren Bedeutung für die Diagnostik und Praxis. Münchn. med. Wschr. *102:* 2391, 2462, 2508 (1960).

GÖLLNITZ, G.: Die Bedeutung der frühkindlichen Hirnschädigung für die Kinderpsychiatrie (Thieme, Leipzig 1954).

HÜNNEKENS, H. und KIPHARD, E.: Bewegung heilt. Psychomotische Übungsbehandlung bei entwicklungsrückständigen Kindern (Flöttmann, Gütersloh 1963).

MATTHIASS, H.H.: Untersuchungstechnik und Diagnose der infantilen Zerebralparese im Säuglings- und Kindesalter (Thieme, Stuttgart 1966).

OSERETZKI, N.: Psychomotorik. Z. angew. Physcol., Beiheft 57 (1931).

PEIPER, A.: Die Eigenart der kindlichen Hirntätigkeit (Thieme, Leipzig 1931).

Adresse der Autorin: Frau Dr. med. H. LANGE-COSACK, Chefärztin der Neurologisch-Psychiatrischen Abteilung des Städtischen Krankenhauses Neukölln, *Berlin* (B.R. Deutschland).

Biomechanics I, 1st Int. Seminar Zurich 1967
pp. 339–343 (Karger, Basel/New York 1968)

From the Neurologic Department of the University of Zurich

Objective Kinesiologic and Electro-tono-myographic Observations on Spasticity and Rigidity

E. Esslen

Spasticity and rigidity are the best known states of pathologic increase of muscle tone. It is noteworthy that the clinician even nowadays characterizes these states in descriptive terms. Rather few trials have been undertaken to record and measure muscle tone by objective methods.

It was our aim to investigate well-defined movements, easily and exactly reproducible and indefinitly repeatable. The measuring device should permit the active and passive performance of the same movement (or cycle of movements). For the legs the movement of bicycling has been chosen. This is a rather complex movement in which at least three joints participate (hip, knee, ankle), though flexion and extension

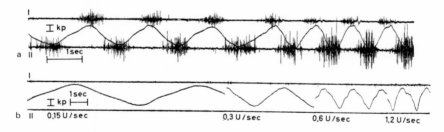

Fig. 1. Bicycle movement of a normal test person. a) Trace I Extensor, trace II Flexor of the knee joint. Mechanogram of active novement between trace I and II. Alternating activation of motor units in flexor and extensor. During activation there is a shift towards increasing activation of the flexor and decreasing activation of the extensor. b) Trace I and II depict the passive bicycle movement. The pedals are driven by an electric motor and the subject is asked to follow the movement in complete relaxation. The normal test person follows without muscle activation even during acceleration from 0,15 rotations/sec to 1,2 rotations/sec.

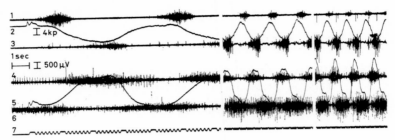

Fig. 2. Male patient with spasticity of the left arm and leg. Passive movement. The extensor
(1) and flexor (3) of the right knee joint show a slightly increased activation during the
stretch phase of the muscle whilst there is a considerable increase of reflex activity in
the extensor (4) and flexor (6) of the left side. One notices a prolongation and an overlap
of the phases of activation in agonist and antagonist. Corresponding to the increased
activation the tonogram of the left side (5) indicates about 8 kp more resistance to muscle
stretch. With higher speed of the movement (middle and right part), there is a further
increase of resistance to muscle stretch on the left side (5) but practically none on the right
side (2). The record illustrates the basic model of spasticity characterized by the marked
dynamic factor causing increase of tone with acceleration of movement. Trace 7 indicates
the angle position of the knee joint.

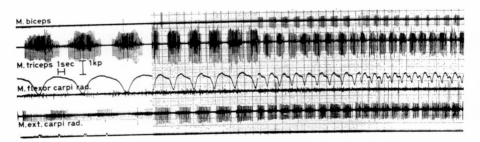

Fig. 3. Rigidity on the other hand behaves differently from spasticity. The record of this
case of Parkinsonism depicts passive flexion and extension of the elbow. With increasing
speed of flexion and extension the resistance to muscle stretch diminishes.

of the knee is the most important. The strength of the active movement or the resistance to stretch the passively moved muscles were
measured by strain gauges fastened on to the pedals. The mechanogram or tonogram was simultaneously recorded with the pattern of
activation of the knee extensors and flexors on both sides. The device
for the arms permits the measurement of simple extension and flexion
of the elbow or wrist. The speed of the mentioned movements can be

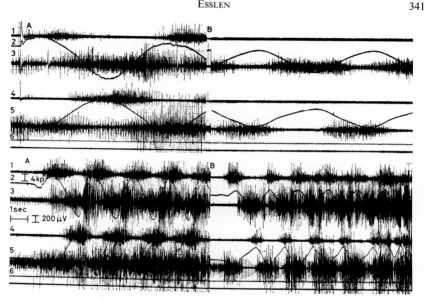

Fig. 4. Case of pseudobulbar palsy with tetraspasticity. The left upper quadrant of the figure shows the passive bicycle movement. There is a strong increase of flexor tone (3, 6) and a less pronounced increase of extensor tone (1, 4). The right upper quadrant shows the same movement 30 min after intramuscular injection of Valium®. There is a diminuation of 8 kp of resistance (2, 5) to muscle stretch. The spastic extensor activation is almost completely inhibited, the flexor innervation considerably reduced though not normalized. In the lower left quadrant the active bicycle movement is recorded. Note the unphysiological co-activation of agonist and antagonist. The mechanogram illustrates the slow viscous movement. Right lower quadrant: Same movement, 30 min after injection of 20 mg Valium®. There is a clear economizing effect on the action of extensors and flexors with improved performance of the movement.

increased within a rather wide range. This is of importance in order to evaluate the dynamic component of increase of muscle tone. As flexion and extension of the arm are performed in a condition neutralizing gravity, the increased muscle tone can be directly indicated in kilopond (kp). In the bicycle movement, however, gravity is not neutralized and therefore the mechanogram or tonogram is composed of the muscle strength (in active movement) or the resistance to stretch (in passive movement) and the weight of the lower legs.

The increased muscle tone in states of spasticity or rigidity can generally be observed in a resting position of the patient though there is a clear facilitatory effect of postural, emotional or locomotor activation. Figure 5 illustrates the unusual case of a 30-year-old woman

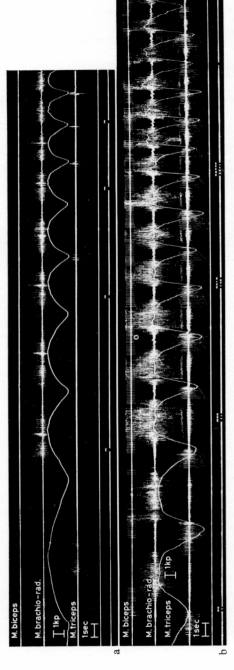

Fig. 5. a) Passive flexion and extension of the right elbow. During slow movement, flexor and extensor can follow without activation. With acceleration of the stretch phase, a tonic stretch reflex appears, first in the brachio-radialis muscle, then, with higher speed, in the triceps muscle. b) On request to perform an active movement, e.g. to put the right foot on the left knee, a considerable increase of tone appears in the passively flexed and extended arm. Again the increase is more pronounced with higher speed.

who did not show any signs of increased muscle tone in a quiet supine position. Even slight active movements, however, provoked a strong increase of muscle tone, especially of the erector trunci, and of the limb muscles as well. One would have supposed a state of tetanus or strychnine intoxication if the disease had not existed for two decades.

Results

The records give a lot more information which cannot be dealt with at this moment. There can be no doubt, however, that biomechanical methods are an important tool in the analysis of pathologic states of muscle tone.

Author's address: E. ESSLEN, M.D., Neurologic Department of the University of Zurich, CH 8006 Zürich (Switzerland).

Biomechanics I, 1st Int. Seminar Zurich 1967
pp. 344–346 (Karger, Basel/New York 1968)

Universität J.E. Purkyne, Brno

Untersuchungen mit Lichtspuraufnahmen als Hilfsmethode in der Rehabilitation

L. Kubálková

In der Rehabilitationspraxis fehlt eine objektive Aufzeichnung der Bewegung zur Ergänzung der übrigen Untersuchungen, wie Muskelkraft, EMG und so weiter, sowie um ein vollständiges Bild vom Stand der Körperbehinderung und vom Grad der Reedukation zu gewinnen. Dieser Mangel macht sich besonders bei der Dokumentation und bei der Kontrolle über die Richtigkeit der methodischen Vorgänge in der Heilgymnastik bemerkbar.

Wir versuchen, diese Lücke mit Hilfe der Lichtspuraufnahme zu schließen.

Bei der untersuchten Person wurden an Kopf, Schultern, Hüfte, Knie und Knöchel kleine Glühbirnen angebracht, die von Mikroakkumulatoren gespeist waren. Die Bewegung wurde von der Seite fotografiert, die stroboskopische Einrichtung ermöglichte die Registrierung des Zeitfaktors und ein entsprechender Raster, der in das Positiv eingezeichnet wurde, ermöglichte eine gewisse Orientierung im Raum.

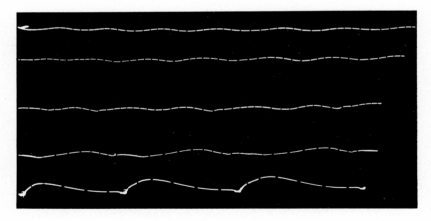

Abb. 1

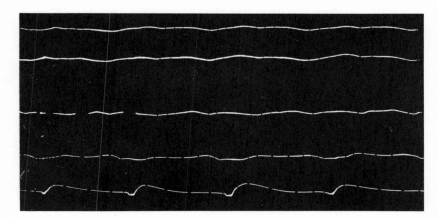

Abb. 2

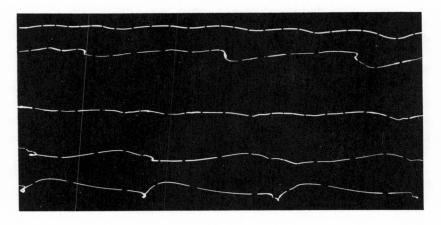

Abb. 3

In Abbildung 1 ist der normale Gang dargestellt. Die obersten drei Kurven haben bei globaler Betrachtung ungefähr die Form einer regelmäßigen Doppelwelle, die Kurve des Knies und des Knöchels sind ausdrucksvoller (man beobachte das Abrollen des Fußes, die Phase des Schwunges und das Auftreten). Bei genauerer Analyse, die sich auf klinische und theoretische Kenntnisse stützt, lesen wir eine Reihe von

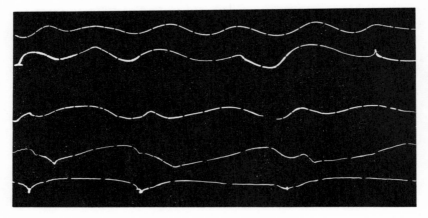

Abb. 4

Grundelementen und gegenseitigen Beziehungen heraus, die den Ausgangspunkt zur Deutung der Aufnahme des veränderten Stereotyps bilden (Abb. 2–4).

Wir müssen bedenken, daß die Aufnahmen eine zweidimensionale Reduktion der dreidimensionalen Bewegung sind. Wenn sie zweckmäßig angewendet werden sollen, ist es nötig, auf Grund von klinischen patho-physiologischen Kenntnissen die Bedeutung und die Dynamik der Zusammenhänge morphologischer Merkmale an den Kurven zu beurteilen und die Aufnahmen nach diesen Merkmalen und ihren Veränderungen zu werten. Das ist der gangbarste Weg zur Unterstützung des Heilgymnasten, für den die Merkmale gewissermaßen als Kodesystem dienen sollen.

Adresse der Autorin: Dr. LUDMILA KUBÁLKOVÁ, Universität J.E. Purkyne, *Brno* (CSSR).

Biomechanics I, 1st Int. Seminar Zurich 1967
pp. 347–350 (Karger, Basel/New York 1968)

Biomechanik als Grundlage der technischen Orthopädie

H.U. DEBRUNNER, Aarau

In einigen Vorträgen dieses Seminars wurde die Bedeutung bestimmter biomechanischer Untersuchungsmethoden für die Konstruktion von Prothesen erwähnt. Es ist angezeigt, einmal nicht von der Methode her, sondern vom Problem der Prothesenversorgung aus zu untersuchen, welches die Bedeutung der Biomechanik für den Prothesen- und Orthesenbau (= technische Orthopädie) ist.

Die Kenntnis des zeitlichen Ablaufes der menschlichen Bewegungen, der Kräfte, die auf den Körper und seine Teile wirken und ihr Verhalten während der verschiedenen Phasen einer Bewegung, vor allem aber des Zusammenwirkens der aktiven Muskelkräfte und ihr Einfluß auf Haltung und Gang, sind die wichtigsten Grundlagen für die Konstruktion von künstlichen Gliedern. Das funktionelle Verhalten der Prothese ist noch wichtiger als deren morphologische und ästhetische Anpassung an den Amputierten. Am Beispiel des Kunstbeines wollen wir uns die daraus entstehenden Probleme etwas näher betrachten.

Die Prothesenmacher haben während langer Zeit Kunstbeine rein empirisch konstruiert und waren damit auch erfolgreich. Erst seit ungefähr 1920 diente die Glieder- und Muskelmechanik als wichtige theoretische Untermauerung für die Kunst, dem Amputierten Ersatzglieder zu schaffen. Die große Zahl von Amputierten im zweiten Weltkrieg war der Anlaß für eingehende biomechanische Untersuchungen über den Bewegungsablauf beim Gehen im Hinblick auf bessere Prothesenherstellung, von denen besonders diejenigen der Universität von Californien erwähnt werden müssen. Diese Untersuchungen brachten uns eine große Menge von neuen Informationen neben der Bestätigung früherer Erkenntnisse. Sie fanden allmählich Eingang in die technische

Orthopädie und beeinflußten in vielen Punkten die Konstruktion von Kunstgliedern.

Die großangelegten biomechanischen Untersuchungen vertieften vor allem unsere Kenntnisse über die durchschnittliche Normalbewegung, über den normalen Gang. Diese Grundlagen sind für die Herstellung von Prothesen sicher notwendig. Für den Amputierten müssen wir jedoch ein Ersatzglied anfertigen, das ihm nicht den ‚Normalgang' ermöglicht, sondern das seinem individuellen Bewegungsmuster angepaßt ist.

Alle Naturformen körperlicher Bewegung sind nach einem bestimmten Grundschema aufgebaut. Jedes Individuum hat jedoch sein eigenes, durch ganz bestimmte Abweichungen von diesem Normalschema bedingtes individuelles Bewegungsbild. Diese individuelle Variante ist so charakteristisch, daß sie als Erkennungszeichen für bestimmte Personen dienen kann. Nach dem Verlust eines Beines hat der Amputierte das Bedürfnis, seine Bewegungsindividualität wieder zu erhalten. Dies wird besonders problematisch, wenn durch weitere Schäden noch pathologische Bewegungsmuster bestehen, deren biomechanische Analyse oft an ihrer Komplexität scheitert. Die Besonderheit des individuellen Bewegungsmusters jedes einzelnen Amputierten ist der Grund, weshalb bei uns die Prothesenherstellung wohl immer eine Kunst bleiben wird, die dem handwerklich geschulten Orthopädiemechaniker vorbehalten ist.

Auch wenn die modernen technischen Hilfsmittel der Biomechanik in der Praxis der Prothesenherstellung kaum zur Verwendung kommen, denkt, konstruiert und beobachtet der gute Prothesenbauer doch durchaus biomechanisch. Seine Beobachtungsmethoden sind jedoch subjektiv, deshalb schwer zu erlernen und schwierig zu diskutieren. Ich glaube, daß es nichts schadet, wenn ich vor diesem Gremium über die uralte subjektive Beobachtungsmethode einige Bemerkungen mache.

Durch die Beobachtung des gehenden Patienten kann man sich ein ziemlich gutes Bild vom Ablauf der Bewegungen beim Schreiten machen. Man beobachtet den ganzen Menschen und erfaßt alle Mitbewegungen, die besonders für pathologische Bewegungen charakteristisch sind. Sowohl Auge wie Ohr gestatten eine Analyse der verschiedenen Bewegungsphasen bis zu Zeitabschnitten von $^1/_{10}$ sec. Unterschiede in der Symmetrie des Gangbildes und Abweichungen vom rhythmischen Ablauf der Bewegungen sind besser erkennbar als statische Unterschiede. Dem geübten Beobachter ergibt sich ein Bild, das dem individuellen Bewegungsschema entspricht, aber zeitlich nicht weit analysiert ist. Auch pathologische Bewegungsformen können auf diese Weise vom Erfahrenen recht gut erfaßt werden.

Die Erfahrung zeigt, daß die subjektive Beobachtung mit Auge und Ohr für die Praxis der technischen Orthopädie meist genügt. Es sind keine technischen Apparaturen notwendig, der Patient wird nicht durch die Methodik belastet und das Resultat steht sofort zur Verfügung. Für die Zwecke der Prothesenkontrolle ist die Gesamterfassung des persönlichen Bewegungsschemas der fortlaufenden Registrierung einzelner Bewegungsabläufe vorläufig noch überlegen. Es scheint mir jedoch durchaus möglich, daß z.B. telemetrische Methoden zur objektiven Darstellung des Bewegungsablaufes in schwierigen Fällen eine bessere Erfassung von Fehlern im Prothesenaufbau, der Anpassung an den Amputationsstumpf und von Fehlbewegungen des Patienten erlauben werden. Versuche mit Lichtspuraufnahmen haben nicht richtig befriedigt, sie zeigen nicht viel mehr, als die subjektive Beobachtung ergibt.

In der Forschung, der Entwicklung neuer Prinzipien der Konstruktion von Kunstgliedern sind jedoch die modernen Untersuchungsverfahren sehr wertvoll. Fast jede meßbare Teilfunktion läßt Rückschlüsse auf den Gesamtablauf eines Schrittes zu und kann dadurch für Forschungsaufgaben verwendet werden. Einige Beispiele mögen illustrieren, welche Probleme damit bearbeitet werden können.

Der Energieverbrauch ist beim Prothesengang größer als beim Gang des Gesunden. Dies hängt u.a. damit zusammen, daß der Schwerpunkt des Körpers eine unregelmäßige Bahn beschreibt. Durch Messung des Energieverbrauches kann die günstigste Konstruktion für ein Kunstglied, ja für verschiedene Kniekonstruktionen oder Fußaufbauten ermittelt werden.

Die passive Kunstbeinkonstruktion sollte eine solche Bewegungscharakteristik aufweisen, daß das Zusammenspiel von Körper, Amputationsstumpf und Prothese einer natürlichen, harmonischen Bewegung möglichst nahekommt. Mit Accelerometer, Elektrogoniometer, Kraftmesser usw. kann die optimale Konstruktion ermittelt werden. Derartige Untersuchungen sind für die Steuerung z.B. der Kniebewegung wichtig, wie sie in der hydraulischen Knie- und Fußsteuerung angewendet wird.

Die Energie für die Bewegung des Kunstgliedes muß vom Amputationsstumpf geliefert werden. Durch Elektromyographie kann die

Funktion der Stumpfmuskeln in der Prothese kontrolliert werden. So
wurde u.a. die Überlegenheit der myoplastischen Stumpfversorgung
bei der Operation nachgewiesen.

Die Steuerung von Fremdkraftprothesen (pneumatische und elektrische Hand) ist ein Problem, das nur mit modernen biomechanischen Methoden befriedigend gelöst werden kann. Hier bieten sich
der Forschung noch große Problemkomplexe an, die in der ganzen
Welt bearbeitet werden.

Adresse des Autors: Dr. H.U. DEBRUNNER, Bachstraße 82, CH-5000 *Aarau* (Schweiz).

Wissenschaftliche Ausstellung am Seminar
Scientific Exhibition
Exposition scientifique

Die nachstehend aufgeführten Firmen haben als Aussteller einen Einblick in den neuesten Stand der einschlägigen Instrumente vermittelt:

Ampex SA 2 via Berna, *6901 Lugano*	Videorecording
Heuer-Leonidas *2501 Biel*	Chronographes et compteurs de sport
Honeywell AG Postfach, *8030 Zürich*	Elektronische Apparate
Kontron AG Hardstraße 235, *8031 Zürich*	Elektronische Instrumente und Apparate
Longines SA *2610 St. Imier*	Horlogerie de précision
Omega *2500 Biel*	Watches
Paillard SA *1450 Sainte-Croix*	Caméras et Projecteurs
I. Weinberger Förrlibuchstraße 110, *8005 Zürich*	Generalvertretung der Photo-, Kino- und Magnettonindustrie

Als Hochschulinstitute beteiligten sich an der Ausstellung:

Université de Genève Ecole de Médecine	Vectograph
Eidg. Technische Hochschule Zürich Kurse für Turnen und Sport	Accelerograph Goniograph Electromyograph Dynamograph Reaktionsplatte Lichtschranke Film-Auswertgerät

BOGNOR REGIS
COLL. of EDUCN.
LIBRARY